HENRY CHANDLER COWLES

PIONEER ECOLOGIST

VICTOR M CASSIDY

kedziesigel

Kedzie Sigel Press
2647 N. Western Avenue
Suite 8042
Chicago, Illinois 60647 USA

51 A Victoria Road
Cambridge CB4 3BW
England

Visit us on the World Wide Web at:
  www.sigelpress.com and
  www.kedziepress.com

Cover and internal design by Harp Mando
Cover Image: Henry Chandler Cowles of the University of Chicago Department of Botany on a field trip, 1911. Credit Line: American Environmental Photographs Collection, [AEP-ILP234], Department of Special Collections, University of Chicago Library.

ISBN 13: 978-1-934087-20-6
ISBN 10: 1-934087-20-3

Library of Congress Cataloging-in-Publication Data

Cassidy, Victor M.
  Henry Chandler Cowles : pioneer ecologist / Victor M. Cassidy.
     p. cm.
  ISBN-13: 978-1-934087-20-6 (pbk. : alk. paper)
  ISBN-10: 1-934087-20-3 (pbk. : alk. paper)
  1. Cowles, Henry Chandler, 1869–1939. 2. Botanists—United States—Biography.
  3. Ecologists—United States—Biography. I. Title.
  QK31.C875C37 2008
  577.092—dc22
  [B]

                                        2007000189

Printed in the United States of America
10 9 8 7 6 5 4 3 2 1

Printed on 100% recycled, 100% post-consumer waste paper.

The author dedicates this book to his wife

DONNA

Whom he will love forever.

kedziesigel

This book is printed on Rolland Enviro100, which contains 100% recycled post-consumer fibre, is EcoLogo, Processed Chlorine Free and FSC Recycled certified and manufactured using biogas energy.

CONTENTS

Part Two: Anthology 97

PART ONE:
BIOGRAPHY

INTRODUCTION

Photographs always show him outdoors—and always wearing a tie. In his professorial mode as Henry Chandler Cowles of the University of Chicago, he wears a dark suit, vest, white shirt, bowler hat, and tie as he escorts his European colleagues through the Indiana Dunes under the summer sun. In his role as "Doctor Cowles," the jovial, cigar-smoking mentor to generations of ecology students, he leads expeditions in calf-high boots, knickers, white shirt, floppy hat—and tie. Short and a bit stout, with a large, well-shaped head and a ready grin, he's someone who seems easy to like.

Cowles (it's pronounced "coals") was a botanist, ecologist, field teacher, and conservationist. At the end of the nineteenth century, he made hundreds of field observations of the sand dunes landscape that rings the southern and eastern shores of Lake Michigan. His study demonstrated that the outdoor environment is a dynamic system in which plants, soil, moisture, climate, and topography interact.

Ecological Questions

Ecology, which Cowles helped to pioneer in North America, investigates the interrelationships between living organisms and the natural environment.

Before Cowles came on the scene, botanists had asked why plants grow where they do, how vegetation changes over time, and whether there is a pattern to the changes, but no one had systematically investigated these questions. Science had yet to clarify the role of vegetation in creating sand dunes—and the effect of the dunes environment on the plants that grow there. The role of wind in shaping dunes vegetation was incompletely understood.

As Cowles looked for answers, he discovered a natural phenomenon called *plant succession*. Though succession was observed and described in antiquity—and was known to many scientists before Cowles—he investigated and described it more comprehensively than anyone else before him. Succession studies have advanced dramatically since Cowles' day, but ecologists still acknowledge his pioneering contributions.

Plant succession denotes the way that communities of plants come into a landscape, flourish, and create conditions for their replacement by other plant communities. Succession is easy to follow in the lightly vegetated dunes landscape. No plants grow at the lake edge, because waves wash constantly over the land. At the back of the beach, where waves come less often, a few plants grow on the sand and stabilize it with their root systems. Over many generations of growth, reproduction, and decay, these pioneers produce humus, which makes it possible for a new group of plants to move in and replace them. A third generation eventually follows this second generation, and a fourth replaces the third, until an ending point, called *climax*, is reached. The climax community—at the dunes it's an oak forest—does not change until something disturbs or destroys it. If the forest burns down, for example, succession starts all over again, but usually from an intermediate stage.

Cowles could face away from Lake Michigan, hike inland, and see the results of centuries of plant succession. As he walked through space, he walked through time. Today, visitors to the Indiana Dunes National Lakeshore can follow his footsteps on a "Succession Trail" that starts on the beach and passes through the successive plant communities.

Cowles' basic ideas, which he published in a long, multipart article called "The Ecological Relations of the Vegetation on the Sand Dunes of Lake Michigan" (1899)[1] have withstood more than a century of testing, discussion, and refinement. He followed "Ecological Relations" with important studies of Chicago-area plant communities, underlying rock and its effects on vegetation, the causes of vegetative cycles, prairies, and more.[2]

Through his publications, lectures, teaching, travels, and leadership of an International Phytogeographic Excursion that brought European scientists to the United States in 1913, Cowles won professional respect for the new science of ecology and a place for American ecologists in the international scientific community. A great joiner, he signed on with many scientific organizations, made presentations at conferences, and helped to found the Association of American Geographers and the

---

[1] Henry Chandler Cowles, "The Ecological Relations of the Vegetation on the Sand Dunes of Lake Michigan," Parts 1–4. *Botanical Gazette* 27 (February, March, April, May 1899): 95–117, 167–202, 281–308, 361–91. Reprinted in this volume.

[2] Henry Chandler Cowles, "Plant Societies of Chicago and Vicinity"; "The Influence of Underlying Rocks on the Character of the Vegetation"; "The Causes of Vegetative Cycles"; and "The Persistence of Prairies" are reprinted in this volume.

Ecological Society of America. He forged connections with every important ecologist of his time and leading botanists, geologists, and geographers.

Later in his career, Cowles advanced scientific education and conservation through the Illinois State Academy of Science, Friends of Our Native Landscape, Geographical Society of Chicago, Chicago Academy of Sciences, and other organizations. He surveyed Illinois natural areas, providing expert data that convinced the state legislature to purchase ecologically important lands for parks. Prior to his time, only historic sites were preserved. During 1916, he testified in federal hearings on behalf of the proposed Sand Dunes National Park in Indiana.[3] This initial effort, though unsuccessful, strengthened the movement to save the dunes that triumphed long after his death.

Born to Botanize

Born in 1869, Cowles was the son of a Connecticut market gardener. His earliest memories were of walks in the woods with his mother, where she taught him the names of plants and trees. In youth, he raised flowers and vegetables on the family farm and roamed the woods, where he found, identified, and collected wild plants. He began reading *Gray's Manual of Botany*, the authoritative flora, when he was just seventeen years old.

High school geology helped Cowles to see relationships between rock, soil, topography, and plant life. In college and graduate school, he outgrew simple plant identification and learned how to read vegetative patterns in the landscape. He evolved an intuitive method of nature study, much like Darwin's, that relied upon close observation, experience, and a highly disciplined thought process. This method brought him success at the Lake Michigan dunes and in other early studies.

As Cowles was completing his dunes work, Frederic E. Clements, a Nebraska grasslands ecologist, developed the numerical and statistical survey techniques used in science today. As Clements' statistical methodology supplanted the intuitive approach, Cowles responded by training students in Clements' techniques, but resisted them in his own work. He published relatively little after 1901, transferred his ambition to his students, and employed his field skills to teach, do personal research, and survey natural areas.

---

[3] Cowles' testimony is reprinted in this volume.

Colleagues always wondered why Cowles published so little of his research. A few weeks after his death in 1939, his widow, Elizabeth, told a friend that she too regretted that he had not published more. "I feel that one reason that he did not ... was that the recognition of his authorship of an idea did not have for him the urgency which the testing of that idea and its promulgation among his colleagues and students, if found sound, held." He did not "hunger and thirst" for recognition, she added, but preferred doing research and teaching to writing up his results.

There was talk, during Cowles' final years, of "shaping his voluminous notes on his particular contribution to physiographic ecology into book form," but this did not happen. He "said more than once 'All I have done is written in my students, it is not lost because I have not published it; they have published it for me.'" However, "Being his student as well as his wife," Elizabeth "privately felt that nobody else could say it quite so clearly and well."[4]

Though Cowles' intuitive approach to nature study is completely out of professional fashion, it's alive and well in today's environmental restoration movement. The professionals and volunteers who restore damaged natural areas venture daily into the unknown. They never know how nature will respond to their initiatives—whether an endangered plant will grow where they place it, for example, or what will happen when they remove invasive species. In making site management decisions, these people combine observation, intuition, and experience with their knowledge of botany and ecology. Cowles is thus very relevant to the most challenging ecological work of our time. His spirit helps heal the land.

Field Teacher

Between 1897 and 1934, Cowles taught physiographic ecology, ecological anatomy, geographical botany, experimental ecology, applied ecology, field ecology, and related courses at the University of Chicago. His students included Victor E. Shelford, the father of animal ecology; George D. Fuller, who became his assistant and successor at Chicago; William Skinner Cooper, who refined his theory of plant succession

---

[4] Elizabeth Cowles to C. C. Adams, 1 November 1939. C. C. Adams Papers, University of Western Michigan, Kalamazoo.

with fieldwork on Isle Royale in Lake Superior; Paul B. Sears, who became professor of conservation at Yale University and an eloquent writer on ecological subjects; Walter P. Cottam, who became chair of the botany department at the University of Utah and co-founder of the Nature Conservancy; and many others. In 1980, Douglas D. Sprugel published a "pedagogical genealogy" that traced Cowles' influence to 1950 on some fifty American plant ecologists.[5] These men and women completed their careers in the 1970s and there is now no living memory of Cowles' teaching.

Students flocked to Cowles because he gave vivid, authoritative lectures, had incomparable field skills, and was happy to be alive. Instead of pushing his opinions on students, he encouraged them to think independently and welcomed a variety of viewpoints. He took many weekend research trips to sites near Chicago and often brought some of his better students along. When he made a discovery in the field that might become a research project, he encouraged students to pursue it, guided their work, and delighted in their successes.

Cowles was best known for Botany 36, a four-week field ecology course that took students into wilderness areas all over North America. In August of 1916, May Thielgaard (Watts) enrolled for Botany 36.[6] Led by the Professor, as the class called him, a party of about fifteen students traveled through the Lake Superior region of Michigan and Wisconsin to study plant communities in beaches, canyons, bogs, forests, and more. The group worked hard all day, cooked over open fires, slept in tents, endured rain, mosquitoes and black flies—and had a wonderful time. Thielgaard wrote this admiring ditty about her teacher:

> Get on your boots and follow him,
> He's half a mile in front,
> It's our own Dr. Cowles himself
> Out on a lichen hunt.
>
> It's our own Dr. Cowles you know;
> They've lost the pattern since
> Of all our friends afar and near
> He surely is the prince.

---

[5] Douglas D. Sprugel, "A 'Pedagogical Genealogy' of American Plant Ecologists," *Bulletin of the Ecological Society of America* 61, no. 4 (December 1980): 197–200.

[6] The papers of May Thielgaard Watts at the Sterling Morton Library of the Morton Arboretum in Lisle, Illinois, include May Thielgaard's student notebook from Botany 36.

CHORUS
Each year we hunt for courses.
Not that we may learned be.
But if you want the reason,
It's not the course, it's he.[7]

Photographers, including Cowles' wife, Elizabeth, accompanied these expeditions and some 10,000 images have survived. Of these, 4,500 are now digitized and available on the Internet as *American Environmental Photographs, 1891–1936.* Though most of the photos show plants and landscapes, the Professor and his students appear in many. We see groups in Packard touring cars traveling on a narrow mountainside road, a mock wedding ceremony with the Professor presiding, a laughing gang of wilderness explorers gathered around a No Trespassing sign, and May Thielgaard (Watts) poling the Professor through a Wisconsin wetland on a raft.[8]

Why this Book?

After Cowles' died, his widow apparently discarded or destroyed most of his papers, saving only his diaries, a few letters, and some family photographs. None of his manuscripts survived and we have just a few tiny pages of undated, barely readable field notes. Some papers were left behind in the Cowles' family house near the University of Chicago when Elizabeth Cowles moved out near the end of her life. These somehow ended up on the curb and were taken away as garbage. A lack of primary material has retarded work on Cowles and made a book-length biography impossible.[9]

---

[7] Ibid.

[8] See http://memory.loc.gov/ammem/collections/ecology/index.html. According to Judith Dartt of the University of Chicago Library (UCL), the botany department ecology photographs were taken by a number of different individuals who were typically members of the field party. Roughly 10,000 photographs exist, but the 4,500 on the website were chosen because they conform to the standards set for the Library of Congress/Ameritech American Memory grant that funded the scanning project. In original format, the images are a mix of glass lantern slides, glass plate negatives, and prints in a variety of sizes. The American Environmental Photographs, 1891–1936, were digitized by the Special Collections Research Center, UCL, for the Library of Congress American Memory website.

[9] Nobody knows why she did this. Harriet Cowles, the daughter, who probably helped destroy the papers, apparently felt that nobody would be interested in her father's work and that there was little point in saving his manuscripts and letters. During the 1980s, the

Three scholars have done important research on Cowles. In 1999, Sarah Gibbard Cook published *Henry Chandler Cowles (1869-1939) and Cowles Bog, Indiana*, a 93-page booklet. Largely biographical, Cook's text includes an appendix with a partial chronology and bibliography. Cook was the starting point for this book.[10]

Professor Eugene Cittadino of New York University has published two long papers about Cowles: "A 'Marvelous Cosmopolitan Preserve': The Dunes, Chicago, and the Dynamic Ecology of Henry Cowles" (1993) and "Borderline Science: Expert Testimony and the Red River Boundary Dispute" (2004). The author has drawn on both of these papers, especially in his accounts of Cowles' activities as an expert witness. *Sacred Sands: The Struggle for Community in the Indiana Dunes* (1983) by J. Ronald Engel, describes the long battle for the Indiana Dunes National Lakeshore and Cowles' role in it. Professor Engel kindly supplied some original materials that he used in writing *Sacred Sands.*[11]

Fortune smiled on this project. Just as the author began, Cowles' daughter, Harriet, gave family papers to the University of Chicago Library. Soon after, the Ecological Society of America donated class notebooks of several of Cowles' students to the University of Chicago Library. The University of Illinois Archives supplied materials that illuminated Cowles' working partnership with Stephen A. Forbes, the father of Illinois ecology.

As research proceeded, the author decided to reunite Cowles' fragmented legacy—to write a biography, reprint the best of his written

---

UCL began to collect historical materials on Cowles. At that time, the complete botany department photograph collection (found in a basement on campus) was preserved and transferred to the Department of Special Collections. In the 1990s, records of the botany department and papers of Professor Paul Voth were acquired. In 1997, the botany department photographs were digitized and put on the *American Environmental Photographs* web site, which includes an online essay on HCC and his contributions to ecology, a chronology of field trip courses, a biographical guide with links to individuals in the photographs, and a selected bibliography on the history of American ecology. This work was done by Daniel Meyer, Associate Director, Special Collections Research Center and University Archivist at the UCL, and Judith Dartt. We thank Mr. Meyer for supplying this information.

[10] Sarah Gibbard Cook, *Henry Chandler Cowles (1869–1939) and Cowles Bog, Indiana.* Revised 1999 [original manuscript was written in 1980.]

[11] Eugene Cittadino, "A 'Marvelous Cosmopolitan Preserve': The Dunes, Chicago, and the Dynamic Ecology of Henry Cowles," *Perspectives on Science* 1, no. 3, (1993): 520–59; Eugene Cittadino, "Borderline Science: Expert Testimony and the Red River Boundary Dispute," *Isis* 95 (2004): 183–219; and J. Ron Engel, *Sacred Sands: The Struggle for Community in the Indiana Dunes* (Middletown, CT: Wesleyan University Press, 1983).

work, and publish updated reference material. If this book is a success, it will inspire and facilitate future work on Cowles—and a reconsideration of his role in ecological history. Ecology has grown immensely since his day, but he remains a great pioneer who gave this important branch of science an excellent start. Through his teaching he birthed an entire generation of ecologists. Through his conservation advocacy he helped protect Illinois wilderness for his own generation, for ours, and for those yet to come. Most of all, he loved the land and taught us to cherish it.

Acknowledgments

This book would have been impossible without the full cooperation of the University of Chicago Library, Special Collections Research Center, and its staff. Thanks go to Daniel Meyer, Associate Director, Judith Dartt, David Pavelich, and especially Barbara Gilbert. Linda Estelle, Executor of the Cowles Estate, was tremendously helpful as was Harriet Cowles (Waller), who gave the Cowles family papers to the University of Chicago and met with me in St. Louis. On behalf of the Ecological Society of America, Prof. Robert K. Peet of the University of North Carolina donated student notebooks from Cowles' classes to the University of Chicago that enabled me to bring the reader into his classroom. Daniel Meyer, Noel Pavlovic, and Eugene Cittadino read an earlier draft of this manuscript, found errors, and made valuable suggestions. Others who helped include Dr. John Arnold, Julia S. Bachrach, Lee Botts, Patricia P. Burg, Sarah Gibbard Cook, L. Ron Engel, Roberta Fountain, Christine Giannoni, Sheila Hoyos, Corasue Nicholas, Randy Nyboer, Joanna Olmsted, Laurel Ross, Tim E. Smith, Michael Steibert; and George Yaskievich. Help also came from the following institutions: Bancroft Library, University of California-Berkeley; Berlin-Peck Memorial Library, Berlin, CT; Chesterton Public Library, Chesterton, IN; Chicago Academy of Sciences; Chicago Historical Society; Filson Historical Society, Louisville, KY; John Crerar Library, University of Chicago; Johns Hopkins University Library, Baltimore, MD; Indiana University Northwest Library, Gary, IN; Nebraska Historical Society, Omaha, NE; Newberry Library, Chicago, IL; New York Botanical Gardens Library, New York, NY; Northwestern University Archives, Evanston, IL; Oberlin College Archives; Prairie Club, Elmhurst, IL; Sterling Morton Library, Morton Arboretum, Lisle, IL; University of Georgia Library; University of Illinois Archives; University of Western Michigan Archives; Wisconsin Historical Society; and Yale University Library.

I would also like to thank my publisher, Thomas Sigel, Josh McClary, Production Editor, and Jessica Sanchez, Marketing Manager at Kedzie-Sigel Press for making this project a reality. I also extend thanks to Harp Mando for creating the cover and interior design.

Note on Sources

Abbreviations used after first reference in notes

HCC   Henry Chandler Cowles
HCW   Harriet Cowles Waller
UCL   University of Chicago Library

In citing works in the notes, short titles are generally used. Works frequently cited are identified by the following abbreviations after first reference:

EC Borderline
Eugene Cittadino, "Borderline Science: Expert Testimony and the Red River Boundary Dispute," *Isis* 95 (2004): 183–219.

EC Dunes
Eugene Cittadino, "A 'Marvelous Cosmopolitan Preserve': The Dunes, Chicago, and the Dynamic Ecology of Henry Cowles," *Perspectives on Science* 1, no. 3, (1993): 520–59.

HCC Papers
The primary source for original material on Cowles is the Henry Chandler Cowles Papers at the University of Chicago Library, Department of Special Collections.

HCW Address
Harriet Cowles Waller, "An Address To Be Given by Harriet Cowles Waller During the Henry Chandler Cowles Memorial Symposium at the Annual Meeting of the Ecological Society of America on August 11, 1983." The University of Chicago Library has a transcript of this talk.

SAF Papers
The Stephen A. Forbes Papers in the University of Illinois Archives, Champaign.

Sacred Sands
J. Ron Engel, *Sacred Sands: The Struggle for Community in the Indiana Dunes* (Middletown, CT: Wesleyan University Press, 1983).

UCBDR
The University of Chicago Department of Botany records are housed in the University of Chicago Library, Department of Special Collections.

USSC
Cowles gave testimony before the Supreme Court of the United States. The transcript of his remarks (In The Supreme Court Of The United States *State of Oklahoma* Complainant v. *State of Texas* Defendant United States of America Intervener No. 20 Original October Term 1921). Stenographic Report of Proceedings Had Before Hon. Frederick S. Tyler, Special Commissioner Vol. 27 September 1921, Oklahoma City, Oklahoma.

Chapter 1

BEFORE THE DUNES

Henry Chandler Cowles grew up on a farm in Connecticut during the years that followed the American Civil War. Kensington, where he was born on 27 February 1869, is a hamlet in the scenic, somewhat hilly, center of the state. Nearby are Berlin (population 1,869 in 1850), an early manufacturing town known for tinware, and New Britain, a production center for builders' hardware and carpenters' tools. Hartford, a major city, lies about ten miles northeast of Kensington, and New Haven is roughly twenty-five miles to the south.[1]

Henry was the elder son of Henry Martyn Cowles (1831–1915) and Eliza Whittlesey (1839–1888). The family traces itself to a John Cowles who emigrated from England in 1640. According to a genealogy, Henry Martyn Cowles was "a farmer and market gardener; member of the Legislature; deacon in the Congregational Church; Sunday school superintendent; Prohibitionist; constable; assessor; justice of the peace; selectman, and member of the board of relief." Dwight (1874–1930), the younger Cowles son, lived locally and never married.[2]

Eliza Whittlesey was the daughter of a Cleveland judge. While she was visiting a relative in Kensington, she met Henry Martyn Cowles and they married on 31 May 1866. Active in church, Eliza was a teacher in Sunday school. She loved the outdoors and taught her son the names of plants and trees as they walked in the woods. Eliza fell ill while Henry was still a boy and became a permanent invalid. After

---

[1] *The Connecticut Guide* (Meriden, CT: Emergency Relief Commission, 1935), 167–71; Arthur S. Hughes and Morse S. Allen, *Connecticut Place Names* (Hartford: The Connecticut Historical Society, 1976), 15–19; and John C. Pease and John M. Niles, *A Gazetteer of the States of Connecticut and Rhode Island* (Hartford: William S. Marsh, 1819), 55–58.

[2] Colonel Calvin Duvall Cowles, *Genealogy of the Cowles Families in America*, 2 vols. (New Haven, CT: Tuttle, Morehouse & Taylor, 1929),779–80. HCC filled out forms for this volume and corresponded with the author.

eight to ten years as a shut-in, she died on 13 September 1888. Henry was devastated by her death.[3]

The Congregational Church

The Cowles were members of the Kensington Congregational Church, the center of their community. This church, which arose in England in the late sixteenth and seventeen centuries, came to New England soon after the Pilgrims did and set up many communities, such as Kensington, which were based on its religious principles. Congregationalists believe in the spiritual autonomy of each congregation; that is, its right and responsibility to decide about its own affairs without submission to any higher human authority. They oppose state establishment of religion and advocate civil and religious liberty.

Congregationalist principles regulated community life as Henry was growing up. Kensington's people worked hard and late, went to church every Sunday, and made civic decisions by consensus in town meetings. The young were expected to participate in church and to become self-reliant. Henry was a committed Christian, who remained a member of the Kensington Congregational Church throughout his life. In Chicago, he joined the University Congregational Church and sometimes worshipped at the Hyde Park Presbyterian Church.[4]

According to a history of the state, Connecticut farmers had "a hard time holding their own" while Henry was growing up. In 1874 the Connecticut Bureau of Labor Statistics surveyed farmers, finding that most of them worked from dawn to dusk and earned less than their counterparts in manufacturing. Farms farther west were more productive, so Connecticut adjusted by raising crops that were "suited to the distinct soil, climate, and seasons of the state such as vegetables, fruits, tobacco, and dairy products," the history states. The Cowles family grew fruits and vegetables in summer and winter crops in heated greenhouses, selling its produce locally. The family always had enough to eat, but there

---

[3] The account of Eliza Whittlesey Cowles comes from the Kensington Congregational Church, *Church Record*, 15 October 1888. The description of Henry as a child comes from HCW Address. The University of Chicago Library Department of Special Collections has a transcript of this talk.

[4] *Encyclopedia Britannica*, 15th ed., s.v. "Congregationalists." See also Clarence M. Webster, *Town Meeting Country* (NY: Duell, Sloan & Pierce, 1945).

was never much for extras. Henry needed jobs and scholarships to finance his higher education.[5]

Like most farm boys, Henry (family name: Harry) had plenty to do. He liked growing vegetables and flowers, checked the fields and greenhouses daily, and became his father's precociously capable assistant. Off and on, from 1880, when he was eleven years old, until 1896, when he was a graduate student, Henry kept a diary in small notebooks. Most of the narrative in this chapter, especially the personal parts, is based upon these diaries.[6]

At the age of eleven and twelve, Henry tended beets, onions, kale, spinach, and flowers, delivered orders in a horse-drawn cart, and kept careful track of the seed supply. "I sent another letter to W. Atlee Burpee & Co. for Cuban Queen Watermelon, Turks Turban tomato, and *dianthus chinensis* [pink] double dwarf mixed," he wrote on 22 January 1882. He described his activities with academic exactitude—"pulled 175 beets," "potted 242 of my tomatoes." He rarely expressed an opinion in his diary, had little to say about his father, and only mentioned his mother when she died.

Each week Henry visited the local library, returned one book, and withdrew another. He favored nonfiction—*Leaders of Men, African Adventurers and Explorers, Curiosities of Human Nature*, and *History of London*. Without comment, he recorded the deaths of local people, also the famous: Mary Todd Lincoln, Charles Darwin, Ralph Waldo Emerson, and the Bey of Tunis. He subscribed to several periodicals, including a now-forgotten magazine about bird's-egg collecting called *The Young Oologist*.

In 1883, when he was fourteen years old, Henry joined the Young Peoples' Society for Christian Endeavor at church. Quite new at the time, this interdenominational missionary organization was founded, in 1881, primarily as an activity for youth. Society policy stated that young people were expected to run their own meetings and every member was strongly encouraged to participate. Christian Endeavor

---

[5] Ruth O. M. Andersen, *From Yankee to American: Connecticut, 1865 to 1914* (Chester, CT: Pequot Press, 1975), 47–48. In 1894, Henry Martyn Cowles, who was then a sixty-three-year-old widower with grown children, apparently sold the farm and moved to nearby Southington, where he remarried and lived for the rest of his life.

[6] Henry Chandler Cowles, Papers at the University of Chicago Library, Department of Special Collections. HCC Papers include diaries dated 1880, 1881–82, 1882–83, 1883–85, 1885–86, 1886–87, 1888, 1890–91, 1892–93, 1894, 1895, 1895–96, and 1898. There are datebooks for later dates, but these contain only brief notations and addresses in back.

gave Henry experience in group activities and public speaking. Presentations about Christian Endeavor missions in China and other foreign countries broadened Henry's view of the world. Years later, he told his daughter that he had learned a lot in church.

Throughout his life, Henry joined organizations and used personal contacts to advance his career, creating opportunities for himself by the impression that he made on his elders. Fully grown he was five feet seven inches tall, with brown hair and eyes, a pleasant open face, and a ready laugh. People liked him, but he was never a leader and he functioned best when men with more forceful personalities gave him direction. His father was the first such influence in his life. John M. Coulter, professor of botany at the University of Chicago, introduced him to ecology. Jens Jensen and Stephen Forbes got him into conservation.

Henry always took time for fun. He saw Barnum's circus and listed every single act in his diary. In the sideshow, he saw "a fat woman with whiskers," "a girl with two heads," "trained monkeys, Zulus, [and] the tortures of Inquisition." With chums, he founded the Kensington Weeding Association and was elected president. For several years, the association had an annual picnic. He and his brother, Dwight, merged their respective "museums of curiosities" into The Cowles National Museum. He attended numerous community gatherings where the people of Kensington entertained themselves with group singing, poetry recitals, oratorical contests, and the like.

New Britain High School

Kensington and New Britain were legally united during the 1880s, so Henry was able to attend New Britain High School. John H. Peck, A.M., a classical scholar and pedagogical martinet, was principal of this first-class institution. According to Edith A. Adams in *The High School, New Britain Connecticut, 1850–1950*, a pamphlet that was apparently produced and circulated in New Britain, Peck "never spared himself nor expected others to coddle themselves. Students knew they were in high school on trial, and they must meet the scholastic and citizenship requirements or be expelled."

Henry took the Classical Course, which included Latin prose composition, Caesar, Virgil, and Cicero. He learned to read and write ancient Greek, studying Homer's *Iliad* and Xenophon's military histories. Other courses included mathematics, bookkeeping, English and American literature, composition, singing, drawing, and penmanship.

Science at New Britain High comprised physiology, physical geography, physics, astronomy, geology, and botany. The botany texts were *How Plants Grow (1858)* by Asa Gray and *Apgar's Plant Analysis; adapted to Gray's botanies* (1874), by E. A. and A. C. Apgar. Henry cherished these books all of his life because they "seemed to open up for him the entire plant kingdom," his daughter has written. Mr. Elliott, the botany teacher, led the class on field trips and had them examine pollens through a compound microscope.[7]

These classroom experiences and his readings in botany spurred Henry to study nature systematically. Roaming the local woods and fields, he collected plants, identified them by their Latin names, pressed them, and recorded where and when he had found each specimen. On 16 July 1885 he had four hundred dried plants. Ten months later, he purchased Gray's *Manual of Botany*, the authoritative flora, and used it thereafter to confirm his field identifications. Quickly mastering the common varieties, he discovered what he termed "a new kind of [T]*rifolium* [clover]" in June 1886. At the end of the summer, he identified "white snakeroot, which is new to me." Once he even went botanizing in a snowstorm.

Local newspapers awakened Henry to public affairs. Characteristically, he pursued these interests through organizations. On 9 February 1886, shortly before his seventeenth birthday, he applied for membership in the Grange, the social, educational, and political organization that serves agricultural interests. At Grange meetings, he listened to political debates and heard speeches by U.S. senators. A staunch prohibitionist, he became Chair of Temperance in the Christian Endeavor Society. In July 1887 he canvassed locally for the Prohibition Party, but hated this and soon quit, declaring that "It is none of my business how people vote."

At about the age of sixteen, Henry discovered girls. He had "a bootyful time" at a social on 3 November 1885 and, somewhat later, "a deli-

---

[7] This account is constructed from: HCC Papers: Diaries; HCW Address; and materials supplied by the New Britain Public Library, New Britain, CT. These include a pamphlet, Edith A. Adams, author & comp., *The High School, New Britain Connecticut, 1850–1950* (n.p., n.d. [1950?]); *New Britain High School, 1884–85*, and *1886–87* (Annual Reports: From Report of the Superintendent of Schools); and *Annual Report of the Selectmen, Treasurer, and the Several Departments of the Town of New Britain* for 1885, 1886, 1887, and 1888.

Henry's religious zeal, faithful attendance at church, and willingness to work brought him pleasing recognition. The Kensington Congregational Church *Church Record* mentioned him by name several times over the years. It published extracts from his high school valedictory oration on patriotism and his poem "Ode on America." (Church records are preserved in the Berlin-Peck Public Memorial Library, Berlin, CT.)

cious time" with Alice Upson, the deacon's daughter. In spring of the next year, he presented flowers to a sweetheart named "her" and later wrote "her" something in Latin. The two went riding in June and he spent the entire day of 5 July with "the best of all my findings." "*Quam amo* [she I love]" may have been a second interest. She appeared in October, but did not last the winter. On 11 February 1887 Henry went out walking with "my new and best 'her.'"

Henry found ways to combine learning with romance. "Our geology class met at the home of Mr. Marlin Wiard to view diatoms, rhizopods, and other minute forms of animal and vegetable life," he wrote on 12 December 1887. "We saw some very minute oysters. Perhaps—does it harm to say it?—the best time was afterwards, for I walked home with her [underlined in the original], and had a very sweet time, of course." Sometimes, after a day of botanizing, he would bring plant specimens to a female classmate. As the two identified and pressed the plants, her parents no doubt exchanged knowing looks. Some of these encounters led to moonlight walks.

Henry got along with almost everyone, except for Mr. Peck, the principal of his high school. "I am on the war-path," he declared on 28 February 1888. "Prof. Peck handed back my [graduation speech] and growled out, 'Won't do, don't do you credit' and so on and so forth. 'Have to be rewritten.' But will it, though. We shall see. It may be and then again it may not be. Really, Mr. Peck, there is a bare chance of its being rewritten, very bare; to be sure, but then, you know, dying people cling to a straw." It seems that no one blinked until a female teacher took Henry aside, consoled him, and explained that he simply had to rewrite the speech. Even after that, Peck made changes. On graduation day, Henry spoke his own words, ignoring most of the unwelcome improvements.

On 27 March 1888 Henry graduated first in his class from New Britain High School. His Class Night prediction was that "I become famous as a prohibition orator . . . also as a musician and a poet. . . . In the future, I am to be an orator, go to the West Indies, marry a Cuban lady, get divorced, come back home, and live the remainder of my days with the love of my youth, Little Mary, whoever that may be." This is complete nonsense, of course, but it suggests that classmates were impressed with Henry's intelligence and speaking skills.

At a loose end after graduation, Henry was offered opportunities. His pastor "desires to have me enter the ministry if I see that it is my duty," he wrote in his diary on 23 August. On 13 September a fruit farmer invited him to become foreman of a peach orchard. On 10 October a relative offered Henry part ownership of an insurance agency for which he would be the salesman. Instead, he earned eighteen dollars a week working for his father, botanized, attended meetings of Christian Endeavor and the Grange, courted girls, and volunteered for the Prohibition Party. In August, he traveled with the party, selling temperance books and campaign buttons in the tent where orators spoke. This was apparently the end of Henry's political career. There is no record that he joined another political party or worked on behalf of any candidate for public office.

Oberlin College

No diary is extant between 10 October 1888, when Henry was living in Kensington, and 6 April 1890, when much of his first year at Oberlin College was behind him. Those nineteen months are a blank and we do not know what Henry was doing, when he decided on college, and why he chose Oberlin.

He probably worked for his father, built up a savings account, and applied for college scholarships. Oberlin may have been chosen because it was an accommodating place for a young man with Henry's background. Founded in 1833 by a Presbyterian minister to train clergy and teachers for the West, Oberlin was a religiously observant school where students were expected to attend chapel. Oberlin also had a tradition of openness. It became the nation's first coeducational college and one of the first to admit blacks. Henry, who had neither money nor high-level social contacts, might have felt isolated in an elite eastern college. These things did not matter at Oberlin. In 1889, when he enrolled, there were 812 men and 901 women in the college, for a total student body of 1,713.[8]

Henry's manner of living did not change much during his first years at Oberlin. He went faithfully to church, joined Christian Endeavor and the Grange, got active in clubs, courted a succession of sweethearts, and botanized whenever he could. He roomed in the houses of faculty members and sometimes played cards with them. In his freshman year, he studied analytic geometry, Horace, rhetoric, and Latin composition.

---

[8] John Barnard, *From Evangelicalism to Progressivism at Oberlin College, 1866–1917* (Columbus: Ohio State University Press, 1969), chap. 3; Oberlin College Archives Finding Guide: RG 30/17, Albert Allen Wright (1846–1905) [description of A. A. Wright Papers]; and *General Catalogue of Oberlin College, 1833–1908* (Oberlin, OH: Oberlin College, 1909). Oberlin may possibly have been chosen in part because Henry's maternal uncle, Henry Whittlesey, lived in nearby Cleveland. He may have provided temporary room and board and kept a benevolent eye on his young nephew.

He became so proficient in classical languages that he composed odes in Latin and delivered a Greek oration to his graduating class. He would later say that he did "not at all regret" the seven years he spent studying Greek and Latin.[9] Other college work included French, German, chemistry, botany, and geology. On 12 December 1890 he made sixty mistakes in a French test, sputtering that "it is beyond the power of language to describe the fiendish character of the same."

Chemistry, especially lab, was more to his taste and he advanced to qualitative analysis. Prof. Albert Allen Wright taught him botany, vegetable histology, cryptogamous forms, and general and glacial geology. Wright also paid Henry fifteen cents per hour to mount plants in the Oberlin herbarium and appointed him his assistant in the botanical laboratory.

Wright would later state in a letter of recommendation that Henry was already "an excellent field botanist" when he arrived at Oberlin with a "quick and sure and wide knowledge especially of vascular plants."[10] According to him, Henry spent his vacations in the field and "brought to light many new species" in the "pretty well worked region" around Oberlin. One of these was *Dirca palustris* or leatherwood, a low, woody shrub with small yellow flowers that grows in moist woods. In spring 1890 Henry discovered the first known specimen in Lorain County, Ohio.

On 26 April Henry and a friend sought *Dirca palustris* and other specimens for Professor Wright. They began the day in a pouring rainstorm, but persevered and found every plant they sought. "When we wished to go home," Henry writes, "we found ourselves on the wrong side of the Black River, two miles from a bridge, so we walked through the river with our shoes on, with the water up to our knees!" They "looked and felt like drowned rats" when they got home. That evening Henry delivered *Dirca palustris* to Wright and brought violets and trilliums to a Miss Clark.

The quest for *Dirca palustris* was one of many expeditions that combined everything Henry liked best: botany, outdoor adventure, and the fair sex. His diaristic accounts of these jaunts tell of encounters with poisonous snakes, conversations with old-time settlers, and suspicious looks from policemen. He usually ended the day with a hearty dinner and a flirtation. At about this time in his life, Henry raised a neat

---

[9] HCC, "The Economic Trend of Botany," *Science* 61, no. 1049 (12 February 1915): 225.

[10] Albert A. Wright , letter of recommendation, 31 January 1896, HCC Papers. Wright (1846–1905) was professor of geology and natural history (1874–97), professor of botany (1878–91), and curator of the Oberlin Museum (1874–1905).

mustache, which hung over his mouth on either side. He kept his hair short, parting it on the left.

Henry's joining ways continued at Oberlin. He attended meetings of the Young Men's Christian Association, an oratorical association, a temperance club, a Greek club, the botany club (he was president), and the Agassiz Association (he was president). Named after the naturalist Louis Agassiz, this association was founded in 1875 on the principle "Study nature, not books." Henry apparently joined the association at its peak, but did not stay long. He was a member of so many groups that his diary often just states: "Went to all the meetings."

After awhile, Henry loosened up in college. He skipped class and chapel to botanize, partied past midnight, and spent hours playing Halma, a Victorian ancestor of Chinese checkers. Viewing girls less innocently than before, he discovered tobacco, and once consumed "a drink of moonshine whiskey." This from a man who had voted a straight Prohibition ticket in his first election.

Geology eclipsed botany during Henry's final year at Oberlin. On a field trip, he found geodes, which he brought to Professor Wright. "He has none like them," Henry's diary states, "and was a bit surprised that they were formed in trap rock." After graduating with high honors in spring of 1893, Henry worked in town for awhile, and took the train home in August. "My trip was made of more interest," he wrote, "by the geological railway guide, which I carried. From Corry, Pa. to Deposit, N.Y., a distance of three hundred miles, we went over the gray Chemung shales and sandstones of the Upper Devonian. All along this whole distance, valley drift, kames, and boulders are to be seen." By 19 August he had "pretty nearly made up [his] mind to specialize in Geology instead of Botany."

The University of Chicago

Professor Wright probably pointed Henry toward the University of Chicago, which was a perfect place for him.[11] The university was founded in 1890 by the Baptist Education Society and John D. Rockefeller, the oil baron. Marshall Field, owner of the Chicago department store that

---

[11] Charles Chamberlain was a year ahead of Cowles at Oberlin and preceded him to the University of Chicago. Professor Wright knew some of the scientists at Chicago and was able to place promising students there, like Chamberlain and Cowles. According to EC Dunes, Chamberlain expected to study botany at Chicago and complained to President Harper when no courses were available. To pacify him, Harper recruited Coulter to lecture at Chicago and later appointed him chairman of the department of botany.

bears his name, donated land in the recently annexed suburb of Hyde Park. William Rainey Harper, the first president, envisioned a university that would combine an American-style undergraduate liberal arts college with a German-style graduate research facility.

The University of Chicago held its first classes in 1892, so it was just two years old on 2 January 1894 when Henry enrolled in a new department headed by glacial geologist Thomas C. Chamberlin. On his first day, he and Professor Chamberlin "talked over matters," and he decided to take general geology, geographic geology (sedimentation), and paleontology.

At Chicago, Henry studied with Chamberlin and Rollin D. Salisbury, the physiographer, hunted fossils along the Calumet River south of the city, and joined the geology club and the University Congregational Church. He conversed with at least one "fair damsel," got into an all-night card game, and went downtown to an evening lecture by Henry George, the economist. In March, he applied for a fellowship. There is no diary from 18 April to 28 June, so we do not know precisely what happened, but it seems that he got no fellowship, ran out of money, went home, and found a teaching job through church connections. On 7 September he was enroute to Gates College in Neligh, Nebraska.

Scandal at Gates College

Neligh is located on a small plateau on the north bank of the Elkhorn River in northeastern Nebraska. Nearby are areas of geologic and natural importance—today's Ashfall Fossil Beds State Historical Park and Niobrara State Park. Gates College was founded in 1882 by the Congregational Church and survived only sixteen years. During Henry's ten months at Gates, the college struggled to meet its payroll and was torn apart by scandal.

All went well at first. On the day after his arrival, Henry began to meet people, fixed his lab, which was "in horrible shape," looked for a place to live, and announced that "I like the place immensely, especially the view from College Hill." On Sunday he went to church, found everyone "delightfully cordial," and inspected a hill north of town where the flowers and soil were "almost entirely new" to him. He taught physical geography, geology, zoology, chemistry, physiology and botany to "some of the cream of the students." Later in life, he would joke that he had occupied "not a chair, but a settee" of the sciences at Gates since he taught so many subjects. Soon he was active in church, playing tennis with friends, and riding horseback with a young lady.

Henry also did some serious reading at Gates. According to his diary, he read the *Omaha Bee* and *Omaha World Herald* every day and absorbed ten weekly journals: *Scientific-American, Journal of Education, Public Opinion, Harper's Weekly, Christian Advocate, Epworth Herald, Golden Rule, Congregationalist, Outlook,* and *Advocate.* He also read six monthly periodicals: *Popular Science Monthly, North American Review, Review of Reviews, Missionary Review, Century,* and *Forum.* On top of all this, he especially liked the Sunday newspaper funnies.

In April 1895 a local newspaper accused Charles E. Pascoe, who had recently joined the Gates College senior class, of plagiarism. The charges were proven and Gates' faculty met on 19 April to consider the case. Twenty-four hours later, the faculty voted to let Pascoe graduate if he fulfilled certain conditions. These conditions [unspecified in Henry's diary] were not fulfilled and it was later learned that Pascoe was three semesters' short of credits toward graduation. Someone was apparently pulling strings to get him a degree that he had not earned.

On 4 June Henry and other faculty members received threatening letters. Six days later, the Gates faculty met to determine which students should graduate. As Henry tells it, "All went fairly smoothly until we reached [Pascoe's] name when we engaged in a general free-for-all scrimmage . . . Dr. Ellis [president of Gates: he supported Pascoe's graduation] accused me of misrepresenting things to him [at an earlier time in a committee meeting] and his wife insulted me outright, practically calling me a liar. The scrap ended in [Ellis'] recommendation for graduation with Miss Chellis' [a faculty colleague] and my emphatic protest. We prepared statements of our side of the case for presentation to the trustees."

On 11 June a meeting of the trustees declined to hear Henry, Miss Chellis, and student representatives, who argued that graduating Pascoe amounted to an abandonment of academic standards. On commencement day, 12 June, five students refused their degrees and demanded Dr. Ellis' resignation. Two days after that, a colleague informed Henry that "my work had been good but that I had told too many things." According to this individual, someone blamed "that boy on the faculty" [i.e., Henry] for causing all the trouble.[12]

---

[12] The Neligh story is reconstructed from Cowles' 1895 diaries (HCC Papers) and contemporary newspaper clippings: "A Personal Word" [letter by Herbert E. Gregory] *Neligh Leader,* 14 June 1895; "Thompson's Yeoman Article: Why the Seniors Refused their Diplomas," *The Yeoman* (Neligh, Antelope County, Nebraska) 21 June 1895; "Why Ten of the Seniors Accepted Their Diplomas—The Standard of Gates Not Lowered" [article signed by P. H. Finfrock, Secretary of the Gates College Faculty] *The Yeoman,* 28 June 1895; "A Trustee's View of the Pascoe Controversy [letter signed by O. A. {name illegible}]

For a few days, Henry got away, leading students on a plant-collecting trip from Neligh, about sixty miles northward to the Niobrara River. He traveled alone in a "lop-sided, dirty-canvassed, shaky-wheeled, jammed-full prairie schooner," while the class used other conveyances. Everyone camped outdoors and numerous specimens were found. By the end of his tenure at Gates, Henry reported that he had collected and pressed 1,046 species and varieties of local plants.

On his return, Henry sat through more acrimonious meetings as he quietly negotiated his return to the University of Chicago. "My Dear Friend Cowles," wrote Professor Chamberlin on 22 June, "[I] am very glad to learn of your desire to study with us the coming year. I have seen Dr. Harper [university president] and he has expressed a desire to do what he can in the matter of a fellowship." Chamberlin also offered Henry paid work during the fall term "compiling paleontological data—especially the distribution of species, and the compilation of analytical geological maps." Later, he sent Henry a "most flattering letter" that offered him "some splendid work in Paleobotany, which is to begin with some collections this summer." Henry accepted "with avidity," resigned from Gates College on 16 July, and was soon Special Field Assistant with the U.S. Geological Survey under Chamberlin's supervision.[13]

August and September were spent hunting for ancient vegetal remains in the Southern Iowa Drift Plain. According to geologists, rock and soil (i.e., glacial drift) in this part of south central Iowa were pushed ahead of the Des Moines Lobe, or southernmost point of glacial advance in the state. Henry looked for subsoil exposed by highway and railroad cuts and excavated very dark layers called *old soil*. He also consulted with well diggers. Discouraged after seven solitary, fruitless days in the sun, he sought Chamberlin's advice and was told, "Stay and dig away."[14]

The Yeoman 5 July 1895; "To the Trustees of Gates College" [letter signed by P. H. Finfrock] *Neligh Leader,* July 13, 1895; "The displeasure with Dr. Ellis..." [unsigned commentary] *Neligh Leader,* 19 July 1895; "Voted by the Faculty of Gates College," [report on Gates College board meeting] *Neligh Leader,* 26 July 1895; "Norfolk Gets a College," *Omaha World Herald,* 8 September 1895.

[13] Thomas C. Chamberlin to HCC, 22 June 1895. Thomas C. Chamberlin, Letterbook 6, University of Chicago Library.

[14] Ibid., 9 August 1895. The account of Iowa geology comes from *Geology of Iowa: Over Two Billion Years of Change* by Wayne I. Anderson (Ames: Iowa State University Press, 1983), 215–30. Susan F. Schultz writes in "Thomas C. Chamberlin: An Intellectual Biography of a Geologist and Educator" (Ph.D. diss., University of Wisconsin-Madison, 1976) that Chamberlin "designated the forest bed between his Kansan and his Iowan tills the

On 21 August Henry found "a bonanza," a "nice lot of sticks and vegetal earth," including one stick that was two feet long. Two weeks later, he discovered "the best specimens yet" and on 24 September he excavated "as much as a bushel" of material. After crating the fragile specimens, he hired two railroad section men to transport them to a depot on a handcar. When the job was done, he set them up to cigars.

John Merle Coulter

All this activity could not disguise the fact that Henry had been drifting—and restless—since his graduation from Oberlin. Finances abruptly ended his first year at Chicago. Gates College was a stopgap and he understandably looked elsewhere during his eventful year in Neligh. Though he was relieved to escape the mess at Gates, he did not enjoy his solitary excavations beneath the Iowa sun. During his second graduate year at Chicago, he failed a test in crystallography and did unsatisfactory work for Professor Chamberlin, while he corresponded with universities in New York and South Dakota. He did not seem to know what he wanted.

John Merle Coulter (1851–1928) came to his rescue. He led Henry back to botany, introduced him to ecology, directed his thesis research, and hired him to teach at Chicago. Coulter and Cowles were similar in background and belief. Son of a Presbyterian missionary, Coulter lost his father early in youth and was raised by his mother in Hanover, a small Indiana town. After studying Latin and science at Hanover College, he spent five months in 1872 as an assistant geologist with the Ferdinand V. Hayden Expedition that explored Yellowstone and the Grand Tetons. When Hayden discovered that Coulter was collecting plant specimens in his spare time instead of playing cards like the other men, he appointed him expedition botanist.

While he was teaching plant taxonomy at Hanover College in 1875, Coulter founded the *Botanical Gazette* "to afford a convenient and

---

'Aftonian' for its exposure at a railway excavation near Afton Junction, Iowa" (p. 227). Cowles visited Afton, but his diary does not state clearly that he excavated there.

Paul Sears writes in *The Biology of the Living Landscape: An Introduction to Ecology* (London: Allen & Unwin, 1962), 77, that Cowles was assigned to find a geological formation and failed because it did not exist. This incident is said to have convinced Cowles that he would never succeed in geology and so he turned to botany. Nothing that the author has seen in Cowles' diaries or his correspondence with Chamberlin supports these assertions. Cowles remained in the department of geology for months after his return from Iowa and the record shows that Coulter actively recruited Cowles into the department of botany.

rapid means of communications among botanists." This professional journal, which is still published, became a leader in its field and a major outlet for Henry. In 1881 Coulter and his brother Stanley compiled the first Indiana flora, cataloging plants that Henry would later study at the Indiana Dunes. In 1893 Coulter became president of Lake Forest College, north of Chicago, expecting to build the college into a major university.[15]

After about a year at Lake Forest, Coulter concluded that he could never raise the money that the college required. At roughly the same time, the University of Chicago received a $1 million endowment to create a botany department and erect a building for it. In 1894 President Harper, who had known Coulter for some years, asked him to deliver botany lectures on Saturday mornings at the university. Roughly a year later, Harper followed this with an invitation to found a botany department. In 1896 Coulter left Lake Forest College to become head professor of botany at Chicago.[16]

Henry attended Coulter's Saturday botany lectures and apparently approached him after one of them. "Talked with Prof. Coulter about my work," he wrote in his diary for 1 October 1895. "[H]e is a fine man to meet and is likely to be of much assistance to me, as my first work [on glacial vegetal remains] must be a study of native woods." On 4 January 1896 the two men talked about Henry's future, and Coulter began to draw a very willing Henry into his orbit. On 29 February Henry had "quite a talk with Dr. Coulter [who] strongly encouraged me to take up some good work in botany." On 21 March they had a "satisfactory talk . . . about next year's work." The two went botanizing on 30 March and the following day. Soon after, Henry joined the botany department for good. Coulter got a capable, enthusiastic botanist with teaching experience, which was precisely what he and President Harper wanted for the new botany department. They envisioned staffing it with two senior professors and "promising younger men."

---

[15] Andrew Denny Rodgers III, *John Merle Coulter: Missionary in Science* (Princeton, NJ: Princeton University Press, 1944) is the source of this history of Coulter's life. Coulter corresponded with William Rainey Harper, president of the University of Chicago, whose letters are in the Department of Special Collections at the UCL. See also "Henry Chandler Cowles," an unpublished memoir by Charles J. Chamberlain in the Department of Special Collections at the UCL.

[16] According to the *University of Chicago Annual Register* for 1893–94, the Department of Botany employed John Coulter as "Professorial Lecturer in Botany" and Henry L. Clarke as his assistant. Coulter gave 9:30 Saturday morning lectures on plant morphology, plant anatomy, plant physiology, and advanced laboratory work. Mr. Clarke taught plant evolution, special laboratory work, and elementary practical botany.

Coulter introduced Henry to ecology through an extension course that he began to teach at Chicago on 11 April 1896. Ecology was very new at the time, having originated in Europe during the 1860s. Coulter knew what was happening, saw ecology as a coming thing, and wanted it to have a presence at the young, ambitious University of Chicago. Eastern colleges viewed ecology as an upstart pseudoscience.

Origin of Ecology

The notion of nature as an interdependent system goes back to the Greeks, but its modern history begins with Charles Darwin, who "made ecology inevitable," says Paul Sears in *Charles Darwin: The Naturalist as a Cultural Force* (1950). Sears explains that Darwin's work "carried in it the seed of two aspects of natural science. One of them—the science of variation and inheritance, now called genetics, he had clearly predicted. The other was implicit in his thesis, and to it in 1866 [Ernst] Haeckel [German zoologist and proponent of Darwin's theory of evolution] gave the name Oecology." Darwin "really made it impossible," Sears continues, "to think of life apart from environment. Biochemistry had already, in its earliest phases, shown life to be dependent upon a continuing interchange of material and energy with the environment. But Darwin went even further, asserting as he did that environment had from the beginning built itself into the very form and organization of life. And so Darwin, dealing primarily with the interrelations of life and environment, was thus himself one of the first and greatest of ecologists."[17]

Botanists were the first people after Darwin to study the interrelationships between organisms and the environment. Plants are visible and they stay put, which makes them easier to study than animals. Gottlieb Haberlandt, the German botanist, pioneered autecology—the study of the response of individual organisms to their environment—in his *Physiological Plant Anatomy* (1884). Among other things, he

---

[17] Paul B. Sears, *Charles Darwin: The Naturalist as a Cultural Force* (NY: Charles Scribner's Sons, 1950). Though Cowles parted from Chamberlin and Salisbury, he acknowledged that they had taught him dynamic geologic processes—the advance and retreat of the glaciers, how melting ice created the Great Lakes, and how water levels rose and fell to erode river valleys. He drew on this knowledge in his studies of the Indiana Dunes and later, as a professor of ecology, he expected his students to learn geology.

explained why identical plants grow thicker, denser leaves in sun than in shade.[18]

Eugenius Warming, the Danish botanist, became a key influence on Cowles. As Sears tells it in *The Biology of the Living Landscape* (1964), Warming made "a minute study" of the glaciated Danish landscape, where "natural forces were . . . at work to restore an equilibrium. Drifting dunes were being anchored by vegetation, lakes being converted to swamps and bogs, while plant succession both on dune and bog was moving on toward stabilized climax." In *Plantesamfund* [Plant Ecology] (1895), Warming demonstrated that "plant communities arise and progress toward stability by succession," Sears writes, "and that this is in effect, part of a geologic process."[19]

Charles J. Chamberlain, who attended Coulter's lectures as a student and later joined the University of Chicago faculty, recalled in a memoir that "none of us could read [Warming's] Danish except a Danish student, who would translate a couple of chapters, and the next day Coulter would give a wonderful lecture on Ecology. . . . Cowles, with his superior knowledge of taxonomy and his geology, understood more than the rest of us, and became so interested that he studied Danish and, long before any translation appeared, could read the book in the original. . . . The treatment of such sand dunes as Warming knew, started Henry on his study of the comparatively immense moving dunes south of the University."[20]

Plantesamfund was translated from Danish into German and published in 1896 as *Lehrbuch der ökologischen Pflanzengeographie* [Textbook of Ecological Plant Geography]. When this German language translation appeared in July 1896 Henry prepared a synopsis for Coulter, who reviewed the book in *Botanical Gazette* (July–December 1896). "The geographical distribution of plants has received much attention for many years," Coulter wrote in this review, "but the earlier observers could do little more than accumulate facts and outline general zones. With the development of plant physiology," he continued, "it became possible to organize these facts upon a scientific basis, and this

---

[18] Gottleib Haberlandt, *Physiological Plant Anatomy*, trans. Montagu Drummond [of 4th German ed.] (London: Macmillan, 1914).

[19] Paul B. Sears, *The Biology of the Living Landscape: An Introduction to Ecology* (London: Allen & Unwin, 1962), chap. 6. This book is one of many sources on the history of ecology, which present a variety of factual material and interpretations. Our purpose here is simply to set Cowles in context.

[20] See also "Henry Chandler Cowles," an unpublished memoir by Charles J. Chamberlain, UCL.

organization introduces us into the great modern field of ecology of which geographical distribution is a conspicuous part." Henry was so taken with Warming, ecology, and plant geography that Coulter encouraged him to assemble a field course in plant geography for summer of 1896. He promised that the course would become permanent if successful. Henry was on his way to becoming a teacher of ecology.

We are getting ahead of ourselves. On Saturday, 25 April 1896, Henry and two friends went botanizing in Dune Park, Indiana. "This was my first experience in a sand dune country," he wrote. "We climbed up the wonderful piles of sand and saw acres and acres stretching up and down the lake, billowy like a prairie or vast drifts of snow. The sand dune flora is very characteristic and new to me." Henry did not know it then, but he had found the place that would inspire his greatest work and make his name.[21]

---

[21] In HCW Address, HCW says that Cowles was visiting the Chicago World's Columbian Exposition in Chicago in 1893, passed by the Indiana Dunes in a train, and was so taken with them that he alighted at the first opportunity and walked back to inspect them. Variant versions of this story place the incident later. Cowles' diary and his introduction to "Ecological Relations" confirm that he first saw the dunes in 1896. He may have concocted this fable for Harriet when she was a small child or she may have invented it herself

Chapter 2

IN HIGH GEAR

Between April 1896, when he first visited the Indiana Dunes, and summer of 1913, when he led European and American plant scientists on the International Phytogeographic Excursion in America, Henry Cowles transformed himself from a gifted graduate student into a plant ecologist of international reputation. He did field research in seventeen states, two Canadian provinces, Belgium, Holland, and the United Kingdom. He published three major studies of plant succession and other important papers, made presentations at professional meetings, and wrote 89 reviews and notices of 281 botanical and ecological books and studies, mostly for *Botanical Gazette*.

At the University of Chicago, he advanced in academic rank from Laboratory Assistant in Ecology (1897) to Assistant (1898), Associate (1901), Instructor (1902), Assistant Professor (1907), Associate Professor (1911), and Professor of Ecology (1915). Starting with a blank sheet of paper, he created an ecology curriculum, expanded it as the field grew, and published *Part Two: Ecology* of the *Textbook of Botany for Colleges and Universities* in 1911. (Part One covered morphology and physiology.) Often called the *Chicago Textbook* by the botanical community, this volume was used all over the United States for almost twenty years.

Prominent in many professional organizations, Cowles helped to found the Association of American Geographers in 1904 and the Illinois Academy of Science in 1907. He engaged with the general public through the Chicago Academy of Sciences and Geographic Society of Chicago, and played an important part in a pioneering ecological survey of Illinois in 1909.

"The Ecological Relations"

Cowles' reputation rests on three studies of plant succession: "The Ecological Relations of the Vegetation on the Sand Dunes of Lake Michigan" (1899 published version of his 1898 doctoral dissertation); "The Physiographic Ecology of Chicago and Vicinity: A Study of the Origin, Development, and Classification of Plant Societies" (published the same year, 1901, in modified form as "The Plant Societies of Chicago and Vicinity"); and "The Influence of Underlying Rocks on the Character of the Vegetation" (1901). In "Ecological Relations," Cowles worked out the process of plant succession at the Indiana Dunes. In "Plant Societies," he expanded the scope of his investigations to include swamps, bogs, prairie, flood plains and other systems in the Chicago vicinity. In "Underlying Rocks," he explored the relationships between vegetation, soil, and underlying rocks in four different parts of the United States. These essays are republished in this volume; full publication details are in the Bibliography.

The Indiana Dunes, where Cowles did field research for "Ecological Relations," stretch roughly twenty-five miles across the crescent-shaped southern shore of Lake Michigan. In the west, closest to Illinois and well back from the shore, are the four-thousand-year-old Tolleston Dunes, completely stable and covered with vegetation. Eastward are younger dunes; Miller Dune, the easternmost, is still forming today. Shore dunes exist on other Great Lakes, on some North American seacoasts, and in Europe, but none compare in size and grandeur to those of Lake Michigan.[1]

Dunes sand originated in the extreme northern portions of the North American continent, where it was once ancient quartz bedrock. This rock erupted to the surface, where glaciers crushed it as they advanced and pushed it into the area where the Great Lakes are now. About thirteen thousand years ago, as the glaciers began to melt, they washed huge amounts of debris into the basins that became today's Great Lakes and the rivers that feed them. Over time, erosion reduced this material to sand, which accumulated on the shores of present-day Lake Michigan and at the mouths of rivers that empty into it. The sand at

---

[1] See Dennis A. Albert, *Borne of the Wind: An Introduction to the Ecology of Michigan Sand Dunes*, Report Number 2000-16 (Lansing: Michigan State University Extension, Michigan Natural Features Inventory, 2000); Elizabeth Tilman-Brockwell and Earl Wolf, *Discovering Great Lakes Dunes* (Muskegon, MI: Gillette Natural History Association, 1998); and Catherine L. Hill et al., *Our Changing Landscape: Indiana Dunes National Lakeshore*, U.S. Geological Survey Circular 1085 (Washington, D.C.: U.S. Government Printing Office, 1991). Tourists today can follow Cowles' footsteps through a succession of plant communities on the West Beach Trail at the Indiana Dunes National Lakeshore. See also Noel B. Pavlovic and Marlin L. Bowles, "Rare Plant Monitoring at the Indiana Dunes National Lakeshore," in *Science and Ecosystem Management in the National Parks*, eds. W. L. Halvorson and G. E. Davis (Tucson: University of Arizona Press, 1996), 253–80.

the Indiana Dunes contains quartz, silica, dolomite, and traces of iron ore and magnetite.

Wave action drove sand grains toward the southern and eastern shores of Lake Michigan. Heavier grains washed onto the beach and stayed there, while wind drove lighter grains further inland where they encountered obstacles, such as vegetation, that trapped and stabilized them. This sand slowly accumulated to become dunes, which range up to 118 feet above lake level in the area that Cowles studied and rise as much as 384 feet above lake level in Michigan.

During the centuries that passed as the Lake Michigan dunes formed, the lake level rose and fell many times. As the shoreline advanced and receded, new dunes formed in front of older ones and a complex of sand ridges, upland forests, oak savannas, and wetlands came into existence, creating a multiplicity of habitats, often within a few feet of each other. The Indiana Dunes are situated at the meeting point of the northern boreal forest, eastern deciduous forest, and the tallgrass prairie peninsula that traverses Illinois from west to east. This unique location and the many habitats at the Indiana Dunes result in a greater diversity of plant species than exists in any comparably sized area of North America.[2]

Botanists and geologists discovered and studied the Indiana Dunes in the nineteenth century. Industry mined the sand and transformed parts of the shore into harbors and plant sites. For decades, commerce and conservationists fought over the dunes. In 1925 the State of Indiana purchased dunes land that, with added parcels, became Indiana Dunes State Park. In 1966 the federal government protected the area's remaining wild lands by creating the Indiana Dunes National Lakeshore. Some Michigan dunes are protected. Mining has destroyed others.[3]

Cowles acquainted himself with dunes topography and flora during the summer of 1896, but no doctoral project jelled until autumn at the earliest. On 9 September he told Frederick V. Coville, a friend from the University of Chicago who had become a U.S. Department of Agriculture botanist, "I am at present endeavoring to strike some problem for my Ph.D. thesis. If I could get a subject suitable for a thesis and at the same time of practical value, I would be delighted."[4]

---

[2] See Jerry Sullivan et al, *An Atlas of Biodiversity* (Chicago: Chicago Region Biodiversity Council; n.d., but probably 1998).

[3] The best history of the battle for the dunes is *Sacred Sands*.

[4] HCC to F. V. Coville, 9 September 1896, HCC Papers.

Professor Coulter suggested an investigation of dunes ecology. He had visited the dunes in 1878 and published "The Flora of Northern Indiana," a scholarly paper, in 1879. He accompanied Cowles on early visits to the dunes, but a childhood accident had permanently weakened his knee and he could not keep up. Cowles, who was eighteen years younger, ventured into remote, little-known areas of the dunes. In "Ecological Relations" he acknowledges that Coulter directed him "along lines of ecological research."[5]

During 1896, 1897, and 1898 Cowles studied the dunes between Dune Park and Furnessville, Indiana, at all seasons of the year, and he visited dunes along the Michigan coastline in summer. He carried William K. Higley and Charles S. Raddin's reference work, *The Flora of Cook County, Illinois, and a Part of Lake County, Indiana*. Knowledgeable assistance came from Ellsworth Jerome Hill, a local amateur botanist, who published an ambitious four-part article, "Sand Dunes of North Indiana and Their Flora," in 1898. In "Ecological Relations" Cowles thanks Hill for his "valuable suggestions." Others who accompanied Cowles at the dunes include Bradley Moore Davis, a colleague in botany at the University of Chicago, and Burton E. Livingston, whose memoirs state that he "became intimate with Cowles at the time of his classic sand-dune studies."[6]

---

[5] John M. Coulter, "The Flora of Northern Indiana," *Botanical Gazette* 4 (1879): 109. On 2 July Cowles wrote in his diary: "Dr. Coulter greatly encouraged me by suggesting a possible permanent course in Plant Geography as a result of a successful summer field course." (2 July 1896; HCC Papers: Diaries). According to the *Annual Register of the University of Chicago* for 1896–97, Cowles, who was then a laboratory assistant in ecology, assisted Coulter in the Plant Ecology course. On 20 July Cowles wrote in his diary that he was "spending a large part of my time nowadays in reading Warming's Ecological Plant Geography for Dr. Coulter" and on 2 October he was "planning work in Plant Geography" (20 July; 2 October 1896; HCC Papers: Diaries). All this confirms Coulter's active role in shaping Cowles' doctoral dissertation and early academic career.

[6] A heavily annotated copy of Higley and Raddin's *The Flora of Cook County, Illinois, and a Part of Lake County, Indiana* (Chicago: Chicago Academy of Sciences, 1891) survives among Cowles' papers. E. J. Hill's "The Sand Dunes of Northern Indiana and their Flora" was published in *Garden and Forest*, no. 445 (2 September 1896): 353–54; no. 447 (16 September 1896): 372–73; no. 448 (23 September 1896): 382–83; and no. 449 (30 September 1896): 393–94. Burton E. Livingston, who was chair of forest ecology at Johns Hopkins University until his retirement in 1940, writes in "Some Conversational Autobiographical Notes on Intellectual Experiences and Development: An Auto-Obituary," *Ecology* 29, no. 3 (July 1948): 235–36, that Cowles' "main interests lay in the details of local plant distribution." He adds that Cowles' "great contribution was toward what he called physiographic plant ecology, which dealt with local features of distribution in terms of the physiographic characteristics of the corresponding plant habitats; he and his students studied vegetation rather than plant individuals or species in bogs and swamps, on beaches, flood plains, and bluffs, on moraines, in ravines." He closes by calling Cowles one of the most important influences on his scientific development.

Cowles completed his doctoral dissertation, "An Ecological Study of the Sand Dune Flora of Northern Indiana," early in 1898, defended it in March, and got his degree in April. Research continued in summer and fall as he revised his dissertation into "The Ecological Relations of the Vegetation on the Sand Dunes of Lake Michigan," a four-part article for *Botanical Gazette*. All notes and drafts for the dissertation and "Ecological Relations" are lost. The bound dissertation has disappeared from the University of Chicago Library. Most of the area that Cowles studied is today the site of a power plant and steel mill.

In "Ecological Relations," Cowles writes that ecology considers "the mutual relations between plants and their environment." He views ecology as "a study in dynamics" and regards flora "not as a changeless landscape feature, but rather as a panorama, never twice alike." Ecologists study "the order of succession" of plant communities "in the development of a region," he continues, and "endeavor to discover the laws, which govern the panoramic changes." To make sense of plant succession, ecologists must find plants whose tissues and organs are presently changing "in response to varying conditions" and plant formations that are "rapidly passing into other types by reason of a changing environment."

These requirements "are met *par excellence* [italics in the original] in a region of sand dunes," he states. Dunes are very unstable, which means that plants must adapt fast or perish. Also, because new dunes are completely devoid of vegetation, ecologists can study plant succession there without facing the perplexities associated with previous vegetation. When dunes advance over a swamp or forest and bury it, they offer plant life "a world for conquest, subject almost entirely to existing physical conditions." Nowhere else, he declares, "could many of the living problems of ecology be solved more clearly [or] . . . ecological principles be subjected to a more rigid test."

Epic in its scope, "Ecological Relations" describes the dynamic topography and flora of more than three hundred miles of the Lake Michigan shoreline. Cowles tells how Lake Michigan dunes behave from their unstable youth to settled old age. "The normal primitive forma-

Stanley Coulter (brother of John) almost certainly visited the dunes with Cowles. In *A Catalogue of the Flowering Plants and of the Ferns and Their Allies Indigenous to Indiana* (Indianapolis, IN: Report of the State Geologist, 1899), he writes that Cowles' researches at the dunes and his personal suggestions greatly improved his understanding of dunes flora and ecology. "So complete and satisfactory was the study of Dr. Cowles," Stanley Coulter states, "that previously prepared discussions of this flora have been discarded and his article [i.e., 'Ecological Relations'] taken as the basis of the presentation of the subject." E. W. Martyn, a professional photographer who served the University of Chicago, took most of the pictures for "Ecological Relations."

tion is the beach," he writes, "then in order, the stationary beach dunes, the active or wandering dunes, the arrested or transitional dunes, and the passive or established dunes."

Cowles next explains how light, heat, wind, soil, and water determine plant distribution on dunes and demonstrates how dunes vegetation modifies topography to create conditions for a succession of plant communities. Vegetation of established dunes passes through several stages, culminating in a deciduous mesophytic forest, the normal climax type in the lake region.

"Ecological Relations" tells literally step by step how plant succession works. Starting from the Lake Michigan beach where constant wave action prevents all plant growth, Cowles walked inland through a succession of plant communities that parallel the development of vegetation in time. He explains how dune flora stabilize the sand, making it possible for successor plants to take root, grow, reproduce, die, and eventually to create humus in which subsequent plant communities can flourish. The climax community, or final stage in succession, remains in place until conditions change.

Like other early natural history studies, such as those of Charles Darwin, "Ecological Relations" is primarily descriptive. Cowles presents much new information, but provides no survey data, and his results are neither reproducible nor usable as a baseline. Also, Cowles was cautious in the claims he made and never announced a complete theory of succession. A new generation of ecologists—some were his students—refined, amplified, and challenged his conclusions. But everyone started from Cowles, for he was the pathbreaker, the pioneer.[7]

---

[7] According to Dr. Noel Pavlovic, plant ecologist at the Lake Michigan Ecological Research Station, Porter, Indiana, Cowles described the pattern of succession, but not its mechanisms. In an e-mail (19 January 2006) to the author, Pavlovic writes that Cowles understood that succession "is not always linear, but can be chaotic, and can regress because of what we now call disturbance," which is important in "resetting successional clocks on the landscape." Today we talk "about succession and disturbance regimes within the context of a vegetation pattern that's driven by the landscape physiography interacting with the scale and patchiness of the biotic and abiotic processes and disturbance," Pavlovic states.

The mechanism of succession is called facilitation, says Pavlovic. An example of this is cottonwood trees whose presence on the dunes "facilitates shrub invasion because trees are perches for birds that defecate seeds." Some plant species retard succession. "Wherever marram grass becomes dominant and sand supply is limited," he says, a "thick thatch of grass litter" develops. This thatch, in combination with a poor seed supply, inhibits development of secondary dune vegetation. Seed supply is poor because prevailing winds blow landward. Fire in the Indiana Dunes prevents oak forest from becoming beech maple forest, thus retarding succession.

In "Ecological Relations" Cowles promised to publish an account of the anatomical adaptations that plants make to the dunes environment, giving special attention to

Right Man, Place, and Time

"Ecological Relations" made Cowles' reputation because he described plant succession in a dynamic landscape with greater clarity than anyone who had come before. He made the ecological point of view essential to field botany and helped create a new branch of the life sciences.

Cowles worked hard for his success, but luck also played its part, for he was the right man in the right place at the right time. He had been developing his field skills since adolescence. When he first saw the dunes, he could identify the plants and understood how they functioned because he knew taxonomy and physiology. In the field, he read the landscape, seeing plant associations, communities, and the process of change. Because of his studies with Chamberlin and Salisbury, he had a dynamic vision of nature, knew the geological history of the Great Lakes, and understood how dunes behave. Also, when he wanted to work in the field, Cowles could take the train from his home to the dunes and return the same day. Obliging engineers sometimes stopped between stations so he could unload his equipment near a study site.

After "Ecological Relations," dunes became Cowles' specialty and he studied them wherever he could. In 1900 he visited dunes on New York's Long Island, reporting in *Science* that the succession of plant communities "along the xerophytic shores strikingly resembles that along the Great Lakes." In 1902 he visited dunes on Cape Cod, Massachusetts, and wrote in *Science* that the similarities between sand dune floras of Cape Cod and Lake Michigan "are more striking and far-reaching than the contrasts." The contrasts "are probably due, in the main, to differences in moisture and wind relations," he concluded.

On 31 August 1911 Cowles delivered a paper, "A Fifteen-Year Study of Advancing Sand Dunes," to the British Association for the Advancement of Science. Referring to moving dunes in Indiana and Michigan, he stated that "Plants which are able to survive partial burial by dunes are not Xerophytes (as the pines and oaks), but swamp plants and Mesophytes" that "put forth adventitious roots and . . . elongate as rapidly as the dune advances." Cowles studied dunes in Holland and Belgium in 1906 and in the United Kingdom during 1911. In 1916 he

---

species that "show a large degree of plasticity, and which are found growing under widely divergent conditions." He projected a paper describing "two distinct types" of Lake Michigan beach formations and promised to experiment with the river bottom and dune forms of some plant species to determine whether they could adapt their anatomy in a single generation. He may have presented some of this information to his students. His *Chicago Textbook* describes ecological adaptations and includes a few paragraphs on dunes flora. The other projects were apparently dropped.

declared that he had studied "nearly all the dunes of the world, having personally visited most of them and read about the others." Cowles loved the Indiana Dunes lifelong and showed them off to numerous groups of students and visiting professionals. His daughter remembers many childhood expeditions to the dunes.[8]

Plant Societies of Chicago and Vicinity

Cowles expanded his studies of plant geography and succession to the area around Chicago in 1901, publishing "The Physiographic Ecology of Chicago and Vicinity; a Study of the Origin, Development, and Classification of Plant Societies" in *Botanical Gazette*. In the same year, the Geographic Society of Chicago republished this text with less literature review as "The Plant Societies of Chicago and Vicinity." In subsequent classroom teaching and publications, Cowles dropped the misleading term "plant societies" in favor of "plant communities."

"Plant Societies" begins with a brief review of Warming's *Plantesamfund*, which bases plant geography on the availability of moisture. Warming divides plants into hydrophytes that grow in water or wet places; xerophytes or plants of dry habitats; mesophytes that grow in places of medium moisture (e.g., forests, meadows); and halophytes that live in salt water or alkaline soil. When Cowles and his students tested Warming's system in northern Michigan during 1898, they found that classification by water alone "put together plant societies radically different in their character, and separated plant societies that were obviously closely related." Water is critical, Cowles states, but the list of determining factors must include soil and physiography. "Topographic conditions determine the exposure, the presence or absence of drainage, and the humus content of the soil, and are thus of overshadowing importance," he writes.[9]

---

[8] See HCC, "Investigations at Cold Spring Harbor: Studies in Ecology," *Science*, n.s., 12, no. 297 (7 September 1900): 371; HCC, "Contrasts and Resemblances Between the Sand Dune Floras of Cape Cod and Lake Michigan," *Science*, n.s., 17, no. 424 (13 February 1903): 262; HCC, "A Fifteen-year Study of Advancing Sand Dunes," *Report of the Eighty-First Meeting of the British Association for the Advancement of Science* (London: John Murray, 1912), 565; "Testimony of Henry Chandler Cowles," *Report on the Proposed Sand Dunes National Park, Indiana by Stephen Mather (October 30, 1916)*. The 1916 testimony is reprinted in this volume, see Bibliography for publication details.

[9] HCC, "The Physiographic Ecology of Chicago and Vicinity; A Study of the Origin, Development, and Classification of Plant Societies," *Botanical Gazette* 31, no. 2 (February 1901): 77. Other quotations come from "Plant Societies," which is republished in this volume.

There are many different topographies and plant communities in young, recently glaciated landscapes, but swamps and lakes fill up, hills wear down, and "plant communities pass in a series of successive types from their original condition to the mesophytic forest . . . the climax or culminating type," Cowles continues. Succession can be rapid or slow, direct or seemingly circuitous, and temporary or permanent.

Cowles classifies the plant communities of Chicago and vicinity, dividing them into the "inland group" (ravine, river bluff, flood plain, pond, swamp, prairie, rock hill, clay hill, and sand hill) and the "coastal group" (lake bluff and beach-dune-sand hill series). He then describes succession patterns of each environment. "Plant Societies" summarizes five years of field study in many natural areas. Cowles squeezed research in between other activities, working in bursts of a day or two and getting around on public transportation. The appendix to "Plant Societies" tells how to reach his study sites on streetcars, buses, and trains. If Cowles had lived in a place with less ecological and topographic variety, and poor or nonexistent public transportation, he would have been unable to do so comprehensive a study.

"The Influence of the Underlying Rocks" expands the focus to include the shore of Lake Superior near Marquette, Michigan; the Allegheny Mountains of eastern Tennessee; northern Illinois and eastern Iowa; and Connecticut, places that Cowles already knew or visited as part of his university work. "Underlying Rocks" begins with an account of an "acrimonious" professional controversy about the influence of underlying rock on the species that grow above it.[10]

European botanists claimed that some ferns changed their physical characteristics (i.e., became a different species) after a few generations when they were moved from a soil underlain with serpentine rock to one that had no serpentine content. Some plant geographers attributed this phenomenon to soil chemistry, which nourishes some plants and poisons others. Other plant geographers claimed that soil structure is more important than chemistry. Rocks that weather easily produce a fine soil that supports plant growth, while rocks that weather very slowly produce a coarse soil where desertlike vegetation grows.

The grounds for debate have changed, says Cowles, because everyone now realizes that they exaggerated the contrasts between flora of different soils. Botanists noticed that most plants can grow in a wide

---

[10] Cowles visited Marquette, Michigan, with students in September 1899 and the Allegheny Mountains of Tennessee in June 1900. Northern Illinois and eastern Iowa were accessible by train from Chicago and the Cowles' family home was in Connecticut.

variety of soils and that many survive anywhere they can. Weeds, for example, live in waste places because better soils are normally cultivated. Also, a soil and the rock beneath it are not always chemically identical.

Physiography or history is the most important influence on plant geography, Cowles writes. Over time, plants bury any kind of rock under humus, making conditions very much the same and allowing plant succession to proceed toward climax—a deciduous mesophytic forest. "If a sand hill or a clay hill or a granite hill or a limestone hill have different floras," says Cowles, "it is not because of differences in the rock nor of the organic soil which comes from it, but it is because one is farther along in its life history than is the other."

In most parts of the United States the vegetation of "all hills in a given region, of whatever chemical or physical nature, is tending toward an ultimate common destiny . . . the mesophytic forest." If succession proceeded at the same speed for all plant communities, no difference would be observed and there would have been nothing to debate about. Cowles demonstrates his thesis with an account of plant communities associated with different kinds of underlying rock and cites examples from the areas that his study covers.

Marriage

On 25 June 1900 Henry Cowles married Elizabeth Lucretia (sometimes Luetta) Waller in Louisville, Kentucky. Elizabeth came from a Protestant family of modest means, and she had many relatives who were ministers and deacons. Her father, William Absalom Waller (1836–1928), began his career as a clerk and bookkeeper, apparently prospering. Successive Louisville city directories show the family moving to better and better parts of town.

Born on 6 January 1873 in Louisville, Elizabeth was the fourth of six children. She completed high school, learning French and German. Louisville city directories dated from 1894 to 1900 list her as a schoolteacher. How long she actually taught is unclear, for she matriculated at the University of Chicago on 1 July 1897, took nine undergraduate botany courses, and met Cowles through one of them. Elizabeth took seven years to complete her S.B. degree in botany, which was granted with honors on 14 June 1904. In October of that year, she transferred to the graduate school and took classes until the spring quarter of 1909, but no degree was granted.

Nothing is known about the Cowles–Waller courtship. They may have met as early as 1897 and waited to marry until Henry had a secure income. The single known photograph of the pair around the time of their wedding shows them seated outdoors on the grass near a wooden fence. Henry, dressed in a dark suit, leans back against a tree with a smile on his face and his eyes almost closed. Elizabeth, in a light-colored, long-sleeved, high-collared dress, gazes up happily at the camera.[11]

A handful of Henry's letters to Elizabeth survives. All are dated in autumn of 1900 when he was exploring the Varney River area in Missouri's swampy southeastern Bootheel. His companions were a guide named Shorty Slater and Hermann Von Schrenk (1873–1953), a mycologist and plant pathologist who specialized in the diseases of timber trees, especially bald cypress.[12]

"My own precious pet," Henry writes on 31 October, "This morning we got a distinct type of the swamp, 'Shorty' Slater, a lean, lank fellow about 6? feet tall, and paddled down the Varney River, one of the many bayous that permeate this country. Shorty is a case. Von Schrenk says he is the most unique man he ever saw. He has a strong dialect, a wonderful humor, and his knowledge of the woods is phenomenal. He knows every animal and plant, though not always by name, and the way he peers ahead into the timber beats anything I ever heard of."

Henry describes the day's explorations. "I had a look into a primeval swamp forest, filled with trees centuries old, and fallen logs many centuries older, for cypress never rots. I almost expected to see Pterodactyls in the air and Dinosaurs among the trees. It was my idea of what a Carboniferous forest was. Gigantic cypresses 15 to 20 feet in circumference, tupelos with swollen buttress bases, floating islands of Coreopsis and Polygonum [smartweeds], oceans of Azolla [aquatic fern], Lemna [duckweed], and Wolffia [watermeal], made up a weird sight, such as I never saw before, but must see often again. We found a few bushes of

---

[11] The life history of Elizabeth Waller is assembled from several sources: Linda Estelle of St. Louis, Missouri, the trustee of HCW, provided genealogical information from Waller family sources. The Filson Historical Society, Louisville, Kentucky, provided information on William Absalom Waller and Elizabeth's education and teaching. The marriage license of HCC and Elizabeth Waller is noticed in the *Louisville Courier-Journal*, 26 June 1900. The University of Chicago archives provided information on Elizabeth Waller's (Cowles) matriculation and degrees.

[12] HCC to Elizabeth Cowles, 31 October 1900, HCC Papers. George Yaskievych, Flora of Missouri Project at the Missouri Botanical Garden, St. Louis, and Tim E. Smith, Botanist, at the Missouri Department of Conservation, Jefferson City, helped make sense of this letter. Smith explains that farmers have long since drained most of the swamps and bayous in the Varney River area for cotton, soybean, and rice fields. A few bald cypress-tupelo swamp remnants survive in state parks and other protected areas. It is no longer possible to determine exactly where Cowles was, for the place may have changed out of all recognition.

Leitneria, the corkwood, which grows only in SE Missouri and the cypress swamps of Florida. I am going to bring up a lot of things and try to grow them: cypress seedlings, tupelo seeds, Azolla, etc."

The letter closes: "I love you dearie, and wish I could hear from you—I am so lonesome for a letter, but it wouldn't have been practicable to send any here. . . .Good night, sweetest. Hugs and kisses from your own loving Harry."

Elizabeth accompanied her husband on his long wilderness field trips, carrying a large geology survey Eastman camera to photograph the landscape and the students. In 1912, when she was thirty-nine years old, she gave birth to Harriet Elizabeth Cowles, their only child. This is so late in life to have a first baby that Elizabeth may well have lost others.[13]

In Classroom and Field

Cowles had an ideal situation at the University of Chicago. Instead of teaching introductory botany, he originated a complete ecology curriculum, beginning with Ecological Anatomy and Field Botany during the 1897–98 term. He added Geographic Botany and Research in Ecology in 1898–99 and Physiographic Ecology in 1899–1900. In 1901–2, he was teaching seven ecological subjects.[14]

Student notebooks of Edgar N. Transeau and Homer C. Sampson take us inside Cowles' classroom. Transeau took Ecological Anatomy in 1900–1901, a class the university catalog describes as a course about plant tissues "from the standpoint of function" with special emphasis on "environmental adaptations." Cowles expected his students to read German because the works of German ecologists had yet to be translated.

In those days, ecological anatomy was still such a young field with so little received doctrine that the class was an adventure for professor and student alike. Since no textbooks existed, Cowles assigned articles, some very recent, from professional literature. According to Transeau's notes, Cowles traced the origin of ecological anatomy to the Englishman Nehemiah Grew, who published a "remarkable book on [plant]

---

[13] Elizabeth is credited on many photographs of Cowles' expeditions. According to HCW Address, her mother "carried a "large geology survey Eastman camera for photographing subjects my father wanted for his lectures." Judith Dartt, UCL, who digitized and edited the Department of Botany photographs, originally created by Cowles and his colleagues, for *American Environmental Photographs* on the Internet, says that all but one of his images was printed from five-by-seven-inch dry plate negatives.

[14] *Annual Register of the University of Chicago*, 1896–97 through 1906–7.

anatomy" in 1672. The modern history of the field began in 1874 with Schwenender's "lectures on mechanical tissues" and continued with Haberlandt's 1880 "discussion of assimilation tissues." Cowles also cited an article by Warming that appeared in 1895, and one by Grevillius published in 1897, just three years before the class was taught. "[N]o one has yet presented a complete and logical account of the ecological anatomy," said Cowles.

Sampson's notebooks from 1913, 1914, and 1917 suggest how rapidly ecology had advanced in a short period of time. Geographic botany, for example, was becoming a settled field with a growing literature in German and English. According to Sampson's notes, Cowles divided the field of geographic botany into floristic plant geography and ecological plant geography. Floristic plant geography describes "what plants grew in different countries, [and] relationships of the flora of the different regions," said Cowles. It must be studied "from the microscope."[15]

Ecological plant geography "dates from the time of Warming," Sampson's notes say. The interest is "not in species, but [in the] response that plants make to climate or region, not a question of distribution but a question of ecological response." Ecological plant geography may be studied "from [an] airplane," said Cowles. Physiographic ecology, which is the "local phase" of ecological plant geography, studies "life forms and their development in [the] plant community" and the "life history of the plant community," says Sampson's notes.[16]

In a sixty-five-page notebook, Sampson records Cowles' Physiographic Ecology class for spring of 1913. There were three lectures each week and weekend field trips. In his lectures, Cowles provided numerous examples from the Chicago region and shared his out-of-state

---

[15] HCC Papers: Addenda Box 8. Acting on behalf of the Historical Records Committee of the Ecological Society of America, Professor Robert K. Peet of the University of North Carolina at Chapel Hill donated the Transeau, Sampson, and other notebooks to the UCL.

[16] Books and readings for Ecological Plant Geography included Cowles' *Ecology*, vol. 2 of *Textbook of Botany* (1911), Drude's *Die okologie der Pflanzen* [Plant Ecology] (1913), Haberlandt's *Physiological Plant Anatomy* (English translation, 1914), Jost's *Lectures on Plant Physiology* (English translation, 1907), Schimper's *Plant-Geography Upon a Physiological Basis* (English translation, 1903), and Warming's *Oecology of Plants: An Introduction to the Study of Plant-Communities* (English translation, 1909). Cowles also recommended readings from Engler and Drude's *Die Vegetation der Erde* series (15 vols., 1899–1923). In a letter to Prof. William Morris Davis (6 February 1925, HCC Papers), presumably at the time of Davis' retirement, Cowles wrote: "I regard my greatest scientific contribution to be that in the field of what I call Physiographic Ecology, and the greatest inspiration to this work came in your very wonderful contributions to the field of Physiography."

research with the class. In speaking of the Florida Everglades, for example, he called them a "vast region of prairies like our coarse sedge swamps of the Chicago region" and predicted that grassy islands in the Everglades would eventually "extend themselves" and cover the area. He went into great detail about plant communities and successional patterns, ending Physiographic Ecology with so masterful an account of sand dunes in the United States and Europe that we can almost hear his voice.

Hazel Wiggers (Olmsted) took Physiographic Ecology in spring of 1930. In a videotaped interview made toward the end of her life, she told what Cowles' weekend field trips were like. It "was often strenuous trying to keep up with instructors and jot down notes, while moving rapidly over rough ground, through thickets, or across a quaking bog," she stated. A bog, for instance, "could have thinly mantled small water holes several feet deep. We were warned to stay clear of the waterlilies for they rooted far below!"

When Cowles stopped to point something out, "Observers were crowded, plants often small, and transitions brisk," Olmsted continued. "Few students had cameras. No one had a portable recorder, and accurate field notes were imperative. For survival we grouped spontaneously. In our trio, one got [a] view of the correct specimen, and even a scribble-sketch. Another got the Latin and common names. The third tried for specifics on soil, microclimate, and so forth."

Much has improved since Olmsted's day. "Now we enjoy the comfort of casual jeans, sneakers, T-shirts, and adequate protective lotions," she stated. "Then we donned rather evident 'field' garb. Knickers, even jodhpurs. If you could afford them, knee-high laced leather boots—otherwise heavy socks to the knee." This footgear was "splendidly unsuited for scaling steep sandy blowouts or mucking about in swamps," she writes, while insect repellents were "limited and heavy on the citronella" and sunscreen "was nil." Students depended on "shade, hats, [and] long-sleeved shirts." Even with these discomforts, Cowles' field trips had an "indelible impact," Olmsted concluded. "We were sensitized for life to our surrounding natural world. We became aware of its vulnerability and our responsibility for it."[17]

---

[17] Hazel Wiggers Olmsted, transcript of comments on HCC from a video recorded by her son, Charles E. Olmsted III, on 5 April 1999. Hazel Olmsted made this video for the Cowles symposium in 1999. Her daughter, Joanna Olmsted, supplied the transcript, a copy of which is preserved with the Charles Olmsted Papers at the UCL, Department of Special Collections.

There are many amusing stories of Cowles in class and the field. He began one lecture by quoting from Joseph Seamon Cotter's sonnet, "And Thou art One—One with th'eternal hills," which he probably had learned in church. He then exclaimed: "The hills are *not* eternal, but changing—even mountains change!" Once, when a student asked how long a term paper should be, Cowles replied that it should be "like a skirt—long enough to cover the subject, but short enough to keep things interesting." How did you pass Cowles' courses? Students said that you had to "climb through the fence, keep up with the teacher, and take notes at the same time." Cowles was even said to carry two watches set one hour apart. If someone proposed lunch, he would pull out the slow watch.[18]

Once, Cowles took his daughter Harriet along on a field trip when she was a child, teaching her in advance to recognize *Galinsoga parviflora*, the Peruvian daisy. After an outdoor lecture, she writes, "when the students had been taking many notes, he leaned over and picked a small weed, which he passed around the class. 'What is it? Does anybody know its name?' No one did. So father turned to me, 'Harriet, do you know the name of this plant?' to which I piped, '*Galinsoga parviflora*.'" When Cowles did not know a plant that a student brought him, he would say "with a serious look '*Ignotus damifino*,'" but then laugh joyfully if the student started to write that name in his notebook."[19]

Colleagues described Cowles as a "remarkably successful teacher" who became "a recognized leader" at the University of Chicago. Charles C. Adams, who began his doctoral research under Cowles in 1900, and

---

[18] The Cotter story comes from Paul Voth, interviewed by L. Ron Engel on 4 April 1980. The stories about the skirt and passing Cowles' courses come from Elbert Little, interviewed by Engel for *Sacred Sands*. I thank Professor Engel for sharing these interview notes with me. According to Little, Cowles had such a wide mouth that he could eat bananas whole. Whether he demonstrated this in the classroom is unknown. The watch story comes from EC Dunes. According to Cittadino, the remark was attributed to Harriet Barclay (presumably an ex-student of Cowles) at the Cowles Symposium in 1983. In 1908 an English visitor, T. L. Prankerd, memorably described the botany department at the University of Chicago: "Within the glass-crowned building devoted to the Botanical Department . . . the genial professors, who are professorial in nothing but their scholarship, the assistants, and the students, from the gay young freshman to the newly-made doctor, form one happy family in which everyone knows, likes, and is not in the least in awe of anyone else." T. L. Prankerd, "Botany at Chicago University: Some Impressions," *The New Phytologist* 8, nos. 9 & 10 (31 December 1908): 260–62. Prankerd watched students and faculty holding discussions as they sat on the stairs and saw "moral little mottoes tucked into the nameplate of a research room door, or framed on an office wall, 'Keep Smiling,' and 'Don't Worry.'"

[19] HCW Address.

George Damon Fuller, who assisted Cowles for many years beginning in 1908, have written that his lectures always emphasized the "regional and geographic aspects of ecology" and "kept the research spirit brightly alive."[20]

Cowles "devoted himself mainly to his students, rejoicing in their progress and in their subsequent accomplishments," they continue. Fair-minded, modest, "never at all aggressive," and "never dogmatic," he preferred "non-technical language, avoiding new terminology and the formulation of any rigid system for his science." Above all, he "brought students to nature as well as to books," they write. "He believed thoroughly in out-of-doors teaching, making nearby vacant lands his ecological laboratory."

The University of Chicago was very collegial in Cowles' day, with a "highly sympathetic core group of faculty members and graduate students in the natural sciences who crossed disciplinary lines, visited each others' classes, and exchanged ideas," writes Paul Voth, a colleague and friend. Cowles, who was pioneering an interdisciplinary field of study, thrived in this environment. His influence "spread to the neighboring zoological department, where Professor C. M. Child's physiological point of view may be regarded as a direct outgrowth of the general ecological atmosphere of the university." Many years later, "That atmosphere exerted a favorable influence in the extension of plant and animal ecology to the still newer field of human ecology. The Chicago ecologists have been characteristically geographically minded," Adams and Fuller conclude.[21]

Personal Research

When he had a few days free, Cowles often took quick research trips out of the Chicago region, bringing some of his better students along. He studied the Mississippi River banks, especially on the Illinois side, Mississippi River islands, and sites along the Ohio and Missouri rivers. His notes from these trips are lost, but he incorporated some of his findings in papers and conference presentations and shared results with his classes.

---

[20] Charles C. Adams and George D. Fuller, "Henry Chandler Cowles, Physiographic Plant Ecologist," *Annals of the Association of American Geographers* 30, no. 1 (March 1940): 39–43.

[21] Voth is quoted in *Sacred Sands*, 74; Adams and Fuller, ibid.

Cowles "studied up and down the Mississippi River . . . to see what the general history of islands was." Islands "furnish one of the most interesting places for ecological study," he says, "on account of their rapid growth."[22] Henry Allen Gleason, a colleague of Cowles, studied Mississippi River island sand deposits and their vegetation in 1907–8. Cowles surely knew of Gleason's work and would have taken a special interest in plant succession on the sand deposits.

Randy Nyboer, of the Illinois Natural History Survey in Champaign-Urbana, has visited some Mississippi River islands in recent years, finding unusual forest compositions with "northern extensions of some southern trees (pecan)" and some southern oaks at the northern edge of their range. Nyboer says that the U.S. Army Corps of Engineers had not built its lock and dam system in Cowles' day, meaning that many of the islands and shore/bluff forests were "still in pretty good shape" despite logging.[23]

An episode in 1913 suggests just how important field research was to Cowles. Early that year, he was offered the opportunity to organize a department, presumably of ecology or botany, at the University of Illinois in Champaign-Urbana. On 12 April he wrote to Charles C. Adams, who was then associate professor of animal ecology at the Illinois State Laboratory of Natural History in Champaign-Urbana.

"I weighed the matter carefully," Cowles stated, "and regretted at the end that I could not stay here [the University of Chicago] and go there [the University of Illinois] too. It is a great opportunity, possibly greater than the one here, as viewed by the world. But with the work of organizing and administering a department on my hands, I should have to forego research for five years at least; this to me was the biggest of the

---

[22] Cowles describes these informal studies in USSC. He mentions a study of the "Musgrove Bar," presumably as part of his expert testimony in the Sunk Lands Cases in 1913 and after. He studied "to determine the age of the bar, and to determine the time when the bar was originally started as an island in the Mississippi River" (USSC, 308–9). He mentions studying Mississippi island history and states that he "made many trips to the Mississippi River at points near Chicago for a week or two at a time, so I have made studies along the Mississippi practically all the way from St. Paul . . . down to the neighborhood of Memphis, and in addition to the Mississippi, I have made similar studies along the Ohio, along the Missouri, and along other rivers" (USSC, 308–12).

On pp. 332–35 and 332–36, he states "My major studies have been made along the Mississippi River." He claims to have made his first studies "about 1900 and I have been working at that ever since, not missing a year probably." He also claims to have "covered with several studies almost all of the Illinois front of the Mississippi, a matter of some three or four hundred miles." Later, he states that he studied "tributaries of the Illinois [River] and Mississippi, especially the Des Plaines River near Chicago."

[23] Nyboer made his remarks in an e-mail to the author (26 May 2006).

arguments for staying here. The future here has been painted to me in very roseate colors; some day I will tell you about it; this also influenced my decision, but not so much as the fear that I could not do any research at Urbana for a long time to come."[24]

"Causes of Vegetative Cycles"

Foremost among Cowles' concerns during his early academic career were professionalizing ecology and making sense of plant succession. When the American Association for the Advancement of Science (AAAS) asked him to summarize the work of the year 1903 in ecology, he called the field "chaos" and stated that ecologists did not agree on "fundamental principles or motives."

The great task ahead, he stated, is to unravel "the mysteries of adaptation." He contrasted the ideas of Jean-Baptiste Lamarck, the French biologist, who wrote that acquired traits are heritable, with Darwin's theory of natural selection. The "Lamarckians have emphasized the direct response of organism to environment, and the inheritance of useful acquired characteristics," he said. The Darwinians "have emphasized the gradual 'working out' of highly useful structures by the influence of selection upon small fluctuating variations." Instead of endorsing either theory, Cowles asked for further study. "Many have taken for granted on one side or the other what ought to be a subject for profound investigation," he concluded. [25]

---

[24] Letters of HCC and Charles C. Adams are housed in the Charles C. Adams Papers at Western Michigan University Archives, Kalamazoo. Adams, who is best known for studies of animal ecology, came to the University of Chicago in 1900, studied with Cowles, and became a personal friend. The two men helped to found the Association of American Geographers in 1904. Both were members of the Central States Naturalists and, later, the Committee on Ecological Survey of Illinois. In 1908 Cowles helped Adams secure his post as associate professor of animal ecology at the University of Illinois State Laboratory of Natural History in Champaign-Urbana. Discussion of the offer from Urbana is in HCC to Adams, 12 April 1913. (This is the only reference we have found to this offer.) Remarks about the future of ecology are in HCC to Adams, 5 May 1914. In 1914 Cowles helped Adams become professor of forest zoology at the New York State College of Forestry in Syracuse. "Personally," Cowles wrote, "I believe that in the future, ecology is going to be strongly developed in our forest schools. I feel this all the more because I have had associated with me this year, a strong Forest Service man." The Charles C. Adams Center for Ecological Studies at Western Michigan University has a collection of academic reprints housed in the university library.

[25] See the chronology and list of contributions at the end of this volume for details. HCC, "The Work of the Year 1903 in Ecology" appeared in *Science*, n.s., 19, no. 493 (10 June 1904): 879–85. Cowles apparently changed his mind over the next six years. In HCC,

On 29 December 1910 Cowles lectured on "The Causes of Vegetative Cycles" to the Association of American Geographers (AAG). Summing up fifteen years of his field research into plant succession, he stated that vegetational cycles are immensely complex phenomena that may play out over eons or just a few years and concluded that he could only describe problems that science had failed to solve. This finely reasoned, vigorously written essay (reprinted in this volume), ranks among his best.[26]

Cowles begins by stating that the climax stage in vegetative cycles varies with the climate. "In the eastern United States," he writes, "the final formation is a mesophytic deciduous forest; farther to the north and in the Pacific states, it is a coniferous forest; in the great belt from Texas to Saskatchewan the final formation is a prairie; and in the arid southwest it is a desert." In every case, the "ultimate plant formation is the most mesophytic which the climate is able to support in the region as a whole."

He then reviews chorographic, physiographic, and biotic successions. Chorographic or regional successions develop over many centuries and can only be studied through fossils. Here the dominating factors are changes in climate that are "too slow to be attested in a human lifetime, and which, perhaps, are too slow to be attested in a dozen or a hundred lifetimes." Some climatic changes take place faster than others, and there are shorter cycles within longer ones—"feeble and short-lived oscillations of great climatic waves," as he puts it.

"Present Problems in Plant Ecology: The Trend of Ecological Philosophy," a paper presented to the Botanical Society of America on 1 January 1908, and published in *American Naturalist* 43, no. 510 (June 1909): 356–68, he denounces Lamarckism.

Cowles made many other presentations. On 1 January 1908 he and five colleagues discussed "Aspects of the Species Question" at a meeting of the Botanical Society of America. Basically, their subject was *lumpers* vs. *splitters;* that is, taxonomists who lump species together so there are fewer of them, and those who distinguish multiple species based on small differences. Cowles, a lumper, reminded listeners that ecologists make "rich contributions of field observation" to plant taxonomy and concluded that both lab work and field observation are necessary. The entire article, "Aspects of the Species Question," *The American Naturalist* 42, no. 496 (April 1908): 217–81, consists of presentations by C. E. Bessey and N. L. Britton on taxonomy; J. C. Arthur and D. T. MacDougal on physiology; and F. E. Clements and HCC on ecology. Cowles' contribution is "An Ecological Aspect of the Conception of Species," 265–71. Discussion followed the presentations.

[26] Cowles and fifty-eight others founded the AAG on 29 December 1904. He helped to found the *Annals of the Association of American Geographers* and became AAG president in 1910. HCC, "The Causes of Vegetative Cycles" was published in *Annals of the Association of American Geographers* 1 (1912): 3–20 and reprinted elsewhere. For details, see the bibliography in this volume.

Cowles associates physiographic succession with erosion and deposition, which result from the activities of "gravity, running water, wind, ice, and vulcanism." Deposition of a flood plain along a river can result in progressive succession (approach toward the mesophytic), and rapid erosion can cause retrogressive succession (departure from the mesophytic). Cowles says that he has observed "rapid topographic change without a corresponding plant succession, either progressive or retrogressive" on clay cliffs by Lake Michigan.

Biotic successions are the vegetational changes caused by "plant and animal agencies," he continues. "If, in their operation, chorographic agencies are matters of eons, and physiographic agencies matters of centuries, biotic agencies may be expressed in terms of decades," he states. "[F]ar-reaching vegetational changes take place without any obvious climatic change, and without "any marked activity on the part of the ordinary erosive factors." Some areas, such as ravines and cliffs, may "exhibit temporary exemption from erosion," meaning that they have short vegetational cycles within much longer cycles.

Humus accumulation changes the water relation of the soil to affect "the trend of succession" in a number of different ways. Major biotic influences also include water, soil organisms, toxicity, food, temperature and aeration, shade, plant invasion, man, and plant plasticity.

The causes of plant succession "differ profoundly in their nature, and also in the rapidity of their action," Cowles continues. The effect of climatic change can only be understood by studying "the record of the rocks." Physiographic factors bring much more rapid change and some vegetative cycles are so brief that "we can see one formation replacing another before our eyes." It is "small wonder," he concludes, "that within this complex of cycle within cycle, each moving independently of the others and at times in different directions, dynamic plant geography has accomplished so little in unraveling the mysteries of succession."

Connections, Local and International

Locally, Cowles benefited from membership in the Geographic Society of Chicago and the Chicago Academy of Sciences. The Geographic Society published his "Plant Societies of Chicago and Vicinity" in 1901 and "Starved Rock State Park and its Environs" in 1918. He lectured at society meetings, served as president from 1912 to 1914, and sat on the board of directors until his retirement.

The Chicago Academy of Sciences (CAS) operated a museum with nature exhibits and had public educational programs. In autumn of

1909 Cowles taught a University of Chicago extension course called Plants and their Field Relations (Elementary Ecology) at the CAS. His students were mostly high school science teachers and the CAS published their appreciative comments in its annual report. He also helped prepare nature exhibits for the museum, gave lectures about his work, and served as CAS president in 1923–24.[27]

More important in career terms was Cowles' relationship with his counterparts overseas. He reviewed so many European books and articles in *Botanical Review* that he became especially knowledgeable about developments there and known to the authors he reviewed. On an extended trip to Europe, from June 1905 until spring of 1906, he says that he studied "at various universities," met "European investigators," and "studied the dune vegetation of Holland and Belgium." In addition, he was a delegate to the International Botanical Congress in Vienna, Austria, 11–18 June 1905 and may have taught field ecology in Scotland from 28 July to 1 September.[28]

---

[27] The Geographic Society of Chicago has lost its early records. In 1998 Susan A. Volkmann wrote (and the Geographic Society published) *Celebrating a Century 1898–1998*, an illustrated centennial history with information about Cowles. The Chicago Historical Society has scattered records of the Geographic Society. The archives of the Gray Herbarium, Harvard University, Cambridge, Massachusetts, have fifteen "Semi-Historic Letters" (as the archives call them) between HCC and Merritt Lyndon Fernald (1873–1950), the Harvard botanist, ranging in date from 1909 to 1924. Among these letters, those dated in 1912 and 1913 involve arrangements for a lecture with the Geographic Society of Chicago. Early records of the Chicago Academy of Sciences are inaccessible. Accounts of Cowles' extension class appear in the CAS *Bulletin* 3, no. 2 (September 1909), and 3, no. 3 (September 1910): 6–9.

[28] *Botanical Gazette* 39, no. 1 (January 1905) p. 79 states that Professors Barnes, Cowles, and C. L. Shear were appointed delegates from the American Association for the Advancement of Science to the Second International Botanical Congress. Cowles and Barnes appear in the official record of the IBC: *Verhandlung des Internationalen botanischen Kongresses in Wien 1905* (Jena, Germany: G. Fischer, 1905), 8. Coulter was in Europe during 1905–6 and may have attended the International Botanical Congress. In an account of the 1911 International Phytogeographic Excursion in the British Isles, A. G. Tansley writes that an international excursion followed the 1905 International Congress of Botanists (Tansley, "The International Phytogeographical Excursion in the British Isles," *New Phytologist* 10, nos. 7 & 8 (July & October 1911): 271–91. Cowles may possibly have joined this excursion. The summer Field Botany course is announced in the *Annual Register of the University of Chicago*, but there is no convincing evidence that it took place. Judith Dartt, of the University of Chicago, says that some of Cowles' environmental photographs are labeled "Belgium" and "Vienna," suggesting that they were taken in 1905–6. Others, labeled "Dunkeld," "Glasgow University," "Blakeney," and "United Kingdom [dunes]," were taken during the IPE in the British Isles, which visited those places during August 1911 (see HCC, "Notes and Comment," *Plant World* 15, no. 2 (February 1912): 46–48). These photographs are labeled in a consistent hand, which may be that of Elizabeth Cowles. Cowles also describes his European trip in USSC, sec. 308, 5.

The European contacts paid off in 1910 when A. G. Tansley, the British ecologist, invited Cowles and Frederick Clements to join a four-week excursion called the International Phytogeographic Excursion (IPE) in the British Isles. Tansley felt that such excursions were necessary to an understanding of an area's vegetation and organized the IPE because he believed that the region's plants and plant geography were hardly known. Starting on 1 August 1911 the party visited sites in England, Scotland, and Ireland, ending at the British Association for the Advancement of Science meeting in Portsmouth. There were convivial feasts at every stop.[29]

Cowles' "Impressions of the Foreign Members of the Party" appeared in *The New Phytologist* and is republished in this volume. He was "amazed," he writes, at the "vast amount of wild country in densely-populated England—the extensive areas of the Broads, the sand dunes and salt marshes, the numerous heaths and moorlands." He benefited greatly from living for a month with his "phytogeographic colleagues of other countries," which deepened his understanding of their work. "Close companionship has made us more sympathetic with opposing viewpoints," he wrote, "and more ready to see some truth in views we thought were wholly wrong." Everyone agreed that phytogeographers should take more such excursions. Before the trip ended, Cowles and Clements promised to organize one in North America for 1913.[30]

The International Phytogeographic Excursion in America in 1913 began in New York City on Sunday, 27 July, and ended there early in October. Cowles and Clements were co-organizers, but most of the work fell on Cowles. At every stop, local scientists hosted the ten foreign visitors and their American companions. Everyone received detailed itineraries and field notes.

Traveling much of the time in a private railway car, the scientists saw the most famous natural areas and tourist sights of the United States. After visiting New York City, the New York and Brooklyn Botanic Gardens, and Niagara Falls, they spent about a week in the Chicago area, journeyed to Lincoln, Nebraska, to see the Great Plains, and thence to

---

[29] Tansley, "Excursion, Isles." Tansley's article includes a detailed description of the sites visited by the party and site vegetation. The foreign guests were Professor Schröter and Dr. Rübel of Zurich, Professor Drude of Dresden, Professor Massart of Brussels, Dr. Ostenfeld of Copenhagen, Dr. Lindman of Stockholm, Professor and Mrs. Clements of Minneapolis, and Cowles and his wife.

[30] HCC, "The International Phytogeographical Excursion in the British Isles: Impressions of the Foreign Members of the Party," *The New Phytologist* 11, No. 1 (January 1912) 25–26.

Colorado Springs and Pike's Peak. After a stop in Salt Lake City, they passed through Idaho on their way to Oregon and Washington, then traveled south to California—Yosemite National Park, California Redwoods Park, San Francisco, the Salton Sea, and more. In Arizona, they saw the Grand Canyon and Tucson, and then passed through Texas, New Orleans, and Washington, D.C., on their way back to New York.

Cowles accompanied the group through much of the excursion, but he was in his glory when he showed them the Indiana Dunes. At Miller, the group walked to Lake Michigan, "traversing the dunes in reverse order of their development (oak dunes, pine dunes, cottonwood dunes)." The next day, at Dune Park and Mineral Springs, the visitors saw "high oak dunes capped with pines." In the depressions between the dunes were "all stages between ponds and fenland." After visiting "an extensive tract of moving dunes" at Dune Park, the scientists climbed a two-hundred-foot-high dune to get "a bird's-eye view of the region." Later that day, they explored Mineral Springs Bog (since renamed Cowles Bog) to see "stages in bog development." Other day trips took the group to a virgin mesophytic forest (i.e., Warren Woods) in western Michigan, limestone formations at Starved Rock, Illinois, prairies in Chicago, and plant communities in Chicago's northern suburbs.[31]

The IPE in America was the pinnacle of Cowles' academic career. Soon after the scientists returned home, World War I broke out and made further excursions impossible. After this time, he produced almost no important research. While he always had abundant ideas and insights, he shared them with classes instead of publishing.

---

[31] The ten European visitors were Schröter, Rübel, H. Brockmann-Jerosh and Marie Brockmann-Jerosh, all of Zurich; Professor Engler (Berlin), Dr. Ove Paulson (Copenhagen), Dr. T. J. Stomps (Amsterdam), Professor C. von Tubeuf (Munich), A. G. Tansley, and Mrs. Tansley. This account of the IPE in America is drawn from two sources: A. G. Tansley, "International Phytogeographic Excursion (I.P.E) in America, 1913," *New Phytologist* 12, no. 8 (October 1913): 322–36; 13, nos. 1 & 2 (January & February 1914): 30–41; 13, no. 3 (March 1914): 83–92; 13, no. 8 (October 1914): 268–75; and 13, no. 10 (December 1914): 325–33; and "The International Phytogeographic Excursion (I.P.E.) in America 1913," the itinerary for the 1913 IPE, which was probably compiled at the University of Chicago and printed there (no publisher listed). Cowles surely outlined the itinerary and wrote the field notes about Chicago. The itinerary was issued as five pamphlets with subtitles: "First Section—New York to Lincoln," "Second Section—Lincoln-Salt Lake City," "Third Section—Salt Lake City to San Francisco," "Fourth Section—San Francisco to Carmel," and "Fifth Section—Carmel to New York."

Frederic E. Clements

Frederic E. Clements, who taught in Nebraska and Minnesota, is today considered the foremost student of plant succession. He originated modern research techniques, used them in his work, advanced a personal theory of plant succession, and wrote more than thirty books. Clements saw vegetation and the landscape as dynamic and in constant flux. Inevitably, the unit of vegetation, which he called an organic entity, would reach a "climax" and stop changing. He likened succession to the stages in the maturation of a plant and believed that it was always progressive.

While Warming influenced Cowles, Clements followed the pioneer plant ecologist Oscar Drude (1852–1933). Drude, a professor of botany at the Dresden Polytechnikum in Germany and director of Dresden's botanic garden, presented a system of plant geography based primarily on physiography and climate in *Handbuch der Pflanzengeographie* [Handbook of Plant Geography], published in 1890. He classified fifty-five forms of plants, defining them by their structure (e.g., broad-leafed trees, graminoids). In 1913 he elaborated his theories in *Oekologie der Pflanzen* [Plant Ecology] and collaborated with phytogeographer Adolf Engler on *Vegetation der Erde* [Vegetation of the Earth], a multivolume series published between 1899 and 1923 that Cowles reviewed in *Botanical Gazette* and recommended to his students.[32]

Cowles denied that plant succession inevitably moved forward toward a climax formation. He had observed retrogressive succession in the field, confusing intermediary stages, and many kinds of climax formation. Instead of advancing a theory of his own, Cowles (in "The Causes of Vegetative Cycles") called succession "a variable approaching a variable," said that he had no final answers, and called for further research. Clements' methods were up to date and his theory, right or wrong, gave ecologists something to respond to.[33]

---

[32] According to Prof. Eugene Cittadino, "Frederick Clements's approach to ecology was influenced by Drude early on, but it was also influenced by social theorists such as Herbert Spencer and Lester Frank Ward, and by the practical needs of the agricultural context in which his views emerged." Letter to the author (9 January 2006).

[33] H. A. Gleason wrote "Thumbnail Sketches of Botanists" in 1961, never published his manuscript, and presented it to the New York Botanical Garden, where it is archived in the library. In "Cowles and Clements," he describes Clements as "a lanky man, probably six feet tall, with a long face, a Roman nose, a solemn expression, and an austere disposition. If he ever told a joke, I was certainly not there to hear it." Gleason called Cowles "a little man, a trifle inclined to stoutness, and even his best friends would never have called him handsome. But in those piggish eyes was a twinkle, and on his face a smile, and

In *Botanical Gazette,* Cowles reviewed four books written by Clements: *The Phytogeography of Nebraska* (1898), *The Development and Structure of Vegetation* (1904), *Research Methods in Ecology* (1905), and *Plant Succession: An Analysis of the Development of Vegetation* (1916). (The reviews are reprinted in this volume.) He praised Clements' rigor, declaring that his quadrat-based field research methods would professionalize ecology, but complained that Clements created Greek-derived ecological jargon instead of using "simpler and more expressive English equivalents."

From the very start, Cowles acknowledged his philosophical differences with Clements. In May 1898, just a month after receiving his doctorate, he reviewed *Phytogeography,* stating that "It may be too early to predict whether the direction to future work in plant geography will be given by Warming or by Drude; and . . . whether we shall speak of ecology or phytogeography, of life forms or of vegetation forms, of plant societies or of formations."

In 1904 he called *Development and Structure* "must" reading and declared that it contained so much important information so well presented that "a satisfactory review would be little less than a verbatim reproduction of the work." He was equally enthusiastic about *Research Methods* in 1905, stating that "One can scarcely praise this work too much; it is what is needed to prevent ecology from falling into a swift and merited disfavor."[34]

---

on his tongue a quip or a word of welcome. Of all the botanists I have ever known, I believe he stood second in popularity, in ability to be friendly and to attract friends. Students flocked to his classes and followed him on arduous field trips even as far as Alaska, almost hypnotized by his inspirational leadership." Gleason continues: "I can not think of an ecological term that was coined by Cowles, although he did establish and popularize the use in an ecological sense of the familiar terms succession and climax. I doubt if he ever charted or counted a quadrat, and he did not care whether a plant community was called an association or a society or even a formation. He wanted his students to appreciate that vegetation was continuously changing, and that they could detect those changes and even predict what their future might be." Summing up, Clements "was the dreamer, the philosopher, the ecological taxonomist and nomenclator; Cowles was the generalizer, the leader, the inspirer. Both filled a useful niche in the development of ecology. Neither of them lived long enough, possibly fortunately, to see their work outmoded, their concepts generally rejected, and at least some of their ideals shattered."

[34] All four reviews are reprinted in this volume: HCC, review of *The Phytogeography of Nebraska,* by Frederic E. Clements, *Botanical Gazette* 25, no. 5 (May 1898): 370–72; HCC, review of *The Development and Structure of Vegetation,* by Frederic E. Clements, *Botanical Gazette* 38, no. 4 (October 1904): 303–10; HCC, review of *Research Methods in Ecology,* by Frederic E. Clements, *Botanical Gazette* 40, no. 5 (November 1905): 381–82; and HCC, review of *Plant Succession: An Analysis of the Development of Vegetation,* by Frederic E. Clements, *Botanical Gazette* 68, no. 6 (December 1919): 477–78.

Cowles had private doubts about Clements' methodology. On 16 June 1914 he told Arthur G. Vestal, who was then a University of Chicago graduate student in botany, "I do very little quadrat counting, even when I am working intensively on a small area. . . . I have more confidence in a subjective method than an arbitrary one like the quadrat. After all, one must select one's quadrats, and that brings in the subjective element."

A quadrat is a unit of area, often one square meter, which is used to sample vegetation. The investigator lays an open one-square-meter framework on the ground, identifies the plant species and number of stems found inside the square, and makes a record. Repeating this procedure over a given area in a consistent pattern allows the investigator to generalize about the vegetation and plant communities. At some future time the investigator can return to the area, lay down quadrats in the same places, and observe changes in the vegetation.

On 2 September, in approving Vestal's plan to survey Montana vegetation, Cowles wrote "Clements alone among American ecologists, professes to disbelieve in general papers, though he is now getting one ready. Had he gotten at it earlier, I think he would have understood his Pike's Peak region much better." William S. Cooper has written that Edgar N. Transeau, a former student of Cowles who had absorbed his ideas, "instilled in me a violent prejudice against an eminent ecologist [F. E. Clements], which was not entirely removed until I became an assistant to that same ecologist, my first years at Minnesota." Cowles was not given to holding "violent prejudices" or inspiring them in others. Thus, it seems likely that Transeau alone detested Clements.[35]

Reading Clements' *Plant Succession* in 1916 must have been painful for Cowles. After waiting three full years to review this monumental work, he wrote that Clements had "conscientiously and sympathetically" assembled "the contributions of all previous workers dealing with the phenomena of succession in vegetation." Clements understandably placed Cowles among the "previous workers" because he had not published a major study of succession for fifteen years.

Henry Gleason was the ecologist who called Clements to task for his organismal view of succession. See H. A. Gleason, "The Individualistic Concept of the Plant Association," *Bulletin of the Torrey Botanical Club* 53 (1926): 7–26.

[35] HCC to Arthur Gibson Vestal, 26 June 1914; HCC to Vestal, 2 September 1914, Arthur Vestal Papers, University Archives, University of Illinois at Urbana-Champaign. William S. Cooper to Jack McCormick, 28 February 1953, William Skinner Cooper Papers, University of Minnesota Archives, Minneapolis.

In his review of *Plant Succession*, Cowles reiterated his differences with Clements. "The chapter in which the views of the author and the reviewer clash most sharply is the one on direction of development," he wrote. Clements "states positively that 'succession is inherently and inevitably progressive.' The reviewer is as positive in his opinion as ever that succession may be retrogressive as well as progressive, although of course progression is much more abundant and important." Cowles then introduced evidence from his own experience and statements of Tansley to demonstrate how Clement's theory did not square with the facts. But Cowles was reviewing a study that he should have written himself.

Chapter 3

CITIZEN COWLES

Cowles' professional life divides roughly into two overlapping periods: the years from 1896 to 1913, when research and publication took precedence, and the two decades from 1914 to 1934, when his priorities became teaching, natural areas surveys, conservation, and expert testimony. Before 1913, he produced one important book, contributed to one book, and wrote twenty scientific articles, including several that broke new ground. From 1914 to 1934, he co-authored three minor books, contributed to eight books, and published nineteen scientific articles. He lectured widely and kept in touch with his counterparts overseas, but wrote less about their work and made no more phytogeographic excursions. He left many projects unfinished, including a major study of physiographic ecology that colleagues and students had awaited for years.

Always active in professional organizations, Cowles helped to found the Ecological Society of America in 1914, and served as president of the Illinois State Academy of Sciences in 1920 and president of the Botanical Society of America in 1922. He was editor for ecology and plant geography of *Botanical Abstracts* from 1918 to 1923 and worked steadily on *Botanical Gazette*. In addition, he volunteered many hours to the Conservation Council of Chicago, Friends of Our Native Landscape, Illinois Forestry Association, National Conference on State Parks, and Wild Flower Preservation Society.

During this time, Cowles worked with three men. Professor Coulter supervised him at the University of Chicago. Jens Jensen, the landscape designer and conservationist, enlisted his help in protecting the Indiana Dunes and ecologically important Illinois sites. Stephen A. Forbes, the natural scientist and ecologist, involved him in projects that benefited Illinois forests. Content to work behind the scenes, Cowles was valued for his professional knowledge, his skill in dealing with people, and his willingness to perform the administrative chores that keep organizations going. As the record shows, he worked dependably for Coulter and Jensen, less so for Forbes.

Sunk Lands Cases

"A good many years ago," Cowles stated in "The Economic Trend of Botany," a 1914 lecture, "I published a paper on the vegetation of the sand dunes of Lake Michigan, depicting the principles of plant succession.... Shortly after . . . I gave a copy to a man of the world who said merely, 'Well, what of it?' Aghast, I said nothing."

This mortifying incident stuck in Cowles' mind until he got a chance to prove how useful ecology could be. In 1910 the U.S. Department of Justice invited him to serve as an expert witness in a lawsuit. "With many misgivings," he wrote, "and with the feeling that ecology, as I represent it, was now specifically on trial, I took up the work assigned to me. To my unalloyed gratification, I discovered that matters which perplexed the Department of Justice were simple enough when examined by an ecologist."[1]

Cowles was asked to determine whether certain bottomlands along the Mississippi River in eastern Arkansas were lakes in 1847 when the United States surveyed the area prior to settlement. The survey maps showed many lakes, which were presumably flooded and thus could not be homesteaded or farmed. These lakes were dry land in 1910 with excellent timber growing on them. Lumber companies persuaded farmers living next to the presumed lake beds that they had riparian rights to the land adjoining their property because it was under water at the time of settlement. The lumber firms then purchased these rights from the farmers and began to cut the timber.[2]

When word of this reached Washington, the federal government sued the lumber companies, claiming the 1847 survey was fraudulent and no lakes had existed on the land at the time of settlement. According to the government, the land belonged to the federal government and there were no riparian rights to sell. The Department of Justice filed a test suit over an area in Arkansas designated as Moon Lake on the 1847 maps.

---

[1] HCC, "The Economic Trend of Botany," *Science*, n.s., 41, no. 1049 (12 February 1915): 226–28. The essay is reprinted in this volume.

[2] In this narrative of the Sunk Lands Cases and the Red River Border Dispute, quotes by Cowles come from "Economic Trend," while the factual narrative comes from EC Dunes and EC Borderline. Since Prof. Cittadino did such massive research into Cowles' expert witness activities, it seemed simpler to adapt his narrative than to repeat the same research and reach the same conclusions. In a personal communication to the author (9 January 2006), Professor Cittadino pointed out that the Sunk Lands Cases "involved repeated visits to Arkansas and Louisiana at least to 1917, and they involved the illegal obtaining of oil leases (in Louisiana) as well as lumbering. The litigation continued into the 1920s."

As he tells it in "The Economic Trend of Botany," it was "ridiculously easy" for Cowles to prove that Moon Lake did not exist in 1847. Accompanied by people associated with the litigation, he inspected the lake area as shown on the survey maps, finding "upland timber of great age" growing there, which indicated that the land had been dry for much more than a century. Tree-ring counts, plant succession data, and physiographic evidence proved that the wooded site mapped as Moon Lake had changed little since 1847. "[T]here have been no lakes in these sites for at least two thousand years," Cowles declared.

During court proceedings, the lumber companies brought in some local old-timers who testified to boyhood fishing trips in the imaginary lakes. The government summoned witnesses who recalled only woods. "It was brought out in court that it was safer to believe a tree than a man!" said Cowles in "The Economic Trend of Botany." "[A] line of investigation which we had supposed to be theoretical only has turned out to have large practical significance." The government won the Moon Lake case.

The 1847 survey was fraudulent because surveyors were paid more for lakes, which were difficult to map because of their shape. Realizing that no one in Washington would know the difference, the surveyors mapped lakes where none existed and pocketed higher fees.

The Moon Lake trial took place early in 1913. Soon after, Cowles returned to Arkansas to gather evidence and testify in five similar cases. In 1914 he testified in a suit involving Ferry Lake, Louisiana, which had undergone recent submergence and was full of many standing dead trees. He found cypress ("a natural lowland tree") in Ferry Lake, but also "such upland species as overcup oak, walnut, mulberry, and the like." The presence of these species, he stated, "show that prior to submergence the tract was not only land but high and dry land." He returned in 1915 to testify about three more alleged lakes.

Using Cowles' carefully gathered evidence, the government won every suit in which he testified. He never forgot this triumph and described it in *The Book of Plants*, a volume of readings published in 1925 for schoolchildren. On one page is a photograph of a tree stump captioned "One of the Witnesses in the Lawsuit." [3]

Cowles was an effective expert witness because he had been studying the sunk lands since 1900. This area along the Mississippi River in Missouri and Arkansas got its name because huge acreages subsided

---

[3] Bertha Morris Parker and HCC, *The Book of Plants* (Boston: Houghton Mifflin, 1925), 174.

during the New Madrid Earthquake of 1811–12. The earthquake, which began on 16 December 1811 and continued through the end of March 1812, consisted of five separate seismic events measuring eight or more on the Richter scale, interspersed with at least two thousand smaller events. According to eyewitnesses, the earth's surface rose and fell in successive furrows like waves on a lake, fissures six to eight feet deep opened in the ground, and warping lifted pond beds as much as twenty feet in the air. The town of New Madrid, Missouri, sank fifteen feet during the earthquakes. Water invaded the plain on which it sat, creating a lake.

The sunk lands and the Mississippi River were ideal outdoor laboratories in which to study succession. In addition to normal patterns of succession, which Cowles found on river sandbars and in cutoffs where the river had changed its course, he discovered how vegetation responded to the catastrophic destruction and sinking that followed the New Madrid quake. He used the term *retrogression* to denote retardation or reversal of natural succession due to a disturbance like an earthquake and determined that succession started up again in affected areas, but from an earlier stage.[4]

Red River Border Dispute

The Sunk Lands Cases were pretty straightforward and the lumber companies did not put up much of a fight. In 1920 and 1921 Cowles did field surveys and testified in the long, complicated Red River Border Dispute, which involved the U.S. government, the states of Oklahoma and Texas, Native Americans, and numerous claimants to oil lands that were worth millions of dollars. Rival teams of geologists, physical geographers, and ecologists studied the same area, sometimes reaching opposite conclusions. Cowles' methodology was sharply questioned in court. After the case was decided, a disgruntled member of the rival team accused Cowles in print of incompetence and bias.

The Red River Border Dispute originated in the 1819 Adams–Onís Treaty between the United States and Spain, which established the

---

[4] Myron L. Fuller, *The New Madrid Earthquake* (Washington, DC: U.S. Geological Survey Bulletin 494, 1912; reprint, Cape Girardeau, MO: Center for Earthquake Studies, Southeast Missouri State University, 1989). Cowles describes his sunk lands and Mississippi River studies in USSC, sec. 308, 4–12; sec. 332, 5–6. Cowles summarized a lecture on the sunk lands (complete text is lost) as "Retrogressive and Progressive Successions in the Arkansas Sunk Lands," *Journal of Ecology* 6, no. 1 (April 1918): 95–96.

border between the Louisiana Purchase and Spain's territories in North America. The treaty stated that the border running east from the 100th Meridian to the Arkansas line was the south bank of the Red River. Roughly 450 miles long, the Red River Valley eventually became the border between Texas and Oklahoma. It was litigated several times in the nineteenth and early twentieth centuries.

When oil was discovered in and near the banks of the Red River in 1918, Oklahoma claimed jurisdiction over the entire riverbed and sold oil leases. Texas claimed the southern half of the riverbed (the area where oil was found) and also sold leases. Native Americans claimed some of the lands. After violent episodes between rival wildcatters and threats of armed conflict between the Oklahoma and Texas state militias, the Supreme Court placed the area in receivership. The U.S. government became a party to the case, siding with Oklahoma and claiming ownership of the river valley, which promised large tax revenues. Because two states were litigants, the U.S. Supreme Court was case court in the dispute. Hearings were held in Oklahoma City, Oklahoma, Austin, Texas, and Washington, D.C. The case was finally argued before the Court in Washington, D.C.

Because its stream was often braided with a course that switched back and forth, and water volumes that varied widely from month to month, it was not easy to locate the Red River decisively. It was simplest to speak of the entire river valley, but this had implications because the federal government claimed it. Most of the survey work was done in the Big Bend area of the river, where the oil wells were.

L. C. Glenn, a Vanderbilt University geology professor, was first to survey for the Oklahoma team, which employed Cowles. Glenn concluded that the south bank of the Red River was located near the Texas bluffs in 1817. Most of the Big Bend valley, he said, was composed of islands that formed in the middle of the river, grew slowly until they joined, then forced the stream northward. These findings supported Oklahoma's claim that it had jurisdiction over the entire riverbed because the Red River had meandered northward over the past century.

Cowles made four trips to the area in 1920 and 1921, determining through his surveys that the floodplain was comparatively young because few older trees grew there. He concurred with Glenn's island-building theory and stated that he had found small sand dunes in early stages of development with cottonwoods and willows growing on them. "Since the age of the bluff is more than 100 years and the age of the flood plain less than 100 years," he declared, "it follows that the Red River must have run along the foot of the Texas bluffs 100 years ago." Isaiah Bowman, the geographer on the Oklahoma team, inspected the area and wondered privately whether Cowles had reached this conclusion in haste.

Cowles had surveyed the valley floor. An expert witness on the Texas team analyzed the soil of the valley's sides and concluded that it was much more than one hundred years old. As he told it, the dunes had formed on dry land and not on islands as Cowles had suggested. He found climax vegetation in the valley, suggesting that it was quite old, but Cowles replied that succession proceeded to climax much faster in arid lands than elsewhere. When a 170-year-old pecan tree was discovered in the valley, Cowles said that it germinated on an island that fused with others. When he was charged with missing this tree during his survey, Cowles acknowledged the omission but stuck to his story.

When the case was decided, Texas retained possession of the Big Bend valley on which many of the productive wells were located. The federal government claimed the bed of the river for itself. Oklahoma landowners were only allowed riparian rights to the median line of the river, but most of the active wells were in the southern half of the riverbed, so the Supreme Court decision basically left Oklahoma out of the picture.

The Red River litigation was far longer and more bitterly contentious than the Sunk Lands Case had been. Court testimony alone filled nine volumes amounting to fifty-five hundred pages, and Justice Oliver Wendell Holmes, who had to read this material, called the dispute a "despairing case." The briefs, he added, "are as long as the Bible—and the record susceptible of cubic measures. I wish they were to hell."

The dispute did not end there. Benjamin C. Tharp, an instructor in botany at the University of Texas who served on the Texas team of expert witnesses, published an account of the case in the *University of Texas Bulletin* during 1923. Attacking Cowles by name, Tharp wrote that his court testimony was "in so far as ecology is concerned, based upon inadequate investigation and upon misinterpretation of the development and structure of vegetation in the area studied." He added that "no competent, unbiased ecologist could go over the ground and come to any other conclusion than that to assume its age as less than 100 years would be the height of absurdity."[5]

---

[5] The description of the Red River Border Dispute is based on EC Borderline. The description of the Supreme Court decision replicates a personal communication to the author (9 January 2006) from Professor Cittadino. The University of Chicago apparently gave Cowles time off to do the expert witness work. In the *Board of Trustees Minutes* 12 (10 January 1922): 298–99, the president of the university reports that the attorney general of the United States had written in high appreciation of the university's liberality "in releas-

Cowles' response to these accusations is unknown. He never published a word about the Red River dispute and never served again as an expert witness. This time-consuming work had brought him little financial or professional reward. Thereafter, conservation and forestry became his main activities outside the classroom. His first important association was with Jens Jensen.

Friends of Our Native Landscape

Jens Jensen (1860–1951) celebrated the natural landscape of the Midwest in his dramatic designs for public parks, gardens, and estates. He was also a prime mover in establishing Chicago's parks, the Cook County (i.e., Chicago and surroundings) Forest Preserve District, the state parks of Illinois, and Indiana Dunes State Park. Jensen grew up on a prosperous farm in Denmark, but left for America at the age of twenty-four because his family disapproved of his wife. Hired as a laborer with the Chicago Parks District, he rapidly rose in the organization and created his first landscape design, an "American garden," as he called it, in Chicago's Union Park during 1888. On weekends, Jensen and his family took trains into the countryside where he familiarized himself with the Illinois prairie, the Indiana Dunes, and their plants.[6]

By 1895 Jensen was superintendent of Union Park, and one year later he took over Humboldt Park, one of Chicago's largest. He joined many social and civic organizations, becoming a charter member of the Geographic Society of Chicago in 1898. It seems probable that Cowles met Jensen in 1900 when the Geographic Society was preparing to publish

---

ing Dr. Henry C. Cowles from his academic labors at various times during the past two years to make ecological investigations along the Red River for use in connection with the litigation styled Oklahoma v. Texas, United States Intervener, original suit in the Supreme Court of the United States. Dr. Cowles' investigations and testimony have been of great value to the Government and to the cause of science in that they bring to the aid of engineering and physiographic investigations the comparatively new science of ecology, whereby the approximate time of the occurrence of changes in rivers, their flood plains and banks, is more definitely determined. The results attained by scientific investigations made in this cause will be embodied in a printed record." Cowles and Isaiah Bowman served on the Oklahoma team in the Red River Border Dispute and became social friends. Johns Hopkins University Library has miscellaneous correspondence between the two men dated from 1927 through 1935, but the letters are mostly meeting arrangements and contain no information about the Red River Border Dispute.

[6] Jens Jensen, "The Live Sand Dunes," *The Club Messenger* 1, no. 4: 3–4. Jensen writes: "For more than a quarter of a century the Dune country in Northern Indiana (ever since 1889) has provided me with all that sort of intimate beauty and knowledge of the out-of-doors in which the city is deficient." Jensen knew the Dunes six years before Cowles did.

"Plant Societies of Chicago and Vicinity" (1901). The two men became friends and botanized at the dunes and elsewhere. On these field trips, Cowles improved Jensen's understanding of plants and helped him see them as members of natural communities.[7]

Cowles and Jensen became allies despite differences in their temperaments and goals. Romantic and showmanlike, Jensen believed that exposure to nature nurtures human character. Seeking to infuse peoples' lives with the natural landscape, he employed native plants in his dramatic landscape designs and created organizations that helped save natural areas. An activist who persuaded prominent people to support his causes, Jensen involved the general public through large outdoor events. Cowles, a scientist, saw nature as a dynamic system that he wanted to study, understand, and explain to others. Not one to give fiery speeches or lead popular movements, he served Jensen diligently for more than twenty-five years.[8]

In 1900 Jensen was fired from his job with the Chicago Park District for refusing to cooperate with corrupt officials. He soon joined the Special Parks Commission, which developed plans for a metropolitan park system in Chicago. In 1903 and 1904 he contributed maps and a "Report of the Landscape Architect" to a longer Special Park Commission report that was submitted to the Chicago City Council. Cowles may have had a hand in Jensen's text, which displays a comprehensive understanding of local geology, physiography, and ecology.[9]

During the first decade of the twentieth century, Jensen made three attempts to acquire land for outdoor laboratories or schools at the Indiana Dunes. The record is incomplete and inconsistent, but it seems that Cowles was involved in the first scheme, a Biological Field and Farm (i.e., an experimental station) to be located in Porter County,

---

[7] Robert Grese, *Jens Jensen: Maker of Natural Parks and Gardens* (Baltimore: Johns Hopkins University Press, 1992), 52. Grese states that Cowles and Jensen met about 1900, but he provides no documentation. Most of Jensen's papers perished in a fire and Cowles' papers are lost too, which makes it difficult to document dates like these.

[8] See William H. Tishler and Erik M. Gheniou, "Jens Jensen and the Friends of Our Native Landscape," *Wisconsin Magazine of History* (Summer 2003): 1–15.

[9] Jens Jensen, "Part Six: Report of the Landscape Architect" in *Report of the Special Park Commission to the City Council of Chicago on the subject of a Metropolitan Park System,* comp. Dwight Heald Perkins (Chicago: The Commission, 1904), 81–105. In a letter to William P. Hayes dated 4 January 1949 Jensen stated that he made "exhaustive studies" of the "outlying districts" of Cook County beginning in 1899. This letter is quoted in William P. Hayes, "Development of the Forest Preserve District of Cook County, Illinois" (Master's thesis, Department of History, DePaul University, Chicago, Illinois, 1949), 3. The thesis is housed at the Chicago Historical Society library.

Indiana. Early in 1903 Jensen apparently approached President Harper of the University of Chicago, proposing that the university purchase 880 acres of dunes and peat bogs on the Lake Michigan shore and 270 acres of adjoining farmland, river bottom, and forest with a variety of soils and habitat types. The estimated purchase price was $15,000 to $20,000, with annual maintenance of less than $2,500.

President Harper appointed a committee comprised of faculty and trustees, including botany professors Coulter and Barnes, to investigate Jensen's proposal. After visiting Furnessville, Tremont, and Mineral Springs, the committee reported favorably, but nothing happened. On 11 May 1906 Chicago's biological departments presented a petition to the trustees' meeting that stated that the proposed Biological Field and Farm was "absolutely necessary" to retain valued faculty who were leaving Chicago because of its inadequate laboratory facilities and support staff. "We believe that it would be wise to take the first step in this direction immediately by purchasing about forty acres of land, which can now be had at a reasonable figure, but will soon be very costly," the petition said. On 8 December 1906 the trustees in Chicago referred the proposal to a group of trustees in New York City to see whether there might be any interest. There was none, and the proposal died.

Long afterward, on 26 January 1925, Cowles told William E. Scott of the president's office at the University of Chicago that he had tried in 1906 to get the university to buy about a thousand acres of natural forests on Lake Michigan. This land had reverted to the state of Indiana for nonpayment of taxes and he wanted it for research purposes. "We could then have secured several thousand acres for almost nothing," he wrote. "I have seen this land rise in value until the latest purchase that I know of was made on the basis of about six hundred dollars an acre."[10]

The Biological Field and Farm proposed by the Chicago faculty was to be about 40 acres, but Jensen's scheme encompassed 1,150 acres of different land types, and Cowles writes that roughly 1,000 acres of forest (or perhaps "several thousand acres") were available in 1906. Cowles' importance to the Field and Farm scheme is open to question because he was in Europe from autumn 1905 until spring 1906, and still a junior faculty member. As subsequent events suggest, Cowles may have been involved in more than one of Jensen's schemes. All we know for certain is that the university bought no land at the Indiana Dunes.

After the proposal for a Biological Field and Farm was rejected, Jensen and Prof. Frank Waugh from the Massachusetts Agricultural

---

[10] HCC to William E. Scott, 26 January 1925, Department of Special Collections, UCL.

College in Amherst tried to set up a horticulture, forestry, and land-scape design school near Tremont, Indiana, where University of Chicago faculty would teach. They could not raise the money. Next, Jensen asked Henry Ford to buy more than three thousand acres of dunes land for an arboretum of natural plants. By this time, Jensen's attentions to the area had drawn speculators, who began driving prices up. Ford backed off when he learned how much the land would cost.[11]

In 1905 a reformed parks' leadership hired Jensen back and he got busy with new designs. He helped to organize the Playground Association of Chicago that sought recreation areas for children in the central city. Cowles and Jensen served on the committee of this organization, which sponsored Saturday afternoon walking trips to create public awareness of nearby natural sites. The walks, which Jensen thought would attract the poor, drew the upper-middle class instead and proved so popular that a new organization, the Prairie Club of Chicago, was established in 1908 to administer the walks. In 1911 the Prairie Club incorporated under that name and still exists today.

Then as now, the Prairie Club was primarily a social organization for professionals. It purchased dunes land, where it built a shack and, later, a beach house and cabins that accommodated members and their families on overnight stays. The Prairie Club was one of several organizations that worked to save the dunes from development. In 1926 the club sold its holdings to the state of Indiana and the site became the

---

[11] The author has found very little independent documentation of Jensen's three schemes to buy dunes land. On pp. 96–97 of *Outdoors with the Prairie Club* (comp. Emma Doeserich, Mary Sherburne, and Anna B. Way, Chicago: Paquin Publishers, 1941), the authors describe Jensen's attempts to save dunes land, but provide neither dates nor documentation. This account, which probably comes from memory, does not mention Cowles. Grese, *Jens Jensen*, 124, repeats the story of Jensen's attempts, adding a few details but no documentation. Engel. *Sacred Sands*, 75, claims that President Harper, "after consultation with Cowles, Jensen and others . . . submitted a proposal to the board of trustees for the purchase of a 'Biological Field and Farm' to be located in Porter County, Indiana." A pamphlet (no author listed, but probably written in part by Cowles), *Preserves of Natural Conditions* (n.p.: Committee on the Preservation of Natural Conditions of the Ecological Society of America, 1921), 9, states "Fifteen years ago [i.e., in 1906], the present site of Gary, Indiana, was public land, having reverted to the state for taxes. ... Now, however, the land is held at an enormous price and the argument that reserves will interfere with commercial development must be met." This would place the availability of land at low cost in 1906. The University of Chicago *Board of Trustees Minutes* 4:246, 258, 462–63; 5:394, 473–74, suggest that Chicago's "Biological faculty," including Coulter and Barnes from the Department of Botany, promoted the Biological Field and Farm in Indiana with token involvement from Cowles and Jensen. *Minutes* 5 (11 May 1906): 394, include the petition from the biological departments signed by C. R. Whitman and F. R. Lillie in Zoology, Coulter and Barnes in Botany, S. W. Williston in Paleontology, Ludwig Nakteen in Pathology, Edwin O. Jordan in Bacteriology, and Albert P. Mathews in Physiology.

nucleus of today's Indiana Dunes State Park. Cowles went on walks with the Prairie Club and served on the faculty of the Dunes summer camp at the Prairie Club beach house in 1922, but he never led walks, never held office in the club, and his name does not appear in its membership records.[12]

On 7 April 1913 Jensen invited Cowles and eighteen other prominent citizens of Chicago to an organizing meeting for Friends of Our Native Landscape. According to Jensen's prospectus, this would be a society to promote "life in the open" and preserve "examples of native landscape types that are fast disappearing before the encroachments of industry." Jensen was founding president and Cowles served as vice-president or first-vice-president for fully fifteen years. Other founders included Harriet Monroe, the poet, Dwight Perkins, the architect, and Mrs. Julius Rosenwald, wife of the president of Sears Roebuck.

Jensen decided that the Friends would have four full membership meetings each year: Pilgrimage to the Crabapple Blossom, in May; Meeting to the Full Leaf, in June; Meeting to the Fall Leaf, to be held in autumn at the Indiana Dunes; and Fireside Meeting, in January. Each June meeting would be held at an important natural site to spur public interest in its preservation.

On 14 June the society held its first annual outdoor meeting in Illinois's only white pine forest. This place, which is today White Pines State Park, was reachable from Chicago in a morning's train ride. More than two hundred men and women ate lunch, strolled through the forest, and heard speeches by local dignitaries. Cowles brought a botany class. Vachel Lindsay recited his poem "Hawk of the Rock," followed by a performance of Kenneth Sawyer Goodman's masque, "Beauty of the Wild." Goodman's plea to protect nature from development featured a single musician and a cast of five: an Indian, a faun, a pioneer, a builder of towns and roads, and a friend. Everyone sang "Illinois" before taking the train home. Jensen was a great believer in such outdoor gatherings and theatricals. He organized events in the Chicago parks with hundreds of costumed children.[13]

---

[12] See Doeserich et al., *Outdoors*, 95–100; Grese, *Jens Jensen*, 122–23; and Cathy Jean Maloney, *The Prairie Club of Chicago* (Chicago: Arcadia Publishing, 2001). Engel, *Sacred Sands*, 83, states that Cowles taught at the dunes summer camp. The author examined membership records and documents at Prairie Club headquarters, Elmhurst, Illinois, and the Prairie Club Archives, Chesterton Public Library, Chesterton, Indiana.

[13] Grese, *Jens Jensen*, 122, 124. The story about Cowles bringing his botany class appears in *Sacred Sands*, 37. The author examined Friends of Our Native Landscape documents at the Sterling Morton Library, Morton Arboretum, Lisle, Illinois, and the Chicago Historical Society.

Nowadays we roll our eyes at such doings, but they were the style of the times and they focused public attention on a still-young conservation movement. The Lacey Act, which prohibited interstate traffic in illegally killed birds and animals was just thirteen years old when Jensen founded the Friends, and the Migratory Bird Treaty Act, an international regulation, did not pass Congress until 1918. Birds are visible and beautiful, but most people saw the prairie as a weed patch that should be plowed and farmed. The public gave little thought to protecting dunes, woods, and wetlands. Cowles and Jensen fought an uphill battle that continues to this day.

Saving the Dunes

In its early years, the Friends worked with the Prairie Club toward creation of a state or national park at the Indiana Dunes. Stephen T. Mather, a wealthy businessman and early member of the Friends, toured America's national parks in 1914 and found their condition deplorable. When he complained to the secretary of the interior, Franklin K. Lane, an old college friend, Lane invited Mather to Washington to "Run them yourself." In August 1916 Mather became the first director of the National Park Service.[14]

On 30 October 1916 Cowles testified in hearings that Mather held on a Senate resolution calling for creation of a Dunes National Park (testimony is reprinted in this volume). "For 20 years," Cowles stated, "I have been studying the dunes . . . more than anything else combined. In fact, that has been my chief reason for existence." Ranking the dunes with the Grand Canyon, Yellowstone, and Yosemite as the top natural wonders in the States, he declared that there are "few places on our Continent where so many species of plants are found in so small compass as within the area suggested for conservation. . . . Within a stone's throw of almost any spot one may find plants of the desert and plants of rich woodlands, plants of the pine woods, and plants of swamps, plants of oak woods and plants of prairies. Species of the most diverse natural regions are piled here together in such abundance as to make the region a natural botanical preserve. . . . Many of these species are found nowhere for many miles outside of the dune region, so that the

---

[14] The Stephen Tyng Mather Papers are at the Bancroft Library, University of California, Berkeley. This information comes from the biographical sketch in the Library's Finding Aid.

failure to conserve the dunes would result in the extinction of this wonderful flora for all time." World War I intervened and Congress did not act.[15]

The high point of the early campaign to save the dunes was Thomas Wood Stevens' *Historical Pageant of the Dunes,* an outdoor event featuring dramatic recitations, music, and dance that was performed at the dunes before fifty thousand people on 3 June 1917. The pageant was intended to publicize the dunes and their history—and demonstrate their importance as a natural area. The *Historical Pageant,* which had a cast of several hundred, began with an invocation to Nanabohzo, the High Manitou, and included scenes with Spanish soldiers, French explorers, Pottawatomie Indians, "nymphs of the dunes," and much more.

Cowles was a trustee of the Dunes Pageant Association, which staged the event. He served on the promotion committee, but what he did is unknown—and his efforts may not have been appreciated. Stevens' script includes a scene in which "three fantastic figures representing professors"—the scholar, the botanist, and the geologist—appear on the dunes and are chased away by a swarm of dancing mosquitoes.[16]

The Prairie Club and Friends of Our Native Landscape were only two of many Chicago-area nature organizations that flourished in Cowles' day. Late in 1914, to improve communications and increase their public impact, local conservation groups formed the Conservation Council of Chicago. Membership included the Chicago Academy of Sciences, Chicago Regional Planning Association, Ecological Society of America, Evanston Bird Club, Friends of Our Native Landscape, Illinois Academy of Sciences, Wild Flower Preservation Society of America, and many others.[17]

---

[15] "Testimony of Prof. Henry C. Cowles" in Stephen T. Mather, *Report on the Proposed Sand Dunes National Park, Indiana* (Washington, D.C.: U.S. Government Printing Office, 1917), 43–46.

[16] See *Sacred Sands,* chap. 1 and p. 74. Thomas Wood Stevens, *Historical Pageant of the Dunes* (unpublished manuscript), Newberry Library, Chicago.

[17] The Wild Flower Preservation Society of America (WFPSA) was founded in 1907 by Elizabeth Gertrude Knight Britton at the New York Botanical Gardens, shortened its name to Wild Flower Preservation Society in 1925, and was dissolved in 1933. Cowles was active in the Chicago chapter before 1919, becoming its president in 1919–20. His correspondence with Britton (1919 through 1927) is preserved in the New York Botanical Garden library with many WFPSA documents.

The WFPSA had outdoor and indoor events—a Wild Flower Pageant and All-Day Festival on 5 June 1920 in Jackson Park near the University of Chicago and annual exhibitions of nature art and lectures at the Art Institute of Chicago. Cowles gave popular talks on the Indiana Dunes and forest policy in Illinois. The Chicago branch, which had 356 members in 1921, issued a pamphlet in 1922 that told how to organize a local WFPSA

Cowles, who often presided at monthly meetings, called the council "a very informal organization," adding that "there is nothing official in any way about the council, and it has no power to commit any of its constituent members to any policy." It is "a clearing house for discussion of conservation matters referred to it," he continued, "and for the initiation of projects which may be referred to the various member societies."[18]

Meeting minutes from the late 1920s bear him out. Members announced events and exchanged news. Invited guests talked about their organizations and activities. When some natural area was threatened, the Conservation Council sounded the alarm. Member groups responded on their own initiative, which meant that the public heard many voices instead of just one. Cowles was remarkable in his willingness to come out month after month for council meetings.

Friends of Our Native Landscape and the Conservation Council sought to influence legislation and the general public. Cowles also worked with the Illinois Academy of Science (IAS), an organization of academics and professionals that focused on state problems including forest conservation, coal mining, water pollution, and agricultural pests and diseases. A charter member of the IAS in December 1907, Cowles soon joined IAS's Committee on Ecological Survey.

---

chapter. By 1923 the Chicago WFPSA had successfully lobbied for a state law that outlawed commerce in endangered flowers (e.g., bloodroot, lady slipper orchid, columbine, trillium, lotus, gentian) and prohibited their removal from public land.

Wild Flower, the national organ of the Wild Flower Preservation Society, describes a slide lecture ("Wild Flowers as a National Asset") that Cowles gave on 23 May 1924 in Cincinnati, Ohio: Cowles "propounded and emphasized four themes" relating to the value of wild flowers: esthetic, educational, sociological, and religious. The beauty of wild flowers "should be fostered as a higher development in well-rounded lives," he said. Wild flowers "stimulate investigation and foster and present scientific studies indispensable to the student of plant life and reflectively the world at large." It is "rare for one who has access to places of beauty surrounded with flowers and other uplifting influences to develop or to foster a criminal instinct," he stated. As for the religious value of wild flowers, he said that beauty of surroundings "begets a worshipful attitude or frame of mind, and awakens the consciousness to a realization of one greater than man as the author of all this great beauty." The lecture ended with a plea for more nature preserves. This is one of very few accounts we have of a public lecture by Cowles—and his only recorded public statement on religion. *Wild Flower* 1, no. 2 (1 April 1924): 13, 24; 2, no. 2 (April 1925): 5–6; 2, no. 4 (1 October 1925): 8.

[18] HCC letter to Stephen A. Forbes, 6 October 1924, Stephen A. Forbes Papers, University of Illinois Archives, Champaign; Conservation Council of Chicago meeting documents and minutes, SAF Papers. George Fuller, Cowles' assistant for many years at the University of Chicago, published an article on the Conservation Council, but it simply reproduces the organization's bylaws. George Fuller, "An Efficient Conservation Organization," *Ecology* 19, no. 2 (April 1938): 2–3.

Stephen A. Forbes

Chairing this committee was Stephen Alfred Forbes (1844–1930), an aquatic biologist and entomologist, who thought in ecological terms before ecology had a name. His seminal article, "The Lake as Microcosm," appeared in 1887 while Cowles was still in high school. It treats lake biology holistically, foreshadowing the ecosystem concept.

Incredibly energetic and productive, Forbes held two or three full-time jobs simultaneously during most of his long career (he worked into his eighties) and did research in spare moments, publishing more than four hundred scholarly papers. He was willing—as Cowles was not—to do tedious lab work. To identify which Illinois birds harm agriculture and which help, for example, he analyzed the stomach contents of 220 birds (fifty-nine species), determining the insect species—injurious or beneficial—they ate at different seasons. Between 1882 and 1916 he published about seventy research papers on the insects that attack corn. He consulted with Illinois farmers about his work and published results in forms they could use.

Forbes, elected the first president of the IAS in 1907, saw his work from an ecological perspective. He formed the Committee on Ecological Survey to improve understanding of Illinois forests and to formulate "public and private policies concerning them." He favored long-term forest management and wanted some areas to become state parks.[19]

When Cowles and Forbes met, Forbes was simultaneously Illinois State Entomologist, founding director of the Illinois State Laboratory of Natural History, and professor of zoology at the University of Illinois. He was twenty-five years older than Cowles, tremendously accomplished, and probably a bit intimidating. He had mastered the art of doing many demanding things at once—and all of them well.

Cowles began to support Forbes in 1907 when he already had a full teaching load, student trips every summer, personal research to do, and volunteer work. Between 1912 and 1917 he made numerous trips to Arkansas and Louisiana for the Sunk Lands Cases. From 1919 to 1921 he traveled to Texas and Oklahoma for the Red River Border Dispute. He wanted to help Forbes, but the record shows that he was not very

---

[19] Robert A. Croker, *Stephen Forbes and the Rise of American Ecology* (Washington, DC: Smithsonian Institution Press, 2001). SAF Papers include Forbes' statement about the Illinois Natural History Survey, which began in 1908 as the Committee on Ecological Survey of the IAS. The statement about the plant associations study appears in Forbes' minutes of a meeting of the Committee on Ecological Survey, 29 May 1908, SAF Papers.

dependable. Cowles may have taken on too much or may have preferred working for Jensen.[20]

In a talk delivered to the IAS on 22 February 1908 Cowles described the ecological survey, which was expected to produce maps "showing the distribution of [plant] associations." A "start has been made at this work in Chicago," he said. On 2 January 1909 Cowles described the Illinois survey to the Association of American Geographers, stating that its "ultimate aim is a most detailed series of maps and a series of monographs that will exclude no groups of plants and animals if workers can be found to survey them." He added that Illinois was fortunate to have much data already gathered and "systematized from an ecological standpoint by Prof. Forbes." [21]

After promising in 1908 to map "the plant associations of portions of the South Chicago area," Cowles never got started and eventually dropped off the committee. On 2 February 1910 he told Forbes that he could not attend the forthcoming IAS annual meeting on 18 and 19 February. "I would have nothing to say, even if I were present," he wrote, "since I have not done a stroke of field work that might count in two years; I have had to put every minute on [his *Textbook of Botany*, which] is now ready for the publishers, but every day counts, as they are on my back in fearful fashion."

Contractually committed to field research in the Everglades under a Carnegie Foundation grant, Cowles expected to leave for Florida as soon as he could after wrapping up his book. His name does not appear in committee reports until 1914 when he reported work of his students. The 1916 report promises that a Cowles study on sand dunes "will soon be complete," but this paper is not mentioned again and there is no further record of any sand dunes study.[22]

---

[20] Professor Cittadino in a personal communication to the author (9 January 2006) suggested that Cowles may have been overworked at this time and unable to respond satisfactorily to Forbes.

[21] HCC, "The Desirability of an Ecological Survey of Illinois Based on Plant Association," *Transactions of the Illinois Academy of Science*, 22 February 1908: 61; HCC, "A Proposed Ecological Survey in Illinois: Preliminary Program with Abstracts," *Association of American Geographers*, 1 & 2 January 1909: 7.

[22] HCC to SAF, 2 February 1910, SAF Papers. If Cowles took two years to write *Textbook of Botany* and was unable to do fieldwork during that time, this might explain why he wrote no more major books. *Transactions of the Illinois State Academy of Science* 3 (1910): 51–56; 4 (1911): 24–27; 6 (1913): 18–23; 7 (1914): 12–16; 8 (1915): 15–17; 9 (1916): 14–16; 10 (1917): 30–34; 11 (1918): 15–18. Forbes' correspondence (SAF Papers) suggests how exasperating it could be to work with Cowles. On 27 October 1914 Cowles wrote Forbes that he wanted to undertake a "a systematic study of our prairie vegetation

"Conservation of Our Forests"

In February 1912 Cowles made a major presentation called "Conservation of Our Forests" (reprinted in this volume) to the Illinois Academy of Sciences. In this speech, he applied current conservation thinking to the problems of Illinois and presented some ideas of his own.

The American conservation movement originated early in the nineteenth century as people began to recognize that poor farming practices were destroying the soil and that excessive timber harvests led to erosion and water pollution. In 1864 George Perkins Marsh, an ecological forerunner, published *Man and Nature*, in which he described the natural world as a fragile balance of interrelationships between plants, animals, and humans. At the end of the nineteenth century, and the beginning of the twentieth, lumbermen, miners, ranchers, farmers, and conservationists struggled for control of land and water in the western states, particularly California. In 1908 the Governors Conference appointed a National Conservation Commission to collect and publish information on America's current and future resource requirements.

The commission issued a three-volume report in 1909, a major conservation statement that Cowles was sure to have known. The report told how forests prevent erosion and minimize floods, condemned wasteful timber harvest and milling practices, advocated tax reforms to encourage reforestation, and recommended replanting and protection

---

before it is forever too late. . . . At the present rate of destruction, it will be only a few years before it is gone." Cowles proposed that his doctoral student, Homer C. Sampson, do this research in summer 1915 with a small travel grant from the State Laboratory of Natural History, which Forbes headed. Forbes found two hundred dollars for Sampson in December 1914 and the work began the following summer. More than a year later, on 23 October 1916 Forbes asked Cowles for an update on "the progress, plans, and prospects of Sampson's work on prairie remnants." He had "read with interest and satisfaction the brief manuscript" that Sampson sent in February, but he needed more facts to complete a report on his activities to the governor of Illinois. Cowles, who had been in California, answered on 23 November that Sampson's work was not yet done. On 7 February 1917 Cowles transmitted a three-page preliminary report from Sampson that incorporated information developed during the summer of 1916. Sampson stated that his 1917 report was also incomplete and that he did not know where he would be living later that year and whether he would be able to collect "quantitative data of the factors underlying the successions of prairie plants." In his letter of transmittal, Cowles called Sampson's work "the most important and thorough . . . ever done on the ecology and vegetation of the Illinois prairies," but acknowledged that he did not know if Sampson would ever finish. On 4 December 1919 Forbes was still waiting for Sampson's report. On 29 June 1920 the Sampson manuscript was still not in Forbes' hands. It was published as: Homer C. Sampson, "An Ecological Survey of the Prairie Vegetation of Illinois," *Bulletin of the Illinois Natural History Survey* 13, article 16 (August 1921).

of sixty-five million acres of cleared forest. Cowles became a public advocate of these policies.[23]

In his speech to the IAS, Cowles stated that Illinois is an insignificant producer of lumber, which makes it an ideal place to experiment with "conservation theories concerning our forests." Lumbering interests won't interfere, he stated, because they have little influence. If Illinois develops sound forest management policies, other states will follow.

Some timber companies want to cut all the forests down, leaving little lumber for tomorrow, Cowles continued, but sentimental conservationists oppose all harvesting. He called for "rational conservation and scientific forestry," even suggesting that Illinois prairies might be planted with trees. This is possible, he stated, because woodlands encroach upon prairies as it is. "If we can determine how and why natural forests develop on prairie soil," he said, "we will have discovered a principle of forestry of the widest significance."

After praising Illinois for buying the land in 1911 that became Starved Rock State Park, Cowles suggested that the state protect "at least one example of each of the forest types of Illinois" from development. He advocated county and township forest preserves and suggested "Bits of forest here and there [might] gradually be restored to the primitive wildness and beauty of the forests of pioneer days." This reference to natural areas restoration anticipates Aldo Leopold by fully twenty years.[24]

George Damon Fuller

Starting in 1907 George Damon Fuller (1869–1961) assisted Cowles at the university, shouldering part of the ecology teaching load and lead-

---

[23] George Perkins Marsh, *Man and Nature* (NY: C. Scribner, 1864). See Joseph M. Petulla, *American Environmental History* (San Francisco: Boyd & Fraser, 1977), 277; and United States, National Conservation Commission, *Report of the National Conservation Commission, February, 1909, Special message from the President of the United States transmitting a report of the National Conservation Commission, with accompanying papers*, ed. Henry Gannett, 60th Cong., 2d sess., 1909, S. Doc. 676. vol. 1 (Washington, D.C.: U.S. Government Printing Office, 1909), 50–74.

[24] "Conservation of Our Forests," *Transactions of the Illinois Academy of Science* 5 (1912): 48–53. According to Kurt Meine in *Aldo Leopold: His Life and Work* (Madison: University of Wisconsin Press, 1988), 328, the University of Wisconsin Arboretum and Wild Life Refuge was dedicated on 17 June 1934. Leopold wanted the Arboretum to become "a collection of landscapes, a recreation of the land as it once existed," Meine writes. Cowles wanted to preserve forest types and anticipated replanting some places where trees had been cut, but he did not advocate recreation of the presettlement landscape. Thus, Cowles' words are prophetic, but he did not invent landscape restoration.

ing some of the summer field trips. Canadian by birth, Fuller taught school in Quebec for several years, then studied botany at Cornell and Columbia before coming to Chicago for his doctorate. Cowles and Fuller met in 1902 at Woods Hole, where Cowles was teaching for the summer.

According to Paul D. Voth, who taught botany at the University of Chicago after 1934, Fuller, with Cowles as "mentor and colleague . . .criss-crossed the Indiana Dunes with ruler, notebook, and camera." His publications, which included books on the vegetation of the Chicago region, evaporation and plant succession, and Illinois vascular plants and forest trees, amplified Cowles' work. Fuller also edited *Readings in Physiographic Ecology* in 1929, updated Cowles' *Textbook of Botany* in 1930, and helped translate Braun-Blanquet's *Pflanzensoziologie* [Plant Sociology] in 1932.[25]

Fuller shared Cowles' sense of fun. According to Charles J. Chamberlain, who taught botany with them at Chicago, a master's candidate in botany was erroneously listed in the university's *Weekly Calendar* as a doctoral candidate and scheduled to take her oral exam. When the candidate arrived for the examination, Cowles picked up the *Calendar* and said, "I see Miss B. that you are up for your doctor's exam. . . I shall begin." Miss B. blushed, said nothing, and Cowles "opened up with his customary line of questions of the Ph.D. caliber," Chamberlain writes. "She was equal to it. If she had faltered, he would have scaled down to Masters style of questions. Then he called on Fuller, who had caught on immediately and he gave her just as hard a grilling," followed by others. Miss B. got her master's degree and reappeared the next year for her Ph.D. exam. This time they asked her "What's your name? Your street address?" and "Do you think it will rain and why?" After a few minutes of this, Cowles said, "Well Miss B., you seem to be pretty well prepared and our time is valuable, so you may be excused."[26]

---

[25] *The Plant World* 20, no. 11 (November 1917): 364, announces that Cowles and Fuller are preparing "an extended publication" on the Lake Michigan dunes. "The younger dunes near the south end of the lake are the ones that have heretofore received the closest study," says *Plant World*, "whereas the present investigation has been largely among the older stabilized dunes of the northern shores of the Michigan side of the lake, some of which bear the highest type of mesophytic forest." No study of this description was published by Cowles and Fuller. Cowles may well have dropped out of the project, leaving Fuller to complete it.

[26] Paul D. Voth, "Remarks at a Memorial Service for Professor George D. Fuller," 26 November 1961, University of Chicago Department of Botany Records, University of Chicago Library, Department of Special Collections (UCDBR); Charles J. Chamberlain, "Autobiography," 36L, 36M, UCDBR.

Harriet Elizabeth Cowles

Harriet Elizabeth Cowles was born on 29 June 1912. An only child, she resembled her father, inherited his temperament, and became the apple of his eye. From early childhood, she joined him in gardening. During World War I, she recalls, "When many people were starting so-called Victory Gardens, my father expanded his back yard garden. . . .Every year, in addition to a few crops, which he knew would do well in that climate, he would order seeds for plants he had never tried . . . so that often he was growing . . . several new varieties each of pop corn, Indian corn, peanuts, potatoes, a delicious little fruit he called a ground cherry (Solanum [i.e., tomato] family), land cress, salad herbs, French endive, and so on and on."

The family took the train to the Indiana Dunes, walked to the shore, and picnicked. Harriet remembers a quaking bog and her father's talk about "new dunes forming, moving dunes, and farther back from Lake Michigan the older established dunes with oak trees and small wild flowers growing in black soil far above the sand." They collected flowers and pressed them in a book at home. Henry taught Harriet the plants and phrases in German that he felt she ought to know.

When Harriet was six, her father took her to the University of Chicago Laboratory School and said, "This is your school. You'll learn to study. You'll learn from books." She read many books and worked with a little sewing machine, but she was often late because she had a hard time getting up in the morning. Her father gave her a penny if she got to class on time. Harriet was often at loggerheads with her mother and characterized her as status-conscious. Elizabeth invited faculty wives to lunch and tea at their home. Harriet served cookies at these gatherings.

Harriet graduated from the Laboratory School in 1929 and applied to Vassar College, but was rejected because of weakness in math. People on campus were shocked that Vassar had turned down the daughter of a well-known professor. She tried again, was admitted, graduated in 1933 and, two years later, earned a master's degree in Italian and French from the University of Chicago. Thereafter she taught languages at high schools and colleges in the Chicago area. She had a hard time at first because she was short, shy, and couldn't control the class. Elizabeth helped her prepare and graded some of her papers.

Until she married, Harriet lived in the family home near the University of Chicago. She claims that Elizabeth broke up a youthful romance, but she did not leave the household, even after her father died. During the 1950s, Edmund Waller, a St. Louis manufacturer and Harriet's first cousin, visited the Cowles household. He and Harriet liked each other, began to correspond, and married on 12 July 1958. Edmund was then a fifty-seven-year-old widower with two grown sons, and Harriet was forty-six.

Elizabeth opposed this union and did not attend the wedding. Harriet moved to St. Louis after her marriage, found a teaching position there, and visited her eighty-year-old mother almost every weekend in Chicago. Eventually, Elizabeth moved to an apartment in St. Louis, where she died, aged ninety, on 1 August 1963. Edmund Waller died on 19 April 1997; Harriet Cowles Waller was living in a St. Louis nursing home when the author met her in April 2004.[27]

Ecological Society of America

On 27 March 1914 Robert Wolcott, professor of zoology at the University of Nebraska, had the idea of establishing a professional society for ecologists. As he envisioned it, the organization would include "both botanists and zoologists" and would be "for field work" rather than "the reading of papers." Wolcott wanted to have spring or summer meetings in different places where members would take field trips during the day and have demonstrations and discussions in the evening. To ensure large attendance at meetings, he favored a "sectional society" that would cover just the center of the United States. Wolcott communicated with

---

[27] This account of HCW comes from three sources: HCW Address; interview with Harriet Cowles Waller, St. Louis, Missouri, 8 April 2004; and interview with Linda Estelle, trustee of Harriet Cowles Waller, 8 April 2004, St. Louis. Linda Estelle kindly showed me genealogical information on the Waller family and a resume that HCW assembled in 1961. When the author met the ninety-two-year-old Harriet Cowles Waller, she gave conflicting accounts of events and often wandered off the subject. According to Harriet, Henry Cowles originally planned to study for the ministry, but gradually realized that geology and botany were his chief interests. Nothing in his diaries indicates that he seriously considered the ministry. More credible is her statement that Cowles did not drink alcohol and returned gifts of wine or whiskey. The 56-acre Mineral Springs Bog near the Indiana Dunes, which Harriet Cowles visited with her father in childhood, was purchased in 1953 by the Save the Dunes Council and renamed Cowles Bog National Natural Landmark in 1965 by the U.S. Secretary of the Interior. While Harriet was a student at the University of Chicago Laboratory School, Bertha Morris Parker of the School of Education, University of Chicago, and her father (as junior author) wrote *The Book of Plants* (1925). Cowles may have taught some classes at the Lab School. *The Book of Plants* consists of short chapters on botany that were intended "to serve as informational silent-reading material for children of the sixth, seventh, and eighth grades." In a letter to Steven Forbes, Cowles claimed that Parker did all the writing for *The Book of Plants*, but the text is in two styles and he probably wrote or heavily edited several chapters (HCC to SAF, 10 March 1928, SAF Papers).

Victor E. Shelford, professor of zoology at the University of Chicago. Shelford liked the idea and told Cowles, who responded enthusiastically. On 30 December 1914 Shelford, Cowles, and about twenty other ecologists met in Philadelphia to discuss what this new society would do.[28]

Shelford had taken elementary ecology with Cowles in 1904 and had visited the Indiana Dunes with the class. He would make pioneering studies of animal ecology at the dunes. Shelford called Cowles one of the most important influences on his professional life.[29]

After the 1914 meeting, Shelford, Cowles, and other members of the organizing committee spread the word to the ecological community. On 30 December 1915, fifty members approved formation of the Ecological Society of America (ESA), with Shelford as president. Cowles advocated a broad-based national membership, and by 1916 the ESA counted 284 members, comprising plant, animal, and human ecologists and those with interests in forestry, grazing, fisheries, entomology, climatology, and paleoecology. From 14–17 June 1916 Cowles, Shelford, and Fuller hosted a four-day ESA field trip to the dunes of Lake Michigan. The "entire expense for lodging, meals, and transportation for the four days will be about $10," said the announcement.[30]

When the ESA was founded, scenic places such as Yellowstone were protected national parks, but development and pollution threatened hundreds of smaller, lesser-known sites. In 1917 the ESA formed a committee for "The Preservation of Natural Conditions for Ecological Study" that proposed to list "all areas in North America north of Mexico, which are suitable for ecological study and are already preserved or should be preserved." Once this list was ready, the committee would urge protection of these areas.

Shelford chaired this committee, Cowles served as adviser on plant communities, and there were advisers on entomology, ornithology, fisheries, grazing, and fires. Eighteen ecologists volunteered to "secure a listing of areas in their states or provinces." Soon the committee was pushing for a redwood preserve on the Pacific Coast and protection of Georgia's Okeefenokee Swamp. At the December 1919 meeting, Shel-

---

[28] Wolcott to Shelford, 27 March 1914, Victor E. Shelford Papers, University of Illinois Archives, Champaign-Urbana; HCC, "A Proposed Ecological Society," (flyer, Chicago, IL, 20 September 1915).

[29] Robert A. Croker, *Pioneer Ecologist: the Life and Work of Victor Ernest Shelford, 1877–1968* (Washington, DC: Smithsonian Institution Press, 1991), 12–15.

[30] The Ecological Society of America, *Announcements of Field Trips Chicago Sand Dune Region*, 1 April 1916, Shelford Papers.

ford reported that "upwards of five hundred" natural areas had been listed. Cowles took responsibility for Indiana, Illinois, and Ohio.[31]

In 1921 Shelford and Cowles co-authored *Preserves of Natural Conditions,* a thirty-two-page pamphlet that presented a strategy to win public support of nature preserves. The authors explained that ecologists need "undisturbed patches of nature" so they can study native plant and animal species in their original habitats. They wanted to close off some areas, but acknowledged that the public wouldn't support them if it lost all access. Accordingly, they propose limited access and provide a map for "suggested management of a 60-acre tract of forest" with picnic facilities, a forestry demonstration area, and a large, closed preserve.

The time for action is now, say Shelford and Cowles. The Indiana Dunes are under attack by commercial interests and must be protected. Dunes land was available at very low cost in 1906, but prices had risen rapidly since then. The pamphlet contains statements signed by Cowles, Shelford, other ecologists, and lines from "Prairies," a poem by William Cullen Bryant.[32]

It took until 1926 for Shelford's committee to complete the list of preserves and publish it as the *Naturalist's Guide to the Americas.* This 761-page volume begins with essays, many written by former students of Cowles. As with *Preserves, Naturalist's Guide* is an early environmental call to arms. Among other things, it says that "environmental complexes" (large habitats, in today's terms) should be kept as complete as possible. It condemns overgrazing in the national parks, tells how habitat destruction hurts birds, and states that nature preserves must be managed.

Cowles, who had been so important to the ESA in its early years (he was society president in 1918) virtually disappears from the *Naturalist's Guide.* He helped to assemble a list of Illinois nature preserves in

---

[31] Ecological Society of America, *Minutes of the Committee on the Preservation of Natural Conditions for Ecological Study,* 1917, SAF Papers; Shelford to SAF, 24 February 1919, SAF Papers; Ecological Society of America, Committee on the Preservation of Natural Conditions for Ecological Study, *Report of the Chairman V. E. Shelford to the Committee on Cooperation with the National Research Council and to Executive Committee of the Ecological Society,* 1917, SAF Papers.

[32] Ecological Society of America, Committee on the Preservation of Natural Conditions, *Preserves of Natural Conditions* (reprinted for the committee, 1921, with the aid of the National Research Council), SAF Papers. On 19 May 1920 HCC wrote to Elizabeth Britton, founder of the Wild Flower Preservation Society of America: "I note that you desire a brief account of the progress of the Ecological Society in saving plant sanctuaries. I am at present engaged in working out a report of our work in cooperation with Dr. Shelford." New York Botanical Garden Library (NYBGL).

1922, but his only signed contributions to the guide are brief descriptions of some preserves. Cowles may have stood aside to give former students a chance to publish or he may have given up on Shelford. Late in 1922 he told Elizabeth Britton of the Wild Flower Preservation Society, "Like yourself, I have gotten somewhat out of patience with Shelford and his proposed naturalists' handbook of natural areas. He outlined it on too big a scale and now it is submerging him."[33]

A committee of ecologists, however well intentioned, could never hope to identify all of North America's important natural areas, ensure their protection, and win support from the general public. Also, ecological study is not the only reason for creating nature preserves. In 1946 some scientists formed the Ecologists Union to focus directly on natural areas preservation. This group changed its name to the Nature Conservancy in 1950 and incorporated as a nonprofit one year after that. Today's Nature Conservancy, the world's largest and most effective conservation organization, follows the path that Cowles and other ecologists laid out before 1920. Conservancy scientists identify threatened natural areas that the organization protects through purchase, restoration, and management.

Botany 36

Cowles originated Botany 36 (Field Ecology) in 1900–1901 and it became his signature course. For four weeks at a time, he took students into natural areas all over North America. These were teaching expeditions, but Cowles used them for personal research and his primary destinations over the years were the shores of Lakes Michigan, Superior, and Huron, which have a common geological history.[34]

---

[33] Victor E. Shelford, *Naturalist's Guide to the Americas* (Baltimore, MD: Williams & Wilkins, 1926). On 18 November 1922 Cowles told R. B. Miller, Illinois State Forester: "Partly in connection with the committee work of the Ecological Society, partly through the search for desirable state park sites in connection with the Friends of Native Landscape, and partly on my own hook, I am endeavoring to get together a list of all the natural preserves of the state, whether public or private, and also a list of all natural areas that should be preserved." He asks whether county agents might be helpful and sends a list of what he has so far. He also wants to know what areas of Illinois should be kept in "permanent forest" and wants data with which to construct a map of existing woodlands in Illinois. HCC to Britton, 29 November 1922, NYBGL. One reason why the *Naturalist's Guide* took so long was that it ran out of money. Shelford asked Britton for a donation from the Wild Flower Preservation Society.

[34] *Annual Register of the University of Chicago* lists Botany 36 expeditions year by year. The expeditions are listed in a chronology at the end of this volume. Tuition fees paid

Cowles planned trips carefully, checking unfamiliar territory in advance. In 1921, as he was preparing to visit California, he wrote to Prof. William F. Badè, an early member of the Sierra Club, who taught at the Pacific School of Religion in Berkeley. Stating that he wanted students to see every kind of vegetation, from lowland chaparral to alpine meadow, Cowles asked how to avoid the crowds at Yosemite National Park. As an alternative to Yosemite, he was considering Sequoia National Park where the giant sequoias are "much more numerous and finer" and the Kern River Valley or King's Canyon, which is "about as good as the Yosemite, and much wilder." Since he wanted to cover much territory in a short time, Cowles asked whether the group could "get about more speedily" in Yosemite or Sequoia. He wanted hotel recommendations, too, and closed with an apology for asking so much of Professor Badè.[35]

When students signed up for Cowles' Field Ecology, they got an instruction sheet that estimated their costs and told them where to be

---

Cowles' salary and expenses on these trips. He also found summer teaching and research work at the Cold Spring Biological Laboratory, Long Island, New York (1900) and at Woods Hole, Massachusetts (1902).

The Carnegie Institution of Washington supported field trips to the Florida Everglades in 1904 and 1906. For details, see Carnegie Institution of Washington, *Yearbook No. 6, 1906* (Washington, DC: Carnegie Institution, 1907), 19, 126–27. Cowles called his project Origin, Distribution, and Physiographic Development of the Flora of the Everglades. He started work in 1904 with support from Chicago's Department of Botany. When funds ran out, he asked the Carnegie Institution for a grant, explaining in his application that this study made special reference to "the structure, origin, and physiographic development of the plant formations (particularly the hammocks and everglades proper). With this will be coupled an analysis of the soil and climate as related to the vegetation." During autumn and early winter 1906 Cowles did research in the Everglades supported by a three-hundred-dollar Carnegie Foundation grant. In October 1907 D. T. McDougal, director of botanical research at the Carnegie Foundation, sought to defer funding for another Cowles' trip to the Everglades. "Dr. Cowles is now preparing a work dealing with some of the features of the plant geography of North America," McDougal wrote, "and [wants] to use all his available time for completion of this work." No such study was published. Cowles planned to complete his Everglades research during the winter of 1909–10 and the Carnegie Institution granted him five hundred dollars, but the accidental death of Professor Barnes in the botany department meant that Cowles and others had to teach his courses at Chicago and could not get away. It is not clear from correspondence and grant records at the Carnegie Institution whether Cowles ever completed the Everglades work as originally planned.

In USSC, sec. 308, 7, Cowles stated "I have a contract with the Carnegie Institution to publish a monograph on the sand dune vegetation of the lake regions of the United States in comparison with dune vegetation elsewhere in the world, and for that I have spent much time on dunes." The Carnegie Institution has no record of this contract and Cowles never published a monograph of this description.

[35] HCC to William F. Badè, 27 January 1921, William F. Badè Papers, Bancroft Library, University of California, Berkeley, CA.

and when. "It is imperative," these instructions stated, "that each member of the party be a 'good sport,' putting up cheerfully with rain, hot or cold weather, mosquitoes, black flies, and with inadequate or unsatisfactory accommodations." Cowles wrote that he would not tolerate a "spirit of complaint" and reserved the right to "dismiss summarily from the class any who complain" or "fail to harmonize with the other members of the party." Students must have "stout tramping shoes, with leggings, if the shoes are low," he continued, and both sexes need trousers. The "most satisfactory field garb for women," he stated, "is a riding habit made of khaki or other suitable material." Students were expected to bring Gray's *Manual of Botany* with them and handbooks for the local area.[36]

Botany 36 students had plenty of fun. Frederick Grover, a student on the expedition to Oregon, Washington, and British Columbia in June and July 1907, recalls the night on the train "when the men returned to berths in which the girls had stealthily placed all the pots and pans of our kitchenette." There was also a birthday party "celebrated with a bottle of rare Amontillado . . . which grew so boisterous that the occupants of the car ahead came back to find the cause of all the hilarity." We were "all young together, then," Grover concludes, "and what a glorious good time we had!"[37]

The expeditions were intense and instructive. May Thielgaard (Watts) toured the Lake Superior region with Botany 36 during August 1916. In five weeks, the party visited sixteen towns, observed climax forests, hydrarch, bog, xerarch, and retrogressive successions, and identified numerous plants. When she returned home, Thielgaard transformed her field notes into an eighty-seven-page expedition notebook with hand-drawn maps, photographs, and plant lists.[38]

In 1919 Paul B. Sears, who was preparing to seek a doctorate in botany at the University of Chicago, traveled to Wisconsin's Door County with Botany 36. Cowles promised that the group would inves-

---

[36] Botany 36, Summer 1919, First Term (Instruction Sheet signed by Cowles). Cowles probably wrote a similar sheet for every expedition. This one is in HCC Papers. Paul Sears kept a copy from a 1919 Rocky Mountains expedition (Paul Bigelow Sears Papers, Manuscripts and Archives, Yale University Library, New Haven, CT) that is virtually identical.

[37] Frederick Grover to Elizabeth Cowles, 6 March 1940, HCC Papers. Grover typed this letter of consolation on letterhead of the Bureau of Plant Industry, Division of Forage Crops and Diseases at the U.S. Department of Agriculture. Grover was also a fellow graduate of Oberlin College and requested information on Cowles for its files.

[38] Papers of May Thielgaard Watts, Morton Arboretum, Lisle, IL.

tigate "the successional relations along the eroding limestone shores, the depositing sandy shores, the lakes, bogs, and glacial uplands, terminating in the climax forest."

A lifelong friendship began on this trip. "Dear Paul," Cowles wrote on 30 August, "I wanted to tell you how much of a fancy we had taken to you, and how we shall be looking for you again in the very near future. Very few in my experience have taken such a hold on us in so brief a time. You seem to have become inoculated with the Chicago spirit, and we hope you will be one of us always." Sears did his doctoral work with Professor Coulter, but asked to be Cowles' assistant on a field ecology trip to Alaska in 1920 and produced some of the most vivid accounts we have of Cowles.[39]

According to Sears, Cowles was a "superb field teacher." He used to say "If you are going out on a field trip to show something to a class, be sure it's there if you have to sneak out the night before and put it there." While this sounds somehow fraudulent, Sears explains that Cowles was "using his delicate gift of whimsy to make clear that field teaching is a serious, responsible business." Too many field instructors point out anything that catches the eye and make impressively erudite comments, Sears continues, but they leave students "with no sense of the unity and interrelationship of what they have seen." Cowles always had clear notions of what students should see, learn, and take away from field trips.[40]

"As an interpreter and inspirer, [Cowles] excelled, writing and speaking with clarity and force," Sears wrote. "More than this, he had that priceless gift which is a sure sign of a feeling for proportion—a great sense of humor. This kept him from becoming doctrinaire, from ever relying on method as a substitute for judgment." Sears adds that Chicago's botany department "brought in students from all over the world and subjected them, whatever their specialty, to [Cowles'] leavening influence." Teaching rather than publication was his gift to the generation that followed him.[41]

---

[39] HCC to Sears, 25 May 1919; HCC to Sears, 30 August 1919; Sears to HCC, 6 August 1920, (Sears Papers, Yale University Library.)

[40] Sears, "Teaching Ecological Relationships Through Biological Field Trips: Interrelations Between Man and the Environment," *The American Biology Teacher* 8, no. 5 (February 1946): 101–4.

[41] Sears, "Some Notes on the Ecology of Ecologists," *Scientific Monthly* 83, no. 1 (July 1956): 22–27. Sears adds that another Cowles' virtue was "his blithe disregard for boundaries and barriers." He participated in meetings of geographers when some questioned his presence there and was "far less concerned to chalk off lines between . . . subjects than to

Harriet Cowles also went on summer expeditions, presumably in the 1920s when she was old enough to enjoy them. "My father was seldom happier," she writes, "than when he was on his way to visit a new place, accompanied, preferably, by a small group of interested Botany students." On some trips, the group traveled in large open seven-passenger Packard touring cars with cloth tops. "Often the roads were washed out, at which time we all got out and pushed," she writes. "Every so often the engines would overheat and I would be elected to run down the slope to get icy cold water from a mountain stream. I have since wondered why nothing cracked in those engines."[42]

Conservation Advocate

Starting in 1918, Cowles became a public advocate of conservation. Working through the National Conference on State Parks, the Illinois State Forestry Survey, the Friends of Our Native Landscape, the Illinois Forestry Association, and other organizations, he pressed for creation of nature preserves in Illinois and for a state forestry policy that would balance ecological and economic needs.[43]

---

see them united in a common cause." He was particularly good at "healing breaches between individuals and groups" because he wanted "people around him [to] forget their pettiness and pull together."

[42] HCW Address.

[43] Cowles attended the Tri-State Forestry Conference in Indianapolis, Indiana, on 22–23 October 1919 as a representative of the state of Illinois. The conference was originated by Richard Lieber, director of the Department of Conservation, state of Indiana, and a long-time advocate of Indiana conservation and state parks. Industrial associations and the states of Ohio, Indiana, and Illinois sent delegates to the conference, which sought to define a "practical policy of state forestry which will assure a permanent timber supply, a comprehensive legislative program and adequate legislative backing," says an unsigned report on the conference in the SAF Papers. It seems highly probable that Cowles was present during the Second Forestry Conference at the Union League Club of Chicago on 19 and 20 April 1922. Delegates came to the conference from Indiana, Iowa, Michigan, Minnesota, Missouri, Ohio, Wisconsin, and Illinois to formulate "more adequate programs of forestry for these states," says a program for the conference among the Forbes papers. Coulter is listed in the program by name, but not Cowles. We have no information about the First Forestry Conference or any subsequent meetings of this group. On 27 December 1920 Cowles and Jensen attended a meeting at the University Club on the University of Chicago campus that was called by Mrs. Florence Kaufman, who is described as "one of the leading workers for wild conservation in the state." The meeting outlined ten prospective state park sites in Illinois. An undated [28? December 1920] clipping from a newspaper [name unknown] published in Belleville, Illinois, in the Forbes papers describes this event (SAF Papers).

Starved Rock State Park was the first site that Illinois preserved for its scenic beauty and ecological importance. Prior to 1911, when land was purchased at the Starved Rock site, Illinois had only protected places of historic interest. In 1918 Cowles contributed a chapter on botany to *Starved Rock State Park and Its Environs*, a 150-page Geographic Society of Chicago bulletin. His text is a systematic description of park vegetation, with popular and scientific names of the plants.[44]

In 1920 Stephen Mather at the National Park Service concluded that national parks were overshadowing state parks. Railroads and local business wanted national parks because they drew tourists, but people were proposing unsuitable sites and big crowds were damaging the parks. Also, most national parks were located in the western states, meaning that some people in other parts of the country could not afford to visit them.

Mather wanted only the largest and most important sites to be national parks and expected the states to take responsibility for lesser sites within their borders. Some states were already facing this problem, but others had done nothing, so Mather decided to invite people from all over the country to a public conference that would get a national movement going. In October 1920 he met with Cowles, Jensen and others in Chicago to plan the First National Park Conference for 10–12 January 1921 in Des Moines, Iowa.[45]

Cowles was one of about two hundred delegates to this meeting. Contrary to Mather's intent, there were few presentations on the mechanics of creating state parks and many on peripheral subjects like landscape architecture or biological and historical resources. Cowles, who spoke to the conference on "Making a State Park Survey," stated that Illinois had six million acres of land that were unsuitable for agriculture and should become state parks and forests.

"We dream of the time when we will have many parks in Illinois," he declared in his speech. "We should like to see today a continuous parkway along the entire length of the Mississippi River . . . from Minnesota to the gulf [of Mexico] . . . We should like to see this parkway all along [the rivers of Illinois]." Cowles would be pleased to know that today's Nature Conservancy has programs to protect and restore large areas along the Mississippi and Illinois rivers.

---

[44] Carl Ortwin Sauer, Gilbert H. Cady, and HCC, "Starved Rock State Park and its Environs," *Bulletin of the Geographic Society of Chicago*, no. 6. See Bibliography in this volume.

[45] Ney C. Landrum, *The State Park Movement in America: A Critical Review* (Columbia: University of Missouri Press, 2004), chap. 5.

This first conference closed with resolutions calling upon state, county, and local governments to provide recreation and preserve natural areas in an undisturbed state. Cowles helped create committees to study state park laws, suggest a uniform code, investigate creation of a park-to-park highway system, and plan the next conference. He served the National Conference on State Parks, mostly as a member of its executive committee, until 1932.[46]

In 1918 Cowles began to assist Forbes with an Illinois State Forestry Survey "along ecological lines." According to Forbes, roughly 30 to 40 percent of Illinois was forested when settlers arrived at the beginning of the nineteenth century. By 1918 roughly two-thirds of this forest, mostly on hills along the Mississippi River, was gone. Farmers had cut the trees, cultivated the land to exhaustion and walked away. Forbes wanted to know how much forested land remained in Illinois. Then he could recommend which areas should remain untouched as nature preserves, which could be cut for timber, and which cutover lands should be replanted.

On 22 May 1918 Cowles, Coulter, and Forbes met at the University of Chicago to plan the Illinois State Forestry Survey for that summer. Since there was already earlier work on record, they decided to build on it by surveying in the north half of the state, recording "forest types" rather than "individual species" and relying on soil survey maps in choosing survey tracts. Coulter and Cowles were reimbursed their travel expenses, but otherwise volunteered their summer vacation time and supplied student assistants.

Cowles spent most of August "in the field with a party of advanced students." After making "an intensive survey" of the northern part of Cook County (i.e., environs of Chicago), the group created large-scale (eight inches to the mile) maps. These showed "the distribution of timber in relation to cultivated land and prairie land, designating also the different types of timber, such as bottom land, swamp timber, upland timber, etc." The surveyors also noted the species of trees, their size, and forest composition. Cowles planned to continue the survey in fall, working with Warren G. Waterman, a former student who had become a professor of botany at Northwestern University in Evanston, Ilinois.[47]

---

[46] The Editor, "The National Park Conference at Des Moines, Iowa," *Iowa Conservation* 5, no. 1 (January–March 1921): 14–25.

[47] Croker, *Stephen Forbes*, 176; HCC, "The Illinois Forestry Survey," *The Journal of Ecology* 7, nos. 1 & 2 (May 1919): 120; "Minutes of Conference of May 22 (1918) With Professors Coulter and Cowles at the University of Chicago," unsigned typescript by SAF; HCC to SAF, 14 October 1918; HCC to SAF, 17 October 1918 (all SAF Papers). In-

Henry Martyn Cowles, father of HCC, ca. 1905. *Credit: American Environmental Photographs Collection, ASAS-00965, Department of Special Collections, University of Chicago Library.*

Eliza Whittlesey Cowles, mother of HCC, before 1888. *Credit: American Environmental Photographs Collection, ASAS-00971, Department of Special Collections, University of Chicago Library.*

HCC, almost four years old, 1873. *Credit: American Environmental Photographs Collection, ASAS-00968, Department of Special Collections, University of Chicago Library.*

HCC at high school graduation, 1888. *Credit: American Environmental Photographs Collection, ASAS-00969, Department of Special Collections, University of Chicago Library.*

HCC ca. 1898–1900. *Credit: American Environmental Photographs Collection, ASAS-00967, Department of Special Collections, University of Chicago Library.*

Elizabeth Luetta Waller [Cowles] as a young woman. *Credit: American Environmental Photographs Collection, ASAS-00974, Department of Special Collections, University of Chicago Library.*

Elizabeth Waller [Cowles] and HCC, ca. 1900. *Credit: American Environmental Photographs Collection, ASAS-00966, Department of Special Collections, University of Chicago Library.*

Unidentified man, Elizabeth Cowles, and HCC in a greenhouse, probably somewhere in Europe, 1906. *Credit: American Environmental Photographs Collection, ASAS-00964, Department of Special Collections, University of Chicago Library.*

Elizabeth Cowles and Harriet Elizabeth Cowles, 1913. *Credit: American Environmental Photographs Collection, ASAS-00973, Department of Special Collections, University of Chicago Library.*

Harriet Cowles, ca. 1922. *Credit: American Environmental Photographs Collection, ASAS-00972, Department of Special Collections, University of Chicago Library.*

Harriet, Elizabeth, and Henry Cowles, ca. 1922. *Credit: American Environmental Photographs Collection, ASAS-00970, Department of Special Collections, University of Chicago Library.*

University of Chicago Department of Botany faculty and students in front of the Hull Biological Laboratories, Chicago, Illinois, 1917. Faculty members front row from left: Sophie Hennion Eckerson, George Damon Fuller, HCC, John Merle Coulter, Charles Joseph Chamberlain, William Jesse Goad Land, and William Crocker. *Credit: American Environmental Photographs Collection, AEP-ILP 66, Department of Special Collections, University of Chicago Library.*

Students of a University of Chicago Field Ecology class and their baggage at the train station, Hoquiam, Washington, 1907. HCC is at far right. *Credit: American Environmental Photographs Collection, AEP-WAS 204, Department of Special Collections, University of Chicago Library.*

HCC on a field trip, 1911. *Credit: American Environmental Photographs Collection, AEP-ILP 234, Department of Special Collections, University of Chicago Library.*

HCC, Verne Graham, and Harriet Sulzer at play on a University of Chicago Department of Botany field trip. *Credit: American Environmental Photographs Collection, AEP-ILP 244, Department of Special Collections, University of Chicago Library.*

George Damon Fuller and HCC in academic robes, University of Chicago, probably before 1920. *Credit: American Environmental Photographs Collection, AEP-ILP 230, Department of Special Collections, University of Chicago Library.*

HCC and students defy the law on a field trip. *Credit: American Environmental Photographs Collection, AEP-ILP 246, Department of Special Collections, University of Chicago Library.*

HCC (second from right) and unidentified men at the Indiana Dunes, probably during the Twenties. *Credit: American Environmental Photographs Collection, AEP-INP 85, Department of Special Collections, University of Chicago Library.*

HCC and an unidentified woman encircling a *Morus rubra* (Red Mulberry), Bethel Hollow, Pope County, Illinois. *Credit: American Environmental Photographs Collection, AEP-ILS 33, Department of Special Collections, University of Chicago Library.*

University of Chicago Department of Botany Field Ecology class in autos, Yellowstone National Park, Wyoming, 1923. *Credit: American Environmental Photographs Collection, AEP-WYS 84, Department of Special Collections, University of Chicago Library.*

Field Ecology class on a Sunday afternoon at Mt. Timpanogos, Utah, 1924. HCC is fourth from right in front row, Elizabeth Cowles is third from right. *Credit: American Environmental Photographs Collection, AEP-UTS 6, Department of Special Collections, University of Chicago Library.*

Forbes had to badger Cowles to write up his results. On 24 June 1919, ten months after fieldwork was done, he asked, "Can you give me any idea of the time within which it will be convenient for you to complete your report on forestry work in Cook County?" Forbes asked again on 26 September and Cowles apparently replied that he had not turned in his report because there was more work that he wanted to do. On 9 October Hazel Schmoll, who had assisted Cowles, told Forbes that she had given him her work in summer and had heard nothing since. On 3 December Forbes, who wanted to make a complete report to the IAS, had manuscripts from all participants in the survey work save for Cowles. He did not get Cowles' report until 30 December, and it was apparently incomplete.[48]

While the Illinois State Forestry Survey was in progress, Jensen asked Forbes for a list of "proper sites for State Parks in Illinois." These sites, he explained on 18 February 1919, should be very scenic and "not less than one thousand acres in area." In January of the next year, Cowles, Forbes, and Jensen reviewed prospective park sites and Cowles took his "first reconnaissance trip" to southern Illinois the week of 15–19 March with a photographer in tow.[49]

Cowles' findings became two chapters in *Proposed Park Areas in the State of Illinois* (1921), a 120-page paper-covered book that was published by the Friends of Our Native Landscape. As Jensen's foreword explains, the report is nontechnical, a "work of love and must be accepted as such." *Proposed Park Areas* describes "such sections of Illinois as should be preserved for present and future generations," lands that have "greater spiritual than material value."[50]

---

formation on Warren Gookin Waterman from the Northwestern University Archives, Evanston, Illinois.

[48] SAF to HCC, 24 June 1919, 26 September 1919; Schmoll to SAF, 9 October 1919; SAF to J. L. Pricier, Secretary, Illinois State Academy of Science, 3 December 1919, 30 December 1919, SAF Papers. UCDBR contains miscellaneous plant lists and hand-drawn maps titled "Glencoe, Illinois Report on Ecological Surveying of Cook County-New Trier Township-Sections 1, 5, 6, 7, 8, Survey Made between October 1, 1918, and January 1, 1919." There is a brown envelope with the handwritten inscription "Hazel M. Schmoll 'Probably for my personal files and not to be published.' Henry C. Cowles," but this envelope does not contain the Schmoll materials described in the Cowles–Forbes correspondence. Other survey materials in UCDBR are dated 1919, 1920, and 1922. These relate to work in Cook County, Illinois, some Chicago suburbs, and Porter County, Indiana.

[49] Jensen to SAF, 18 February 1919, 7 January 1920; HCC to SAF, 5 March 1920, SAF Papers.

[50] Cowles' letters to R. B. Miller, Illinois State Forester, are preserved at the University of Illinois Archives in Champaign-Urbana. The letters, which run from 1919 to 1923,

Provided with twelve maps and fifty-four excellent photographs, *Proposed Park Areas* is aimed at a popular readership. True to the spirit of this venture, Cowles describes sites in terms of their scenic beauty and historic interest, scarcely mentioning their ecological value. Locals knew the places he describes and many were favorite hiking and camping spots of long standing. *Proposed Park Areas* was thus a publicity piece, but it had the intended effect, for most of the listed sites are state parks and forests today.

On 28 April 1922 Cowles, Coulter, and Robert B. Miller, Illinois State Forester, attended an organizing meeting for the Illinois Forestry Association (IFA), becoming charter members. The IFA, which included representatives from the lumber industry, conservation groups, and state government (Forbes soon joined), sought to educate the public in forestry issues, formulate a forest policy for Illinois, and establish an Illinois Department of Forestry. The IFA was a lobby.

Cowles was elected IFA president and told Forbes on 18 May 1922 that he saw this as "a great responsibility and a great opportunity." He used his office as a forum for promoting Illinois forestry. Late in 1922 he declared that Illinois would benefit economically if trees were planted on the land that had been lumbered and abandoned. He wanted to extend the Illinois State Forestry Survey to "all barren lands suitable for timber production" and called for studies of "tree planting and care," establishment of forest preserves, tax reforms to encourage tree planting for profit, and courses in farm forestry at state colleges. He

---

primarily concern arrangements for Cowles' visits to southern Illinois for *Proposed Park Areas in the State of Illinois.* This report was delivered to the board of directors of the Friends of Our Native Landscape on 15 February 1921. It recommended preservation of Apple River Canyon of Jo Daviess County, the Savanna headlands on the Mississippi River, the White Pine Forest Tract of Ogle County, and Cahokia Mounds, all of which are Illinois state parks today. Areas that Cowles cited in his chapters are today incorporated into Giant City State Park, Ferne Clyffe State Park, Cave-in-Rocks State Park, the Cache River State Natural Area, Dixon Springs State Park, Fort Massac State Park, Fort Kaskakia State Park, Pere Marquette State Park, and in state forests that form a belt across the southern tip of Illinois. Not all areas recommended for preservation by Cowles appear to have become state parks. His text is confusing at points.

It is entirely possible that Cowles consulted with Mary Minerva Steagall—or invited her on some of these survey trips. She was his student after 1899 and called Cowles one of her favorite professors. On one field trip, Cowles told her, "Your name should be Minerva. You remind me of the goddess of wisdom."

Steagall became an expert in ferns, exploring and collecting in almost uninhabited areas of southern Illinois, where she carried a pistol for protection from moonshiners and their ilk. A member of the National Committee on Conservation and Preservation of Natural Areas and the Ecological Society of America, Steagall shared Cowles' views on natural areas. For details, see Willard M. Gersbacher, "Idols of Egypt XV. Mary Minerva Steagall" *Egyptian Key* 3, no. 3 (September 1950): 27–34.

had said most of these things before and was not the first or the only person to say them. But now he spoke as president of a large public organization.[51]

Forbes' Illinois Natural History Survey produced a *First Report on a Forestry Survey of Illinois* (March 1923) and a *Second Report on a Forestry Survey of Illinois* (1924) that summarized the results of the Illinois State Forestry Survey. These documents helped persuade the Illinois legislature to establish a forestry division in the university experiment station in 1923 and to create the Illinois Conservation Department in 1926. Robert B. Miller was author of the *First Report* and Forbes turned to Herman C. Chapman, professor of forest management at Yale University School of Forestry, for the *Second Report*. Chapman estimated the value of Illinois woodlands, described the economics of forest management and production, and tabulated the supply and demand of forest products in Illinois.

Despite his early involvement with the Illinois State Forestry Survey, Cowles' name appears nowhere in these reports. In 1926 Cowles succeeded Coulter as forestry representative on an advisory body called the State of Illinois Board of Natural Resources and Conservation. He did no more forest surveys for Stephen Forbes or the state.[52]

Botany Department Chairman

In 1923 Professor Coulter was seventy-two years old and he began thinking about retirement. During that year, while Coulter was overseas for several months, Cowles served as acting chairman of the

---

[51] S. F. D. Meffley, "To Members of the Council" memorandum from secretary, Lumbermen's Association of Chicago (n.d., but probably 1922), (SAF Papers); "Illinois Forestry Association plans a State Forestry Program," *Journal of the Illinois State Historical Society* 15, 3–4 (October 1922–January 1923): 729–30. Speaking as president of the IFA, Cowles predicted that the year 1974 "will see the first stages of a timber famine in the United States unless farmers throughout the country heed the warnings of forestry experts and devote their waste land to the raising of trees." He pointed to production declines in pine, redwood, and oak, citing a projected IFA study that was expected to show "the various kinds of soil in [Illinois], which most readily can be adapted to timber production," Press Release, apparently issued by the University of Chicago, 12 September 1924, HCC Papers. One paragraph mentions that Cowles had spent the summer in Utah directing work in field ecology. While there, he "attracted widespread attention by his identification of one of the oldest trees in the world—a juniper, aged 2,000 years, located near Provo."

[52] Croker, *Stephen Forbes*, 176–77. Cowles attended his first meeting of the Board of Natural Resources and Conservation on 26 January 1926 and his last on 20 May 1932, missing very few.

Department of Botany. This temporary honor—and burden—did not affect his salary, but he did the work willingly, writing on 29 September to Dean of Faculties James H. Tufts, "To me, the pleasantest feature of the whole affair is that Dr. Chamberlain and my other botanical colleagues, not knowing of any official action, told me that it was their unanimous wish that I step into the breach during Dr. Coulter's absence."

As Coulter took steps toward retirement, Ernest D. Burton, president of the University of Chicago, became involved in selecting a successor for him. In autumn of 1923 he told Cowles and Tufts that the Department of Botany was apparently scheduling courses with poor attendance and attracting low numbers of students. Acknowledging a recent sag in enrollment, Cowles proposed to expand the department into the growing fields of plant physiology and plant pathology. He wanted Prof. William Crocker, a former faculty member and "certainly the leading plant physiologist of America, if not of the world," to spend a week on campus during the summer quarter as a guest lecturer. The department was already planning to add Dr. George Konrad Karl Link, a plant pathologist, to the teaching staff. Crocker delivered the lectures and Link came to Chicago.

As for departmental efficiency, Tufts told Burton on 11 December (Cowles probably never saw this letter) that botany was one of the university's most efficient departments, turning out large numbers of doctors on a comparatively small budget. The English department, for example, had two-and-a-half times the budget of botany, but produced half as many doctors. Tufts added, "I recall some extremely caustic remarks by Mr. Coulter with reference to certain inquiries which he thought showed gross ignorance as to what they were trying to do . . .we should proceed with great caution."

In April 1924 Coulter was back and definitely making retirement plans. He told President Burton that "Dr. Cowles should be appointed [to take over as department chairman] for his service in that capacity during my absence was more than satisfactory." Instead of appointing Cowles to succeed Coulter, Burton named him department secretary, giving him Coulter's administrative work but not his policy-making responsibilities.

On 16 June Harold H. Swift, a university trustee from 1914 to 1955, denounced Cowles to President Burton. Quoting the words of an anonymous acquaintance, Swift wrote, "It may interest you that I have had to hear many groans concerning the Botany Department at the University from many sources. A recent story is that Cowles has an uncle on the board of trustees that assures him the headship." After stating that he knew nothing about Cowles' qualifications, Swift declared "We should be careful not to drift into giving him the job."

On 21 June, apparently without investigating these anonymous accusations, Burton replied that the "situation in Botany is a serious one, and I see no remedy for it except within a year to find some young man of first rate ability. There is no one in the department who can in any adequate measure fill Mr. Coulter's place and carry on as a leader in the Department."

Burton died before he could act and Cowles became chairman of a huge department with five full professors, including himself, four associate professors, and two assistant professors. In 1927–28, under Cowles' chairmanship, two introductory and five general botany courses were offered, along with twelve in morphology and paleobotany, ten in physiology, eleven in ecology, five in pathology, three in genetics, and two designated seminar and research. The eleven ecology courses, all taught by Cowles and Fuller, included Elementary Field Ecology, Applied Ecology, Ecological Anatomy, Geographic Botany 1 and 2, Physiographic Ecology, Forest Ecology, Field Ecology, Experimental Ecology, Experimental Methods in Field Ecology, and Problems in Ecology.[53]

On 16 March 1925 Coulter recommended that his son, Merle C. Coulter, be made editor of *Botanical Gazette*. Instead, Cowles became Coulter's coeditor in 1926, 1927, and 1928, succeeding Coulter when he died in 1929. The phrase "Founded by John Merle Coulter" appeared on the cover of *Botanical Gazette* after 1929 and the front cover was redesigned in 1932, but otherwise Cowles made no changes in the *Gazette*.

In 1926 Cowles got the outdoor research station that he had been wanting for years. He became a trustee of Wychwood, a sanctuary for native Wisconsin plants and animals, located roughly seventy-five miles northwest of Chicago. In 1901 Charles and Frances Hutchinson of Chicago had purchased a tract of unimproved land on Wisconsin's Lake Geneva. Some of this land was completely undisturbed and the Hutchinsons decided to make it a nature preserve. With guidance from a horticulturist, they added native plantings. Cowles eventually became involved as their adviser. In 1926 Frances Hutchinson, who was by then a widow, deeded the property to the University of Chicago as an

---

[53] This account is constructed from correspondence in the University of Chicago Archives involving Burton, Cowles, Swift, and Tufts. As a trustee, Swift deserves considerable credit for developing the University of Chicago into the major institution that it is today. These letters are quite odd, for Trustees normally do not get involved in departmental personnel decisions.

"Experiment and Research Station" with limited public access. Cowles may have done research in this preserve, but we do not know what he did or when. The university sold Wychwood in 1957 and the land was developed for luxury housing.[54]

The last two important papers that Cowles published (both reprinted in this volume) are "The Succession Point of View in Floristics" (1926) and "Persistence of Prairies" (1927). Cowles begins "Succession Point" by contrasting the floristic and ecological points of view in plant geography. The floristic view considers floristic composition and the ecological view looks at associations and successions.

"From the floristic point of view, the flora of a region is considered as to its origin and immigration," Cowles writes. Plants may be divided into those that are "strictly proper to the region" and distributed equally in all directions; plants near the edge of their range and unequally distributed; plants that are discontinuous or disjunct; and endemics (plants that occur in small numbers in very limited areas). Cowles then reviews Chicago-area plant associations in their "dynamic relations or order of development" and compares the floristic character of regional associations—the beach dune succession, pond-bog-forest succession, and other successional series.

Cowles reviews changes in the Chicago region that followed the retreat of the glaciers as plants advanced over the area from south to north, but also from the southwest to northeast and southeast to northwest. He identifies relics "left behind in connection with a northern retreat of glacial ice and ... the northern movement of the flora following this retreat" and closes with an account of endemics. One of these, *Thismia americana* (Thismia) is related to a plant of the East Indies and known only from a small area inside Chicago. Thismia, he writes, "presents a situation of extraordinary difficulty." Since Cowles' time, Thismia has disappeared, presumably extinct. "Succession Point" closes, typically for Cowles, with no firm conclusion and a call for further study.[55]

---

[54] Frances Kinsley Hutchinson, *Wychwood: The History of An Idea in Three Parts* (Chicago: Lakeside Press, 1928); *Wychwood Lake Geneva, Wis. A Sanctuary for the Native Plants and Birds of Wisconsin* Pamphlet: (1928) UCL, Department of Special Collections.

[55] HCC, "The Succession Point of View in Floristics," presented before the International Congress of Plant Sciences, Section of Ecology, Ithaca, New York, 20 August 1926. Published in *Proceedings of the International Congress of Plant Sciences*, August 16–23 1926 (Menasha, Wisconsin: George Banta, 1929) 1, 687–91. In *A Natural History of the Chicago Region* (Chicago: University of Chicago Press, 2002), Joel Greenberg writes (229–31) that Norma Pfeiffer, a graduate student in botany at the University of Chicago, discovered the plant in Chicago's Calumet wetlands on 1 August 1912 and "saw speci-

In "Persistence," Cowles says that treeless prairies grow in dry temperate places like the Great Plains, but also in Illinois where prairie and forest thrive next to each other. Cowles attributes this to drainage, evaporation, fire, and grazing, but also proposes soil evolution as a possible cause. After the glaciers retreated, he writes, Illinois was bare and two types of vegetation—prairie plants, and forest trees—began to grow. Slowly Illinois soil evolved into a type in which prairie plants grow and a type that supports trees.

Forests may invade prairies in the absence of fire or grazing and trees may retreat. Cowles calls this phenomenon the *prairie-forest conflict* and says that prairie and forest have battled back and forth over many centuries as climate changed. The "existence of a prairie in a given place in our middle west may be due in part to factors operating at the present time and in part to the influence of cumulative soil factors operating through past centuries," he writes. The evolution of a prairie soil through the influence of prairie vegetation favors the persistence of the prairie and evolution of a forest soil through the influence of forest vegetation favors the persistence of the forest. Climatic change "may disturb the prairie forest balance either way," he concludes.[56]

Last Years

Parkinson's disease attacks nerve cells in the human brain that help control bodily movement and balance. Science does not know what causes the disease or how to cure it. Symptoms include slower than normal movement and tremors or stiffness in the hands and legs. Rigidity in the face or neck can cause problems with speech or swallowing. Parkinson's afflicted Cowles from the late 1920s, forced him to quit teaching, and ended his life on 12 September 1939 when he was only seventy years old.

Paul T. Voth, who came to Chicago as a student in 1929 and later taught botany there, recalled that "When it became evident that Cowles was stricken with Parkinsonism, Professor Ezra J. Kraus . . . was

---

mens at the site over the next four years," making her last observation on 1 September 1 1916. Late in life, she stated that only three other graduate students had seen the plant at the site, but she may well have shown it to Cowles, who would have insisted on seeing such a rare plant.

[56] HCC, "Persistence of Prairies," presented before the Ecological Society of America at its meeting in Nashville, TN, 29 December 1927. Published in *Ecology* 9, no. 4 (October 1928): 380–82.

appointed 'Secretary of the Department' with full administrative responsibilities. He insisted that the title of Chairman be retained by Cowles until Cowles retired. One of the first classes I attended in the Department of Botany was one in ecology. Cowles by that time mumbled his words and wrote small script on the blackboard. I was the departmental assistant who projected the lantern slides. After Cowles left the room, all students remained to see a rerun of the slides and to gain new insights into the lessons of the day. It was a sad situation."[57]

In 1930 Cowles made his last trip abroad to the International Botanical Conference in Cambridge, England. "He was no longer quite his old self," Tansley would write in an obituary, "though keenly interested in what we could show him." He characterized Cowles as "essentially a field teacher, whose excursions were a vital part of his teaching, and on these . . . he was always the centre of a crowd of enthusiastic and devoted students." Tansley added that Cowles was a man "of infectious gaiety and high spirits and of infinite humanity and humour, a loyal and affectionate friend who never spared himself in giving help, and always quick and generous in his appreciation of the good work of others."[58]

Cowles ceased teaching in 1932 and retired in 1934. Late that year, several of his colleagues in the Ecological Society of America—William S. Cooper, Charles C. Adams, Helen Dixon, George D. Fuller, and George E. Nichols—decided to honor him with a special number of *Ecology*. They passed the hat and collected three hundred dollars to pay for printing extra pages. The Cowles' number, which appeared in July 1935, seemed almost to summarize his professional career. It began with Tansley's "The Use and Abuse of Vegetational Concepts and Terms," which included a lively discussion of succession that Cowles surely enjoyed. Charles C. Adams contributed "The Relation of General Ecology to Human Ecology." Frederic Clements' "Experimental Ecology in the Public Service" nodded toward Cowles' service to conservation, but also mentioned the numerical–statistical techniques that he resisted lifelong. Victor Shelford wrote on animal ecology and Edgar Transeau's article "The Prairie Peninsula" touched on issues that Cowles had raised in "Persistence." Hugo Osvald's "A Bog at Hartford,

---

[57] Paul D. Voth to Frank Yoder, 18 March 1991, UCDBR. In "Remarks Concerning Charles E. Olmsted as a Friend" for the memorial service for Olmsted on 12 January 1977 (Archival Biographical Files University of Chicago Archives), Paul Voth stated that even though "Prof. Henry C. Cowles was becoming incapacitated with parkinsonism, Charles was able to meet this pioneer plant ecologist in his home."

[58] Arthur G. Tansley, "Obituary Henry Chandler Cowles, 1869–1939," *Journal of Ecology* 28, no. 2 (August 1940): 451.

Michigan" stated that the article originated in 1927 on a field trip with Cowles.[59]

The Cowles' number began with William Cooper's tribute to Cowles. According to him, "The concepts of succession and climax" found "their first adequate expression" in Cowles' "Plant Societies." Because Cowles was "always cautious, never dogmatic," he did not try to create a rigid system and so his ideas, "to a remarkable degree, have stood the test of time." He added that Cowles' "basic viewpoint." as expressed in his *Textbook of Botany*, was "that of mechanical causation rather than teleology and adaptation."

Cooper called Cowles an inspiring teacher who, "very early in his career . . . gathered about him a group of men scarcely younger than himself, who enthusiastically entered with him the fresh field of dynamic ecology and applied the principles he was formulating to new regions." He also showed future teachers "how to bring their pupils directly to nature, and, above all, to unfold to them the myriad mysteries of biology without recourse to the cheap and easy fallacies of anthropomorphism."

Cooper closed with a tribute to Cowles as a man. "Merely because it is a joy to do so, we make mention of a few of his many lovable traits—his unfailing good humor, his far-famed ability in the telling of a story, his readiness to give ungrudgingly of time and effort in the service of students and friends, his eagerness to discover and commend whatever is meritorious in the work of a fellow scientist or admirable in the man himself."[60] We can say no more.

---

[59] Ecological Society of America, n.d. [1934] circular letter announcing special issue of *Ecology* and soliciting contributions, Archives of the Ecological Society of America, University of Georgia Library, Athens, Georgia. People responded to this letter with reminiscences and praise of Cowles. These letters were apparently given to Cowles and lost, for they are not in the archives at UGL.

[60] William S. Cooper, "Henry Chandler Cowles," *Ecology* 16, no. 3 (July 1935): 281–83.

PART TWO:
ANTHOLOGY

ANTHOLOGY

NOTE: Herewith a selection of Cowles' articles and presentations. To aid the reader, the author has done minor editing as follows:

- When Cowles uses the scientific name of a plant, the common name is added in brackets the first time the name occurs in a text. If he writes *Hypericum kalmianum*, the editor adds [Kalm's St. John's Wort].
- When Cowles uses an antiquated scientific name, it is silently updated and the common name follows. Thus, *Rhus toxicodendron* becomes *Rhus radicans* [Poison Ivy].
- Here and there, the editor has added the word 'and' in brackets to clarify the meaning of a sentence. A few punctuation marks are silently added.
- Spelling is silently updated. Thus Alleghanies becomes Alleghenies, bowlder becomes boulder, sumach becomes sumac, etc.
- Place names are updated. Thus Crystal lake becomes Crystal Lake.

The authority for plant names is **Plants of the Chicago Region** by Floyd Swink and Gerould Wilhelm (Lisle, Illinois: The Morton Arboretum) Fourth Edition, 1994. The author also used **Manual of Vascular Plants** by Gleason and Cronquist (New York: NY Botanical Garden), 1991. Plants not found in either of these sources were searched on the Internet. There are some tiny inconsistencies because Cowles used Flora that split some species into subspecies based on small differences, while Swink and Wilhelm tend to lump such subspecies together.

If a reader gets lost, there is a plant list at the end of this section with all the scientific names used in these texts and their corresponding common names.

In addition, to access historic photos which relate to The Ecological Relations of the Vegetation on the Sand Dunes of Lake Michigan (1899) and Plant Societies of Chicago and Vicinity (1901), visit www.sigelpress.com. Special thanks is extended to the Special Collections Research Center at the University of Chicago Library for permission to showcase these.

Anthology: The Core

THE ECOLOGICAL RELATIONS OF THE VEGETATION ON THE SAND DUNES OF LAKE MICHIGAN.

PART I. GEOGRAPHICAL RELATIONS OF THE DUNE FLORAS. (WITH FIGURES 1–26)

I. Introduction.

The province of ecology is to consider the mutual relations between plants and their environment. Such a study is to structural botany what dynamical geology is to structural geology. Just as modern geologists interpret the structure of the rocks by seeking to find how and under what conditions similar rocks are formed today, so ecologists seek to study those plant structures which are changing at the present time, and thus to throw light on the origin of plant structures themselves.

Again, ecology is comparable to physiography. The surface of the earth is composed of a myriad of topographic forms, not at all distinct, but passing into one another by a series of almost perfect gradations; the physiographer studies landscapes in their making, and writes on the origin and relationships of topographic forms. The ecologist employs the methods of physiography, regarding the flora of a pond or swamp or hillside not as a changeless landscape feature, but rather as a panorama, never twice alike. The ecologist, then, must study the order of succession of the plant societies in the development of a region, and he must endeavor to discover the laws which govern the panoramic changes. Ecology, therefore, is a study in dynamics. For its most ready application, plants should be found whose tissues and organs are actually changing at the present time in response to varying conditions. Plant formations should be found which are rapidly passing into other types by reason of a changing environment.

These requirements are met *par excellence* in a region of sand dunes. Perhaps no topographic form is more unstable than a dune. Because of this instability plant societies, plant organs, and plant tissues are obliged to adapt themselves to a new mode of life within years rather than centuries, the penalty for lack of adaptation being certain death. The sand dunes furnish a favorable region for the pursuit of ecological investigations because of the comparative absence of the perplexing problems arising from previous vegetation. Any plant society is the joint product of present and past environmental conditions, and perhaps the latter are much more potent than most ecologists have thought. As will be shown in another place, even the sand dune floras are often highly modified by preexisting conditions, but on the whole the physical forces of the present shape the floras as we find them. The advancing dune buries the old plant societies of a region, and with their death there pass away the influences which contributed so largely to their making. In place of the rich soil which had been accumulating by centuries of plant and animal decay, and in place of the complex reciprocal relations between the plants, as worked out by a struggle of centuries, the advance of a dune makes all things new. By burying the past, the dune offers to plant life a world for conquest, subject almost entirely to existing physical conditions. The primary motive, then, which prompted this present study was the feeling that nowhere else could many of the living problems of ecology be solved more clearly; that nowhere else could ecological principles be subjected to a more rigid test.

This particular investigation was also prompted by the fact that the previous ecological studies of sand-dune floras have been carried on chiefly in European countries, and almost exclusively along marine coasts. There has been considerable difference of opinion as to the influence of salty soils and atmospheres upon the vegetation. It would seem that a comparison of dunes along an inland fresh water lake with those along the sea should yield instructive results.

An ecological study of this character has a natural twofold division. In the first place the plant formations are to be investigated. The species characteristic of each formation must be discovered, together with the facts and laws of their distribution. The progressive changes that take place and the factors in the environment which cause these changes must be discussed. This phase of the subject is largely geographic, and will be the special feature of the present paper. In another paper it is the author's purpose to discuss the adaptations of the plants to their dune environment, paying especial attention to those species which show a large degree of plasticity, and which are found growing under widely divergent conditions. This second phase again has a natural twofold division, one part treating of gross adaptations such as are shown in plant organs and plant bodies, the other dealing with the anatomical structures of the plant tissues.

The material for the present paper has been gathered chiefly from the study of the dunes in northwestern Indiana in the vicinity of Chicago.

These studies were carried on in the seasons of 1896, 1897, and 1898, frequent visits being made to various points at all seasons of the year. A portion of the summer seasons of 1897 and 1898 was spent in a more rapid reconnaissance along the entire eastern shore of Lake Michigan, including the group of islands toward the north end of the lake.

The work resulting in this paper has been carried on in connection with the Hull Botanical Laboratory of the University of Chicago, and the author gratefully acknowledges the kindly interest and cooperation shown by his associates among the faculty and students of the botanical department, especially Head Professor John M. Coulter, through whose influence the author was directed along lines of ecological research. The author further desires to express his great indebtedness to Dr. Eugen Warming, professor of botany at Copenhagen; his textbook on ecology and his treatises on the sand-dune floras of Denmark have helped greatly to make clear the true content of ecology, and they have been a constant incentive to more careful and thorough work. Most of the photographs were taken especially for this paper by Mr. E. W. Martyn, a Chicago photographer. Some of the views were taken by Messrs. S.M. Coulter and H.F. Roberts, students in the Hull Botanical Laboratory. The map was prepared by Mr. S.M. Coulter.

II. General features of the coast of Lake Michigan.

Along the eastern shore of Lake Michigan there are hills of wind-blown sand almost continuously fringing the border of the lake. This line of sand hills also continues around the southern end of the lake and along the western shore as far as Chicago. These sand hills or sand dunes form striking topographic features in the landscape, and in this respect present a strong contrast to the level prairies or fields beyond.

Geologically speaking, the sand dunes belong to the most recent formations, as they are entirely post-glacial. In most cases the origin of the existing topographic forms is to be referred to the most recent phases of post-glacial history, and in many instances the topographic forms are either being made or unmade at the present time. As a rule the dunes are directly superposed upon the beach. On the northeastern shores of the lake, however, the dunes are commonly superposed upon bluffs of clay or gravel, sometimes 120 meters above the present beach.

In the lake region there is a decided prevalence of westerly winds, chiefly from the southwest or northwest. As a consequence, the dunes are found along the entire eastern and southern shores of the lake, whereas the dunes on the western shore, due to easterly winds are merely small hillocks of sand. Such small dunes have been seen at Waukegan, Ill., and on North Manitou and Beaver islands. The dunes toward the southern portion of the lake were created and fashioned, as a matter of necessity, almost entirely by the northwest winds. In order to secure any extensive formation of sand dunes, it is necessary for the wind to gather force by sweeping over the lake and to strike the coast almost at right angles to the shore line. It will thus be seen that the most favorable theoretical locality for dunes in a region of northwest winds is on the southeast shore of a body of water in that region. As a matter of fact, the dune region increases in area and the dunes themselves increase in height and complexity as one passes from Chicago around the south end of Lake Michigan. The culmination of the dune formations actually occurs between Dune Park and Michigan City, and an examination of the accompanying map (*fig. I*) will show that these localities have a shore line running nearly southwest to northeast. The contour of the dunes themselves also shows that they were shaped by northwest winds, as does the path formed by the sweeping of the wind.

The Dune Park region furnishes the most extensive area of present dune activity to be found along the southern coast of Lake Michigan, although the altitudes of individual dunes are much greater at many points in Michigan. Elsewhere the active dunes are usually confined to a very narrow belt fringing the shore, but at Dune Park the dunes are active from one to two kilometers inland, the front of the advancing dunes varying from 6 to 30 meters in height. The dune complex or area of dune activity at Dune Park covers perhaps 1000 hectares. The established dunes here as elsewhere cover a far greater area than do the active dunes, reaching inland three to eight kilometers. Between Chicago and Dune Park there is a most interesting series of parallel ridges, alternating with depressions, which often reach below the water level throughout the entire year. The origin of these ridges is scarcely within the province of this paper; their extreme regularity of contour, in addition to their persistent parallelism, seems hardly consonant with a dune origin. Because of the low altitude of these ridges and their protection from shore conditions, their flora is not typically xerophytic. Whatever the origin of these ridges, they represent a phase in the lake's history when its waters were much farther inland than at present. The active dunes at Dune Park are scarcely ever more than 30 meters in altitude, but there are several established dunes, which are more than 36 meters above the lake. The coast charts issued by the Corps of Engineers of the United States War Department figure a dune near Porter, Ind., which reaches an altitude of 57 meters above the lake. Of course, altitudes of individual dunes are subject to much change, although in the case of established dunes the figures need but slight revision. The highest series of dunes is along the Michigan shore between Michigan City and St. Joseph. A large number of dunes reach an altitude of more than 60 meters; several are over 90 meters high; and one is figured on the coast chart which has an altitude of 117 meters above the level of the lake. An inspection of the map will show that these dunes must have been shaped primarily by northwest winds.

The Michigan shore between St. Joseph and Frankfort, a distance of more than 250 kilometers, is fringed almost continuously with a narrow belt of dunes. Perhaps at no place within this region are there such extensive dunes in activity at the present time as at Dune Park, nor do the established dunes reach inland as a rule for more than a kilometer. At Dune Park there is a gradation in the altitude of the dunes as one goes inland, until the low sand ridges pass all but insensibly into the prairies beyond. Along the Michigan shore, however, there is a narrow fringe of dunes close to the lake, commonly much higher than at Dune Park, and the transition between these dunes and the normal inland country is rapidly passed and plainly marked.

A very striking feature along the Michigan shore is the tendency of rivers to form small lakes near their mouths. These lakes determine the presence of cities, since they furnish the best of harbors. An inspection of the map (fig. 1) shows the presence of such natural harbors at the mouths of rivers at Holland (Ottawa Beach), Grand Haven, Muskegon, Whitehall, Pentwater, Ludington, and Manistee. A large amount of the silt brought down by the rivers is deposited at the mouth, where the river currents are slackened by their opening out into the lake and by wave action. The waves pile up this sand along the beach and the winds pick it up and form extensive dunes at the river's mouth. All along the Michigan coast the most extensive areas of active dunes are likely to be at the mouths of the rivers, so that dune formation is thus seen to be regulated by the supply of sand as well as by the relation of the coast line to the direction of the prevailing winds. Since the general direction of the Michigan coast line is north and south, and the prevailing winds southwest and northwest, dune formation tends to close up the mouths of the rivers on both sides. The result of this conflict between the river and air currents is seen in the formation of lakes whose entrance into Lake Michigan is constricted by a narrow passageway. The tendency of the wind to close these passageways is so great that navigation is often difficult, and the necessity for constant dredging and erection of windbreaks is obvious.

The dunes at the mouths of rivers furnish a rough measure for determining the relative influence of northwest and southwest winds in dune formation, since those on the south side are largely shaped by southwest winds and those on the north side by northwest winds, although each wind modifies the action of the other. At Saugatuck the southwest winds appear to dominate, since the dune south of the river is 78 meters high, while to the north the heights are inconspicuous. The course of the Kalamazoo river has been deflected to the northward at this point, although it is interesting to observe that the mouth is now being deflected to the southward, the river filling in on the northwest bank and eroding on the southeast. At Ottawa Beach, the dunes are about equal on both sides, and less than 60 meters in height. At Grand Haven there is an immense active dune on the north side of the river, 66 meters high, and with an advancing lee slope 45 meters in height. This dune is deflecting the river to the southward, and attempts to stop its progress are not particularly successful. The dunes at Muskegon are largest on the south side of the river. At Pentwater, Ludington, and Manistee the dunes average about 45 meters in height. The fringe of dunes is interrupted at several points by clay bluffs, but this latter formation is far more extensive farther northward.

Active dune formation is conspicuous on projecting points of land as well as at the mouths of rivers; for example, active dunes are to be found on Little Point Sable, south of Pentwater, and Big Point Sable, north of Ludington. At many points along the coast the winds are breaking through the fringe of established dunes, so that the older dunes may be said to have started into activity again or to have become rejuvenated. In summation concerning the area between St. Joseph and Frankfort, it may be said that the influence of northwest and southwest winds in dune formation is nearly equal. Indeed, the two winds commonly work together to produce a composite result, so that the winds sweep and the dunes advance, as a rule, from west to east.

In northern Michigan, between Frankfort and Glen Haven, and also on North Manitou island, most of the dunes are perched high up on bluffs of clay or gravel. The bluffs are steep and approach the water's edge, varying in height from nothing up to more than 120 meters. Dunes are to be found upon the tops of the very highest of these bluffs in the district south of Glen Haven. These perched dunes are almost wholly established, and it seems as if their formation took place years ago when the lake was perhaps at a higher level. The most remarkable dune formation along the entire coast of Lake Michigan is to be found on Sleeping Bear point, just south of Glen Haven. The point stretches out into the lake, and is constantly growing to the northward and eastward by reason of the joint action of waves and winds. The point proper is geologically quite young, and, apart from the present beach and stationary beach dunes, is covered by an immense and active dune complex. At many points the wind has scooped out great hollows in the complex, exposing the gravel of a former beach. The advance of the dunes in this area is chiefly eastward, the exposed fossil beaches being chiefly toward the west. Two or three kilometers southward from the point, the region of low active dunes passes somewhat suddenly into an immense flat-topped hill, rising abruptly from the lake like a mesa or terrace. The height of the dunes on the point is seldom greater than 30 to 45 meters, while this peculiar gravel terrace, or mesa, has an average height of 120 meters above the lake level and an area of more than 2000 hectares, since it extends inland for about two kilometers, and along the coast for, perhaps, 15 kilometers. The Sleeping Bear itself, which gives its name to the point, and also to the bay, is a long established dune, with an altitude of 30 meters above the terrace on which it stands, or 150 meters above the lake. This dune stands alone, and is a landmark for miles in all directions. Farther to the south, dunes are perched upon these bluffs almost continuously, and there are reasons for supposing that the Sleeping Bear is but the last remnant of such a chain of dunes formerly superposed on the bluffs near Glen Haven. Toward the east and north, as well as toward the lake, the slopes of the mesa-like formation are quite abrupt, and beyond these slopes there is to be found an extensive dune complex, the grandest in variety and beauty to be found along Lake Michigan. It seems almost certain that the source of the sand for this dune complex was an ancient row of dunes at the top of the mesa toward the west. This is made more probable by the fact that the Sleeping Bear, once firmly established, is now being torn up by the winds and carried northeastward. The dune complex is moving toward the east, the line of advance being parallel to the lake shore, as usual. This advancing dune is far and away the grandest along Lake Michigan, presenting an almost continuous front, measuring four kilometers from north to south, all in active progression. The average height above the country on which it is encroaching is about 60 meters, so that it presents a most imposing sight when viewed from the fields in front of its line of advance. The dune complex at Glen Haven is like that at Dune Park, but on a far grander scale; sometimes there are hollows within it more than 30 meters in depth scooped out by the wind, and reaching down to an ancient beach. Within the dune complex there are extensive old soil lines and many scarred trunks of trees, long buried by the dunes and now resurrected, though not to life.

At many other places along the northern shore of the lake there are high bluffs of clay, or gravel, whose summits are crowned by established dunes. Only rarely are these dunes in action at the present time, and, where such action is observed, it is clearly due to the rejuvenation of dunes that had become established. The origin of these perched dunes is obscure and hardly within the province of this paper. The formation of dunes at the summit of a bluff is not unknown. A wind laden with sand may sweep up the slopes of a hill. As it reaches the summit its path is no longer narrowly restricted, and as it spreads out, its energy is dissipated and its load deposited. However, no such action was anywhere observed; on the contrary, at many points the wind is removing the dunes from just such locations. Consequently the author rather inclines to the belief that these perched dunes represent an earlier phase of dune formation, when lake or wind conditions were different from the present. Another possible mode of origin will be discussed in connection with the rejuvenated dunes.

The greatest altitude reached by the clay and gravel bluffs is at Empire, a few miles south of Glen Haven; at this point a height of 128 meters is attained. There is a high degree of oscillation in the altitudes even within a few meters. Where the clay bluffs are highest, the perched dunes are seldom as high as where the bluffs are lower. The greatest observed height of the perched dunes above the top of the clay was 60 meters. The greatest total observed height above the lake at Empire was 162 meters; at Frankfort 153 meters. South of Frankfort and north of Glen Haven the altitudes are much less. At Charlevoix and Petoskey there are no cliffs; the dunes are low and superposed directly upon the beach.

The islands in the north end of the lake are of great interest to the student of dunes, since they are exposed to winds from all directions; the position of the dunes thus indicates the direction of the dune-forming winds. In all cases the chief dune formation is on the west coast, and the most conspicuous active dunes are usually restricted to a narrow area at or near the southwest point of each island. Observation from the steamboat revealed the presence of such dunes on South Manitou, South Fox, and High islands. The dunes on North Manitou and Beaver islands were visited. On North Manitou there are prominent areas of dune activity along the southwest coast, the dunes being superposed on bluffs of clay or gravel. There is a flat-topped terrace here, like that at Glen Haven, but in miniature, the height being only 15 meters and the area scarcely half a hectare; the dune perched on this bluff has been rejuvenated and carried inland a few meters, the greatest altitude being 45 meters above the lake. There are also small wandering dunes superposed directly upon the beach. On the west coast the bluffs are steeper and much higher, at times perhaps 60 meters above the lake; the summits are occasionally crowned by established dunes. On Beaver Island, the southwest coast was not visited, but there are rejuvenated dunes at various points along the west coast, sometimes 45 meters in height; these dunes are superposed upon the beach. The beach dunes here are exceedingly varied and extensive. As previously stated, there are low beach dunes along the east coast of Beaver island. On Mackinac island there are steep clay bluffs, but no dunes. Thus the islands plainly show that westerly winds, and especially winds from the southwest, are the chief dune formers.

Surveying the lake region as a whole, the dunes are created and shaped almost entirely by westerly winds. In the southern portions of the lake, the northwest winds have the greater sweep and are the chief dune-formers. Northward the southwest winds are the chief factors in determining the location of dunes. In intermediate localities all westerly winds contribute about equally to dune formation, and there is progressive movement of active dunes to the eastward.

III. The ecological factors.

The distribution of the plants in the various dune associations is governed by physical and biotic agencies which will be considered somewhat in detail in another place. At this point it seems advisable to give a general survey of these factors, especially in so far as they affect the distribution of plant societies in the region as a whole.

LIGHT AND HEAT.

Nearly all of the dune societies are characterized by a high degree of exposure to *light*. Particularly is this true of the beach and the active dunes. The intensity of direct illumination is greatly increased by reflection; the glare of the white sand is almost intolerable on a bright summer day. The *temperature* relation is even more marked in its influence upon plant life. Because of the absence of vegetation and the general exposure of sand dunes the temperature is higher in summer and lower in winter than in most localities. This great divergence between the temperature extremes is still further increased by the low specific heat of sand. On sandy slopes protected from cold winds the vegetation renews its activity very early in the spring, because of the strong sunlight and the ease with which the surface layers of sand are heated. Willow shoots half-buried in the sand frequently develop fully a week in advance of similar shoots a few centimeters above the surface. Similarly in the autumn the activity of plant life ceases early largely because of the rapid cooling of the superficial layers of sand, as well as because of direct exposure to the cold.

WIND.

The wind is one of the most potent of all factors in determining the character of the dune vegetation. The winds constantly gather force as they sweep across the lake, and when they reach the shore quantities of sand are frequently picked up and carried on. The force with which this sand is hurled against all obstacles in its path may be realized if one stoops down and faces it. The carving of the dead and living trees which are exposed to these natural sand-blasts is another evidence of their power. Fleshy fungi have been found growing on the windward side of logs and stumps completely petrified, as it were, by sand-blast action; sand grains are imbedded in the soft plant body and as it grows the imbedding is continued, so that finally the structure appears like a mass of sand cemented firmly together by the fungus. The bark of the common osier dogwood is red on the leeward side, but white on the windward because the colored outer layers of the bark have been wholly worn away. On the windward side of basswood limbs the softer portions are carved away while the tougher fibers remain as a reticulated network. On the leeward side of these same limbs, the outer bark is intact and even covered more or less with lichens.

The indirect action of the wind produces effects that are considerably more far-reaching than any other factor, for it is the wind which is primarily responsible for sand dunes and hence for their floras. But more directly than this, the wind plays a prominent part in modifying the plant societies of the dunes. The wind is the chief destroyer of plant societies. Its methods of destruction are twofold. Single trees or entire groups of plants frequently have the soil blown away from under them, leaving the roots exposed high above the surface; as will be shown later this process is sometimes continued until entire forests are undermined, the débris being strewn about in great abundance. Again, swamps, forest, and even low hills may be buried by the onward advance of a dune impelled by the winds; in place of a diversified landscape there results from this an all but barren waste of sand.

SOIL.

The soil of the dunes is chiefly quartz sand, since quartz is so resistant to the processes of disintegration. The quartz particles are commonly so light colored that the sand as a whole appears whitish; closer examination reveals many grains that are not white, especially those that are colored by iron oxide. With the quartz there are conspicuous grains of black sand, largely hornblende and magnetite. These black grains often accumulate in streaks, persistent for considerable depths and apparently sifted by the wind; large quartz grains are mingled with these grains of magnetite and hornblende so that it would seem as if grains of higher specific gravity are sifted out together with those of greater absolute weight. The sand of the dunes is remarkably uniform in the size of the particles as compared with beach sand; this feature is due to the selective action of the wind, since the latter agent is unable to pick up and carry for any distance the gravel or large sand particles of the beach.

As is well known, soil made up chiefly of quartz sand has certain marked peculiarities which strongly influence the vegetation. The particles are relatively very large; hence the soil is extremely porous and almost devoid of cohesion between the grains. These features are of especial importance in their effect upon the water and heat relations as shown elsewhere. As a rule, sandy soils are poor in nutrient food materials, nor do they rapidly develop a rich humus soil because of the rapid oxidation of the organic matter.

WATER.

A factor of great importance, here as everywhere, is the water relation. Nothing need be said of atmospheric moisture, since that is sufficient to develop a rich vegetation if properly conserved, as is shown by the luxuriance of neighboring floras. Because of the peculiar physical properties of quartz sand, precipitated water quickly percolates to the water level and becomes unavailable to plants with short roots. The water capacity of sand is also slight, nor is there such pronounced capillarity as is characteristic of many other soils. Again, the evaporation from a sandy surface is commonly quite rapid. All of these features combine to furnish a scanty supply of water to the tenants of sandy soil. The rapid cooling of sand on summer nights may, however, result in a considerable condensation of dew, and thus, in a small way, compensate for other disadvantages.

The ecological factors thus far mentioned act together harmoniously and produce a striking composite effect upon the vegetation. A flora which is subjected to periods of drought is called a xerophytic flora and its component species have commonly worked out various xerophytic structural adaptations of one sort or another. Again, a flora which is subjected to extreme cold, especially when accompanied by severe winds, takes on various structural adaptations similar to those that are characteristic of alpine and arctic floras. The dune flora is a composite flora, showing both xerophytic and arctic structures. In those situations which are most exposed to cold winds, one finds the best illustrations of the arctic type, while the desert or xerophilous type is shown in its purest expression on protected inland sandy hills. The discussion of the various arctic and desert structures and their relations to each other will be deferred to the second part of this paper.

OTHER FACTORS.

Certain other factors are of minor importance in determining the character of the dune flora. *Forest fires* occur occasionally, and, as will be shown later, they may considerably shorten the lifetime of a coniferous plant society.

Near cities the vegetation is unfavorably influenced by *smoke* and other products issuing from chimneys. In the neighborhood of the oil refineries at Whiting, Ind., the pine trees especially have been injured or destroyed. A careful study would probably show many plant species that have suffered a similar fate.

The *topography* is often a factor of considerable importance. Dune areas are conspicuous for their diversified topography. This factor determines to a great extent the water relation which has been previously considered, the hills and slopes being of course much drier than the depressions. The topography indirectly affects the soil, since it is mainly in the depressions that humus can rapidly accumulate. The direction of slope is a matter of importance, as will be shown in discussing the oak dunes; the greater exposure of the southern slopes to the sun results in a drier soil and a more xerophytic flora on that side.

Animals do not appear to exert any dominating influences on the dune floras. The dispersal of pollen and fruits by their agency is common here as elsewhere; so, too, the changes that animal activities produce in the soil. Near the cities the influence of man is seen, although such influences are slight unless the sand is removed bodily for railroad grading and other purposes.

The influence of *plants*, which so often becomes the dominant factor, is relatively inconspicuous on the dunes. The most important function which dune plants perform for other plants is in the contribution of organic food materials to the soil. The oxidation or removal of decaying vegetation is so complete on the newer dunes that the accumulation of humus is not important. On the more established dunes the mold becomes deeper and deeper, and, after the lapse of centuries, the sandy soil beneath may become buried so deeply that a mesophytic flora is able to establish itself where once there lived the tenants of an active dune. The advance of a wandering dune often results in the burial of a large amount of organic matter; when this matter becomes unburied years afterward it may again furnish a soil for plants. Many fossil soil lines have thus been uncovered on the Sleeping Bear dunes at Glen Haven, Mich.

IV. The plant societies.

A plant society is defined as a group of plants living together in a common habitat and subjected to similar life conditions. The term is taken to be the English equivalent of Warming's *Plantesamfund*, translated into the German as *Pflanzenverein* [Plant Societies]. The term formation as used by Drude and others, is more comprehensive, in so far as it is not synonymous. It may be well to consider the individual habitat groups in a given locality as plant societies, while all of these groups taken together comprise a formation of that type, thus giving to the word formation a value similar to its familiar geological application. For example, one might refer to particular sedge swamp societies near Chicago, or, on the other hand, to the sedge swamp formation as a whole; by this application formation becomes a term of generic value, plant society of specific value.

Plant societies may be still further subdivided into patches or zones; the former more or less irregular, the latter more or less radially symmetrical. Patches are to be found in any plant society, where one or another constituent becomes locally dominant; zones are conspicuously developed on the beach and in sphagnous swamps. The term patch or zone has a value like that of variety in taxonomy. Authors disagree, here as everywhere, upon the content and values of the terms employed; this disagreement is but an expression of the fact that there are few if any sharp lines in nature. The above, or any other terminology, is largely arbitrary and adopted only as a matter of convenience.

In the following pages, an attempt is made to arrange the plant societies in the order of development, the author's belief being that this order more faithfully expresses genetic relationships than any other. In the historical development of a region the primitive plant societies pass rapidly or slowly into others; at first the changes are likely to be rapid, but as the plant assemblage more and more approaches the climax type of the region, the changes become more slow. In the dune region of Lake Michigan the normal primitive formation is the beach; then, in order, the stationary beach dunes, the active or wandering dunes, the arrested or transitional dunes, and the passive or established dunes. The established dunes pass through several stages, finally culminating in a deciduous mesophytic forest, the normal climax type in the lake region. Speaking broadly, the conditions for plant life become less and less severe through all these stages, until there is reached the most genial of all conditions in our climate, that which results in the production of a diversified deciduous forest. On the beach there are to be found the most extreme of all xerophytic adaptations in this latitude, and, as one passes through the above dune series in the order of genetic succession, these xerophytic structures become less and less pronounced, finally culminating in the typical mesophytic structures of a deciduous forest.

A. THE BEACH.

As the author hopes to show in a subsequent paper, the beach formations of Lake Michigan are of two distinct types. One may be called the xerophytic beach, the other the hydrophytic beach. The conditions that determine these two types are not altogether clear, though their distribution suggests some factors which will contribute to the solution of the problem. Dunes are invariably absent from an area occupied by hydrophytic beaches, partly perhaps because hydrophytic beaches are seldom sandy, and partly because they are commonly found in protected locations. The hydrophytic beaches are found where the gradient of the lake bottom is very slight; as a consequence there is a wide zone of very shallow water in which typical swamp and shallow water plants flourish in great abundance. The bottom is very thickly strewn with gravel and shingle, closely resembling a reef in structure. On the other hand, a xerophytic beach is often sandy, is commonly associated with steep clay bluffs or dunes, and the gradient is much steeper, so that there is a comparatively narrow zone of shallow water. As a consequence, wave action is much more pronounced on the beach proper, as is shown by the great amount of driftwood stranded there. The scanty flora is in striking contrast to the diversified flora of the hydrophytic beach. The greater luxuriance of the flora on the hydrophytic beach is due, in part at least, to the greater freedom from the destructive action of the waves on account of the low gradient. The water supply is also conspicuously greater on the hydrophytic beach, again chiefly because of the low gradient. Inasmuch as dunes are associated only with the xerophytic beach, no further reference will be made to the other beach type.

The xerophytic beach is essentially a product of wave action and comprises the zone which is or has been worked over by the waves. Hence the beach may be defined as the zone between the water level and the topographic form produced by other agents; in the region under study the upper limit of the beach is commonly a fringe of sand dunes or a bluff of clay or gravel. The xerophytic beach in its typical expression is very naturally subdivided into three zones, which may be called the lower beach, middle beach, and upper beach. The lower beach is that zone which is situated between the water level and the line reached by the waves of common summer storms. The middle beach is the second zone, extending up to the line reached by the highest winter storms. The upper beach is essentially a former middle beach which is now beyond the reach of the waves, and yet is unoccupied by dunes or other topographic forms.

1. The lower beach.

The lower beach has been defined as the zone of land washed by the waves of summer storms. It might almost be defined as that portion of the beach which is devoid of vegetation. Perhaps there is no flora in the temperate zone quite so sparse as that of the lower beach, unless we except bare rocks and alkaline deserts. A survey of the life conditions in this zone reveals at once the reason for the scanty vegetation. Land life is excluded because of the frequency and violence of storms; the waves tear away the sand in one spot only to deposit it in another. Even though a seed had the temerity to germinate, the young plant would soon be destroyed by the breakers. Nor is there great likelihood that the seeds will find a lodgment in this unstable location. As will be seen later the seeds ripened by tenants of the middle beach are almost entirely scattered away from the lake instead of toward it. The action of both wind and wave tends to carry seeds away from the lower beach. Again, few seeds could endure the alternate extremes of cold and heat, wetting and drying so characteristic of this zone.

Water life is excluded because of the extreme xerophytic conditions which commonly prevail on the lower beach. While algae may propagate themselves in the shallow pools or even in the wet sand during a prolonged season of wet weather, a cessation of activity if not death itself soon follows the advent of dry weather. During a period of rainy weather in the autumn of 1897 green patches were observed in wet sand a few meters from the mouth of a creek near Porter, Ind. Microscopic observation showed that the green coloration was due to the presence of millions of motile Chlamydomonas forms. These unicellular biciliate algae were in process of active locomotion in the water held by capillarity between the grains of sand. In all probability these forms migrated to the beach from the waters of the creek during a period of wet weather. It is possible that they might pass into resting stages and live through a season of drought, were it not for the wind which gathers much of its dune material from the lower beach.

Thus the lower beach is a barren zone between two zones of life. Below it there exist algae and other hydrophytic forms which flourish in the fury of the breakers; above it there exists the flora of the middle beach, a flora adapted to the most intense xerophytic conditions. At no particular time, perhaps, are the conditions too severe for some type of life; vegetation is excluded because of the alternation of opposite extremes.

2. *The middle beach.*

The middle beach is situated between the upper limits of the summer and winter waves, comparatively dry in summer but washed by the high storms of winter. It may also be defined as the zone of succulent annuals. The upper limit of this beach is commonly marked by a line of driftwood and débris. The instability of the beach conditions is often shown by the presence of a number of such lines, marking wave limits for different seasons. A very heavy storm will carry the débris line far up on the upper beach, to all intents and purposes carrying the middle beach just so much farther inland, as the flora of the next season testifies. Another season may be without the visitation of heavy storms and the middle beach will encroach upon the territory of the lower beach. The limits of the middle beach are altered more permanently by changes in the lower beach. In many places the lower beach is growing outwards, reclaiming land from the lake, while at other points the lake encroaches upon the land. Speaking broadly, the middle beach advances or recedes *pari passu* [at the same speed] with the advance or recession of the lower beach To some extent the débris lines register these changes, as their notable departure from persistent parallelism may indicate; however, there is a considerable lack of parallelism in the débris lines of a single season, owing to variations in the direction of the wind and other factors.

The life conditions in this zone are exceedingly severe, and result in a flora of the most pronounced xerophytic characters. The fury of the winter storms as they wash over the middle beach, tearing up here and depositing there, excludes almost entirely the possibility of survival through that period. In other words, biennials and perennials are practically excluded from maturing flowers and fruits, although their vegetative structures may flourish for a single season. In the summer the xerophilous conditions are extreme. Nowhere in the dune region are the winds more severe than here; the middle beach is close enough to the lake to feel all the force of its winds and yet far enough away for the wind to pick up sand from the lower beach and bring to bear upon the flora the intense severity of the sand-blast. No flora is more exposed to the extreme desiccating influences of the summer sun than that which grows upon the bare and open beach. Even though the roots can readily penetrate to the water level, the great exposure of the aerial organs to wind and sun results in the working out of that most perfect of all xerophytic organs, the succulent leaf. Just as succulent plants inhabit deserts where no other high grade plants can grow, so, too, they are able to withstand the severe conditions of the beach.

Along the entire eastern shore of the lake, the dominant plant of the middle beach is *Cakile edentula* [Sea Rocket]. At many points this succulent crucifer is almost the only plant species found in this zone, and it is always the chief character species. Two other fleshy annuals are very common tenants of the middle beach: *Corispermum hyssopifolium* [Bugseed] and one of the spurges, *Euphorbia polygonifolia* [Seaside Spurge]. It is a matter of interest to observe that two of these three character plants of the middle beach, Cakile and Euphorbia, are also characteristic inhabitants of the beach on the Atlantic coast. The significance of the presence of these and other marine forms along the shore of Lake Michigan will be discussed in another place. The above plants are rarely distributed uniformly over the middle beach. The favorite place for growth is along the lines of débris previously referred to; along these lines a greater number of seeds find lodgment than elsewhere, because the waves wash them up from lower levels and the protection of the driftwood prevents the winds from carrying them on farther. Then, too, the driftwood may furnish some protection to the growing plants, especially protection from winds which might otherwise uproot them. Cakile and Euphorbia reach their culmination on the beach, and when found farther inland it is chiefly on the upper beach or on windward slopes of active dunes. Corispermum, on the other hand, appears to be rather more characteristic of the active dunes than of the beach. Cakile is much the hardiest of the three species, venturing farther out toward the lower beach than either of the other two. Of the three, Cakile is the most succulent and perhaps thus best adapted to the extreme xerophilous conditions to which beach plants are subjected. Euphorbia, however, has a copious supply of latex and its prostrate habit would seem to offer some advantages of existence on the beach. Cakile and Corispermum are readily dispersed by the wind, the latter by means of its winged seeds, while the former is a sort of tumbleweed; broken Cakile plants are common sights all over the dunes in the autumn and winter. Corispermum and Euphorbia become less and less common toward the north; at Charlevoix and Petoskey, Cakile is almost the only plant growing on the middle beach, and even this latter species is less common than farther to the south. Thus it seems as though the life conditions on the middle beach are more severe northward than southward, as indeed might be expected.

3. The upper beach.

In the strictest sense the upper beach is not a portion of the beach at all, since it is beyond the reach of the waves; it might perhaps be called a fossil beach, but the fact that it is continuous with the beach proper seems to exclude that term, as does the recency of its fossilization. The expression fossil beach will be reserved for a formation of greater geological age and separated from the present beach by other topographic forms. Where dunes are superposed upon the beach, the upper limits of this third beach zone are quite vague, though the theoretical line of demarcation is where the sand is first accumulated by the wind. Where clay bluffs are present at the water's edge, the beach is quite narrow and the upper limit fairly well defined, though at times obscured by alluvial fans. Occasionally the upper beach approaches very close to the water's edge; this is the case where the lower and middle beaches are very narrow because of a high gradient. Sometimes the lower or middle beach zone is replaced by a tiny cliff; in such a case the upper beach may approach to the edge of this cliff. The limits of the upper beach, as of other beach zones, are constantly shifting. The lower limits are carried lakeward or landward by the waves of winter storms, but on the whole the lower limits are pushed out more and more lakeward, keeping pace with the advance of the lower beach. The shifting of the wind causes variations in the upper limits, but on the whole the dunes likewise are commonly formed more and more lakeward, as will be shown further on. The three beaches, then, shift from year to year with apparent irregularity, but there appears to be as a resultant a general progressive movement of them all out into the lake. As a whole the three beach zones slope gradually and somewhat evenly upward, toward the dunes or bluffs beyond; depressions, however, are not at all uncommon, and at times they reach down to the water level, so that a beach pool results.

The life conditions are much less severe than on the middle beach, and chiefly because of the freedom from the wave action of the winter storms. The exposure to the sun is almost as great as on the lower zones, but there is more protection from the wind because of the abundance of driftwood. The protective influence exerted by piles of débris is finely shown on the beach at North Manitou island. The upper beach

along the south shore of the lake is usually very sandy and comparatively free from driftwood, while the North Manitou beaches are composed chiefly of gravel and shingle with heaps of driftwood piled about
in the greatest confusion. The North Manitou flora is one of marked
luxuriance, compared with the more southern type, and many mesophytic species are able to get a foothold in the more genial conditions
there obtaining. The decay of the driftwood may also add no inconsid-
erable portion to the food materials of the beach plants.

The flora of the upper beach is much richer than that of the middle
beach, both in species and in individuals, but here as there the vegetation is so sparse that the tone to the landscape is given by the soil. In
the region as a whole the most characteristic species of the upper beach
are *Artemisia caudata* [Beach Wormwood] and *A. canadensis*
[*Artemisia caudata*: Beach Wormwood.]*.[1]

At nearly all places visited between Chicago and Beaver island
Artemisia was present and commonly in abundance. Another plant associated almost everywhere with Artemisia is *Cirsium pitcheri* [Dune
thistle, Pitcher's thistle]; this thistle is seldom so common as Artemisia,
but scattered specimens are pretty sure to be discovered on any upper
beach. A species scarcely less important in this connection is the beach
pea, *Lathyrus japonicus glaber*, another marine plant; locally the beach
pea is often the dominant character plant, especially northward. Three
other species are character plants over wide areas, as the above three
are throughout. *Euphorbia polygonifolia* is a character plant at many stations between Chicago and Glen Haven; its absolute abundance is
often as marked on the upper as on the middle beach, though its relative importance is much greater on the latter. *Agropyron smithii* [West-
ern Wheat Grass] and *Oenothera biennis* [Common Evening Primrose]
are as characteristic of upper beaches northward as Euphorbia is southward; Agropyron especially is usually a dominant character plant north
of Glen Haven.

None of the above six species are confined to the upper beach.
Artemisia is found in most dune societies inland, especially in comparatively naked places. Cirsium is frequent on the dune complex, though
less abundant than on the beach, as is also true of Artemisia. Lathyrus
appears to be more restricted in its habitat, and in that sense is more

---

[1] Typical forms of both Artemisias have been found, as well as all intermediate gradations,
and it is all but hopeless to try to determine which is the more abundant, without careful examination of all the plants in time of fruit. Both species are pubescent in beach and
dune habitats, although *A. Canadensis* is the more so. *Swink and Wilhelm lump *A. caudata* and *A. canadensis* into one species, *A. caudata*, making this footnote meaningless.

typical of the upper beach, though it sometimes occurs on clay bluffs. Euphorbia occurs on the middle beach and also on naked dunes, though less frequently. Agropyron, though characteristic of northern upper beaches, is still more characteristic of the embryonic dunes. Oenothera occurs on oak dunes and commonly also as a mesophyte.

At this point it will be well to emphasize one of the fundamental principles of ecological plant groupings. It is comparatively seldom that any single species can be regarded as perfectly characteristic of a formation, while a group of five or ten species can be so selected as to enable one to detect that formation almost anywhere within a large area. No one of the above six species can be regarded as perfectly typical of the upper beach, although Lathyrus approaches such a type, but together they form an assemblage that cannot be found in any other formation, except perhaps locally on the closely related beach dunes. Even on these beach dunes, which grade into the upper beach, the relative proportions existing between the above species are very different from those found on the beach, and, as will be shown later, plant species occur on these dunes which are absent from the beach altogether.

Of the six chief character species of the upper beach, three (Oenothera, Artemisia, Cirsium) are commonly biennials. Euphorbia is an annual, while Lathyrus and Agropyron are perennials with decidedly social habits through extensive rhizome propagation. Thus the perennial habit is much less common on the upper beach than on the dunes. The three biennials pass through the winter in the form of ground rosettes, tall shoots being sent up in the spring. Cirsium has a noteworthy protective covering of woolly hairs.

There are several plant species very characteristic of the embryonic dunes on the beach, which also occur on the upper beach proper, though rarely in great abundance. Notable among these plants are *Ammophila brevigulata* [Common Marram Grass], and *Elymus canadensis* [Canada Wild Rye]. Ammophila occurs about equally throughout, while Elymus is much more characteristic northward; indeed on the northern upper beaches Elymus is sometimes as abundant as Agropyron or Artemisia. About Chicago Elymus is a common character plant of the dunes, but rarely of the beach. Between Chicago and Muskegon *Asclepias syriaca* [Common Milkweed] is a frequent tenant of the upper beach. *Calamagrostis longifolia var. longifolia* [Prairie Sand Reed], one of the chief character plants of the active dunes, is sometimes found on the beach, as are *Solidago racemosa var. gillmani* [Dune Goldenrod] (plants large, but leaves not sharply toothed) and *Lithospermum croceum* [Hairy Puccoon], which are more characteristic of rejuvenated dunes, fossil beaches, and heaths. *Cakile Americana* and *Corispermum hyssopifolium* occur but are less abundant than on the middle beach, although the latter is sometimes a prominent upper beach type. The forms discussed in this paragraph are perennials, with the exception of the last two; as they are all of secondary importance, in reality representing the vanguards of a flora which is more at home farther inland, there seems no necessity for any further defense of the idea that the upper beach flora is not typically composed of perennials.

All of the species discussed up to this time are herbs, passing the winter near the surface of the soil or underneath it. The exposure to which shrubs and trees are subjected during the winter is so severe on the upper beach that few of the many dune species have representatives there. The individual shrubs which brave these conditions are relatively scattered, while the plant body is stunted and bears signs of the severe environment provided by the beach. Much the commonest shrub, and the only one which occurs throughout, is *Prunus pumila*, the sand cherry. Poplars occasionally occur, *Populus deltoides monilifera* [Plains Cottonwood] southward and *Populus balsamifera* [Balsam Poplar](both the type and the var. *candicans)* northward; so too, the willows, *Salix glaucophylloides* [Blue-Leafed Willow], *syrticola* [Dune Willow], and *interior* [Sandbar Willow].

The most striking feature of the plant life on the upper beach is the difference in its development at different localities. The luxuriant flora of the north is in marked contrast to the impoverished flora at the south end of the lake. The Dune Park beach, for example, is tenanted only by Artemisia, Cirsium, Corispermum, and a few scattering plants of other species. An upper beach on North Manitou island showed a great abundance of Elymus, Artemisia, Lathyrus, Oenothera, and *Populus balsamifera*, together with thirty-four other species which were rare to frequent. Among these other species several are of considerable interest: *Anemone multifida* [Pacific anemone], which also occurs on the beach at Beaver island and on several fossil beaches; *Prenanthes alba* [White Lettuce], common in woods and thickets but seemingly out of place on the beach; *Equisetum hyemale* [Tall Scouring Rush], which grows almost anywhere. On similar beaches at Empire, *Achillea millefolium* [Yarrow] and *Equisetum arvense* [Horsetail], two plants which never grow on the beach farther south, are very abundant. *Arabis lyrata* [Sand Cress] and *Polygonum ramosissimum (?)*[Bushy Knotweed],[2] the former growing on the inland oak dunes about Chicago, occur on an exposed upper beach at the north end of Beaver island. The reasons for

---

[2] A remarkable dwarf Polygonum with six stamens, very different from the type.

this great luxuriance of the northern upper beaches are not obvious. It has been previously stated that the greater abundance of driftwood on the more northern beaches may furnish considerable protection. This cause seems hardly adequate to account for the great differences, and it may be that climatic or other less apparent factors may have to be called upon. The luxuriance of the northern forests as compared with those about Chicago may need in part a similar explanation.

Interesting beach conditions are to be found on some small islands that have recently formed on reefs in the vicinity of Beaver island. During the winter and spring blocks of ice laden with stones are stranded on these reefs; thus they are gradually built up to the lake level. Wave action comminutes the reef materials forming a soil suitable for plant life; the waves and winds also constantly add to the area of the islands. One such island is about 200 meters in length, five or ten meters in width, and scarcely thirty centimeters high. The flora of this unprotected island is a swamp flora, *i.e.*, the island is in its entirety a hydrophytic beach. Another island, somewhat larger and considerably older, has an altitude of one or two meters at its highest point. The beach toward the southeast, east, and northeast is hydrophytic, while that toward the northwest, west, and southwest is xerophytic. Undoubtedly the degree of exposure to the wind is the chief cause which determines the nature of the flora on this island. Not only is the wind more severe on the west beach, but the waves pile up more sand on that side of the island and hence produce a drier soil. The flora on this xerophytic upper beach is remarkably complete and diversified, showing a distinct zonal distribution. Above the middle beach there is a zone characterized by the dominance of *Elymus canadensis*, then a zone of *Geranium robertianum* [Herb Robert], then a zone of *Artemisia canadensis*, and finally a zone in which *Cornus stolonifera* [Red Osier Dogwood] (or *C. baileyi* [Red Twigged Dogwood] into which it grades) is the chief character plant. Scattered more or less with these are *Prunus pumila, Oenothera biennis, Lathyrus japonicus glaber, Cirsium pitcheri, Agropyron smithii*, and *Populus balsamifera. Pastinaca sativa* [Wild Parsnip] and *Geranium robertianum* are common here, and are remarkable inhabitants of a xerophytic beach, since both are usually inland mesophytes. Two other plants occur on this beach that are south of their chief range and rare in the Lake Michigan region, *Tanacetum huronense* [Eastern Tansy] and *Anemone multifida*. The flora of this isolated island beach is remarkably prolific; scarcely a single upper beach type is absent. It is obvious that the means of plant dispersal are so uniformly successful, that almost an entire flora may be transported to a newly formed island within a few years.

One other common feature of the upper beaches should be mentioned. As noted above, there are irregularities in the slope of the beach often resulting in depressions which reach below the water level. Such depressions may be called beach pools and of course have a hydrophytic flora; this flora, however, is not the flora of a hydrophytic beach. Beach pools are relatively protected from the action of winds and waves; the chief difference from a hydrophytic beach is that the latter is washed by the fresh waters of the lake, while the beach pools are far less constantly supplied with fresh water. The conditions in the latter approach somewhat those of the ill-drained inland sloughs between the sandy ridges, By far the most characteristic plant about the pool margins is *Juncus balticus littoralis* [Lake Shore Rush]; this species is more xerophytic than most of its genus, and often creeps well up on the xerophytic upper beach. *Triglochin maritima* [Common Bog Arrow Grass], *Potentilla anserina* [Silverweed] and several species of Salix also occur about the margins of the pools.

4. Fossil beaches.

In regions where dunes are superposed upon the beach, portions of the beach may remain unoccupied by the wind-blown sand, appearing as islands in a sea of dunes. Or a beach which has been covered by the dune-complex may later be uncovered, exposing the gravel and shingle of an ancient shore. In any case these ancient or fossil beaches, separated as they are from the present beach by dunes, are more highly protected from the wind than the beaches which have been previously described. The cold winds lose little of their energy while sweeping up the gradual slopes of an ordinary beach, but their force is considerably broken by a line of dunes. Fossil beaches which have been uncovered by the dune complex occur at Dune Park, but to such a limited extent that a typical flora is not developed. The most extensive fossil beach observed was at Glen Haven, where an area several hectares in extent has been denuded of its covering of sand to help supply the extensive dune complex. Similar but smaller fossil beaches were seen at Saugatuck and North Manitou island. Associated with the fossil beach is a formation which may not represent a beach at all. In the general description of the region, reference was made to the high terrace-like bluffs along the northern portions of the lake shore. These miniature plateaux, from which former sand dunes have doubtless been removed, exhibit a surface of gravel, which produces the appearance of a fossil or a true beach. The most extensive of these flat gravel-topped hills are at Glen Haven; similar but less extensive formation of this type were seen at Frankfort and North Manitou island.

The floras of the fossil beaches and the gravel terraces 120 meters above the present beach are essentially identical, although the latter apparently have a greater exposure. Both the beaches and terraces have a flora which resembles that of the upper beach in a general way, but there is a pronounced decrease of most of the typical beach forms and a pronounced increase of the more inland types. Thus the flora clearly illustrates the greater protection from exposure which is enjoyed on the fossil beach. The Artemisias are as characteristic of the fossil beaches and terraces as of the upper beach, but none of their five chief beach associates retain their prominence here. *Cirsium pitcheri* occurs frequently, but chiefly at the lower level; *Euphorbia polygonifolia* and *Oenothera biennis* were observed but rarely and only at the lower level; Lathyrus, Corispermum, and Agropyron were not found at all. In place of these upper beach plants the Artemisias have a new crowd of associates. In general the terraces and fossil beaches have four dominant character plants, *Artemisia canadensis, Solidago racemosa var. gillmani, Lithospermum croceum,* and *Andropogon scoparius* [Little Bluestem]. Solidago and Lithospermum were noted as occurring at times on the upper beach, but they are far more common here. Andropogon was not observed on the true beach, but is very common on fossil beaches and terraces, its scattered bunches or tufts forming one of the chief landscape features.

On the more northern fossil beaches several species are almost as characteristic as those named in the preceding paragraph. Prominent among these forms are *Zygadenus glaucous* [White Camass], *Campanula rotundifolia arctica* [Harebell], and *Arenaria michauxii* [Rock Sandwort, Stiff Sandwort]; northward these types are almost wholly confined to the fossil beaches or terraces, although Zygadenus is sometimes present on the upper beach. *Anemone multifida, Koeleria cristata* (?) [Prairie June Grass] and *Arabis lyrata* [Sand Cress] occur northward but are less frequent. A very interesting plant which sometimes frequents fossil beaches is *Hudsonia tomentosa* [False Heather], a species noted for its habit of forming scattered clumps of densely tufted growths. Other occasional tenants of the terraces and fossil beaches are *Populus deltoides monilifera, Prunus pumila, Calamagrostis longifolia var. longifolia* [Prairie Sand Reed], and *Solidago nemoralis* [Old-Field Goldenrod].

While the fossil beach looks backward to a true beach history, it commonly looks forward to a heath. Largely protected from the accumulation of sand, they furnish a situation favorable for the development of a juniper-bearberry heath. Such heaths are in process of formation at Manistee, North Manitou and elsewhere, and will be described in another place.

B. THE EMBRYONIC OR STATIONARY BEACH DUNES.

1. Dunes of rapid growth (primary embryonic dunes).

Many of the lake winds which blow across the beach have a surplus of energy, and are able to select out the finer grains of sand and carry them farther from the shore. The action of the wind in transportation is analogous to that of water. The finer particles are picked up bodily by the air currents, while the larger particles are blown or rolled along on the beach. Whenever an obstacle is met, some or all of the load is necessarily deposited by the wind. The coarser particles are deposited upon or about the obstacle, while the finer particles form a diminishing trail on the lee side. As soon as the deposition is sufficient to relieve the over-laden wind, the trailing of sand ceases, and the wind continues with its lessened load until another obstacle is reached. So long as the wind blows continuously from one direction, the mound of sand keeps growing and the trail to the leeward becomes more and more conspicuous. Indeed, the growth increment is often greater during the later stages of a continuous wind current, since the growing mound of sand becomes more and more an obstacle to the progress of the laden wind. As a result of this action there appears a topographic form with a steep windward side and a gently sloping leeward side.

When the wind changes, the trails of sand are no longer in the lee of the obstacle, but are more or less exposed to the wind, and hence are rapidly removed. The contour of the mound is changed and there results, just as before, a topographic form, steep to the windward but gently sloping to the leeward. It will thus be seen that it is always possible in dry weather to determine the direction of the last strong wind by observing the position and direction of the leeward trails of sand. A clump of grass with a poorly developed leeward trail may be seen in the foreground of *fig. 4*.

Under ordinary conditions no permanent results follow from such wind action as has been described, since one wind destroys the products of another. There is, perhaps, a tendency for sand to accumulate on the landward side of obstacles, since the energy of the lake winds is likely to be greater than the energy of winds from other directions. But no extensive dune formation can occur on the beach, unless the obstacle, which compels the wind to deposit its load, is itself increasing in size. A mound of sand, which is being built up by the wind, becomes more and more a formidable obstacle to the progress of the sand-laden currents, and it might be supposed that the growth of such a mound would continue indefinitely. Such does not appear to be the case on the beaches studied. The wind blows over the beach from so many directions and with such resistless energy that mounds of sand rarely accumulate without the aid of other factors.

The formation of beach dunes, then, depends upon something more than wind and sand. An obstacle is needed which will grow *pari passu* with the dune, and such an obstacle is furnished by a number of perennial plants, which spread by means of rhizome propagation. These dune-forming plants must be perennials; otherwise the dune would be destroyed at the end of the growing season. Such annual dunes are very common on the beach. Clumps of Cakile have been seen, about which there is piled a miniature dune. In the same manner there may be formed biennial dunes about individual plants of Artemisia or Cirsium. A perennial dune, however, requires perennial dune-formers. A second necessity in a dune-former is the ability to spread radially by rhizome propagation, for only in this way can the area of the obstacle and the area of the dune be enlarged. The only notable exception to this rule is found in the case of cottonwoods and such perennial grasses as Andropogon and Elymus; these plants grow in groups or tufts and will be described later.

The plant which serves as an obstacle for the wind must also possess the power of growing out into the light when buried by the sand. This property permits the rise of the dune in altitude, as rhizome propagation permits the increase in area. Most plants are excluded by reason of this third requirement, partly because they are unable to rise above the sand when buried, and partly because stem elongation increases the difficulty of drawing up a sufficient supply of water from the soil. The roots of dune plants are often uncovered and exposed to wind and sand-blast action; hence plants unable to survive a period of root exposure cannot live in such a habitat. In short, a successful dune-former must be able at any moment to adapt its stem to a root environment or its root to a stem environment. The vicissitudes of existence on an embryonic dune are greater than anywhere else, except at a few points on the dune-complex. In addition to the above particular requirements, a dune-former must, of course, be perfectly equipped with a set of the most extreme xerophytic adaptations. Nowhere else except on the beach is there so great exposure to heat, cold, and wind.

The most typical and successful of all dune-forming plants along Lake Michigan is the sand reed [i.e., Marram Grass], *Ammophila brevigulata*. The life history of an Ammophila dune will now be given, and may be taken as the average life history of a stationary beach dune. Whenever a tuft of this or any similar grass gets a foothold on the upper beach, the sand drifts along and is lodged in between the stems and leaves, as already described (see foreground, *fig. 4*). The leeward trail of sand changes its position as the wind varies its direction, but the sand deposited around the blades of grass is not easily dislodged. The radial propagation of the tuft of grass causes an areal extension of the miniature dune. So, too, there is an increase in altitude, since the grass constantly grows higher in its endeavor to lift itself above the sand. This upward growth enables more sand to accumulate; in other words, the grass and the dune grow *pari passu* outwards and upwards. The result of several years of this symbiotic growth of dune and grass may be seen in *fig. 2*, which represents a small embryonic dune on the beach at South Chicago, Ill. The general contour of the dune is seen to be determined by the Ammophila; toward the left is the leeward trail of sand left by the last wind. *Fig. 3* represents an older and larger Ammophila dune on the same beach, viewed from the lakeward side and hence not showing any leeward trail of sand. Not only is the general contour of this dune determined by the Ammophila, but there will be observed a somewhat sinuous trough toward the center, where there happens to be no vegetation. This shows how readily the dune would be removed were it not for the plant life present. Thus Ammophila is not only an efficient dune-former but also a dune-holder.

While Ammophila is the most common dune-former and perhaps the best adapted for that difficult task of all our lake shore plants, many other species play a similar role. On the northern beaches *Agropyron smithii* is very common as a dune-former; its habit is exactly that of Ammophila, and consequently needs no description. *Elymus canadensis* and *Calamagrostis longifolia var. longifolia* may be regarded as dune-formers, but they are of less importance than Ammophila and Agropyron. A typical Elymus dune, as found on the South Chicago upper beach, is represented at the center of *fig. 4*. These grasses grow in tufts and do not have any extensive vegetative propagation, but the tufts may be so close together as to act like a large social clump of Ammophila.

Certain shrubs are of almost equal importance as dune-builders with the grasses. Among these, the willows, *Salix syrticola* and *S. glaucophylloides*, and the sand cherry, *Prunus pumila*, deserve especial mention. All of these shrubs have social habits, and rapidly increase their area of control in all directions. The willows are particularly well fitted to build up a perennial beach dune. They are about as well adapted to a xerophytic environment as are any of the grasses, and their vegetative increase is about as rapid. The fact that they are shrubs and have a greater power of vertical stem elongation makes them even better fitted to rise above the sand. When a shoot of one of these willows is buried, roots are sent out from all the buried portions, even up as far as the floral axis. The willows, too, can be uncovered without suffering serious injury. In short, the species of Salix are able to adapt their stems to a root environment, or *vice versa*, better than any other plants found along the coast. Hence the willows stand abreast of Ammophila as dune-formers. Another shrub that seems to have all the necessary requirements for a dune-builder is *Cornus stolonifera* (or *C. baileyi*), though it is probably less fitted for a xerophytic life; however, Cornus dunes are by no means rare on the beach.

The only trees which make any significant contributions to dune formation are the poplars, *Populus deltoides monilifera* and *P. balsamifera*. Of these, the former is the more important, especially southward. These trees have little or no vegetative propagation of the willow type. Every year great numbers of cottonwood seeds germinate in protected depressions on the upper beach. As the young plants grow rapidly, it is not long before they form groups dense enough to retard the sand-laden winds. Thus a cottonwood dune is formed, a type which characterizes the Lake Michigan shore at very many places. A cottonwood dune a number of years old is shown in *fig. 5*. It is possible to see, even from the photograph, that the lower portions of the trees are covered by the sand. The growth of a cottonwood dune, therefore, is of a symbiotic nature, exactly as is the growth of an Ammophila dune, in spite of the great difference between the life habits of these two dune-formers.

The controlling part which plants play in dune formation is still further shown by the variations among the embryonic dunes as to area, shape, and height. Dunes that are formed by Agropyron, Ammophila, or Salix are capable of indefinite areal expansion, since these plant types have extensive vegetative propagation. Populus or Elymus dunes, on the other hand, always retain essentially the same area, since there is little or no vegetative reproduction, and since the opportunity for any further development of seedlings is removed. Young seedlings are often found in the moist sand of the depressions, but never in the dry sand of the dunes. The Agropyron dunes are always very low, seldom if ever a meter in altitude. The Ammophila dunes are higher because this latter plant type has a greater power of upward growth than has the former. Both the Agropyron and Ammophila dunes are alike in being relatively large and low, with slopes almost as gentle as those of the beach. The Salix dunes are equally large, but higher and steeper because of the greater power of upward growth. The Prunus dunes are very small because of the slight vegetative propagation, and yet they are relatively high and steep because of the pronounced power of upward growth.

The cottonwood dunes are the highest of all, often having an altitude of several meters, because the cottonwoods grow higher than any other dune-former; they are also the steepest because there is no vegetative propagation. The steep slope of a cottonwood dune is shown in *fig. 5*;

the marks in the sand at the right are the paths made by the movement of the sand down the steep slope, and indicate a gradient of about 30°. *Figs. 2* and *3* indicate the gentle slope of the Ammophila dunes. The cottonwood dunes are commonly long ridges parallel to the lakeshore. This is partly due to the fact that the depressions in which the seeds germinate are parallel to the shore, because of wave action. The prevalence of lake winds perpendicular to these ridges also helps these topographic forms to retain their original shape. Summing up this matter, then, the area of a beach dune is determined chiefly by the amount of the vegetative propagation of its tenants, the steepness is determined by the rapidity of this propagation, and the altitude by the power of the dune plants to increase in height.

Of the dune-forming species, *Ammophila brevigulata* and *Salix syrticola* are the most abundant, occurring almost everywhere that beach dunes exist. These two species are most at home when half-buried in the wind-blown sand, and occur much less frequently in other associations. *Prunus pumila* and *Calamagrostis longifolia var. longifolia* occur throughout the region, but are less characteristic of the beach dunes than are the first-named species. Prunus is common on the upper beach, as already shown, and also on the heath; Calamagrostis is particularly characteristic of the larger active dunes. *Agropyron smithii* is very common at Glen Haven and farther north, and, like Ammophila, is most at home on the beach dunes. *Populus deltoides monilifera* is very common south of Glen Haven; the cottonwood dunes are usually formed farther inland than the other types. This species is replaced northward to some extent by *Populus balsamifera* and its variety *candicans* (both sometimes on the same tree!), though this poplar is much less of a dune-former than the cottonwood. *Salix glaucophylloides* is frequent on the beach dunes, especially southward, but is more characteristic of the swamps; the same may be said of *Cornus stolonifera*. *Elymus canadensis* is not abundant anywhere on the beach dunes.

An interesting corollary may be deduced from the last three paragraphs. Since various dune forms are caused by differences in the life habits of the dune-forming species, it follows that the distribution of certain topographic forms coincides with the distribution of the dune-formers. Low dunes of the Agropyron type area not found at the south end of the lake. The steep ridgelike cottonwood dunes are common southward, but rarer northward, since cottonwoods are rarer northward. This is only one of the many cases where ecology helps to interpret physiography.

The dune-forming plants are not the only tenants of the beach dunes. Most of the species that grow on the upper beach are also frequently present on the dunes. Those of especial importance are *Artemisia canadensis* (or *A. caudata*), *Cirsium pitcheri*, *Lathyrus japonicus glaber*, *Euphorbia polygonifolia*, and *Corispermum hyssopifolium*. By reason of its extensive vegetative propagation, *Juncus balticus littoralis* sometimes serves as an obstacle to sand-laden winds, and by a limited subsequent growth results in the formation of miniature dunes. *Lithospermum croceum*, though more characteristic of embryonic heaths and rejuvenated dunes, sometimes ventures out upon the beach dunes. It should be likewise noted that any of the dune-forming species are likely to grow on dunes that are formed in the main by others, although the vegetation of individual embryonic dunes is often composed of a single species.

Though no plant formation anywhere can have a much larger percentage of plants that are entirely independent of other plants, the beach dunes, nevertheless, have occasional forms that are parasitic, saprophytic, or epiphytic. Various unidentified Basidiomycetes [Club Fungi] have been found in the most open places, deriving their nutriment from buried driftwood. The most notable parasite found was *Aphyllon fasciculatum* [Broomrape], a plant which derives its nutriment through attachment to the roots of Artemisia. Lichens are abundant on the cottonwoods at all places that are not directly exposed to a fierce sand-blast action. Common lichen species in such places are *Physcia stellaris*, *Theloschistes concolor*, and *Placodium sp.*

Interesting beach dunes were seen on the shores of two small inland lakes, Crystal lake near Frankfort, and Fount lake, on Beaver island. In each case the lakes approach a dune area near the shore of Lake Michigan, suggesting the probable origin of the sand; there can be no question, however, but that the sand composing these beach dunes was washed up by the waves of the small inland lakes and worked over by the winds; exactly as described in the preceding pages. The dune-forming winds at Crystal lake are easterly winds, chiefly because the source of sand is on the west side of the lake, and it is on the west shore that the dunes are located. There are typical Ammophila dunes at this point. Among the other plants growing here are Artemisia, Cirsium, Populus, Cornus, Prunus, Lathyrus, Oenothera, Corispermum, Calamagrostis, Elymus, and Juncus. At no place on Lake Michigan was a more typical and varied beach and beach dune flora observed than on the west shore of Crystal lake.

2. Dunes of slow growth (second embryonic dunes).

Dunes formation is by no means confined to the upper beach, but may take place anywhere that the sand is able to collect, provided that plants at that place are fitted to be dune-formers. The formation of dunes on the dune-complex and on rejuvenated dunes is essentially like that on the upper beach, and will be discussed later. New dunes of a very interesting type are in process of formation on many fossil beaches and on the gravel terraces. As has been previously stated, the terraces and fossil beaches are better protected from the wind than is the upper beach, and there is in consequence not only a more luxuriant flora, but also a different plant assemblage. The sand which blows across these places, though less in quantity and less furiously driven, nevertheless is capable of dune formation if the proper plant species are present. Several of the beach dune-formers also occur on the terraces and fossil beaches, and build up small dunes. Among these are Ammophila, Calamagrostis, Prunus, and Populus.

Among the dune-formers on terraces and protected fossil beaches, one of the most interesting is *Andropogon scoparius*. This grass grows in tufts and is very abundant, as has been already stated. About each tuft a mound of sand has often collected. A photograph showing the striking appearance of an area of Andropogon dunes was unfortunately spoiled, but its appearance is much like that of an area of *roches moutonnées* [glaciated rocks], as figured in geological works. Hundreds and sometimes thousands of these miniature dunes may be seen in a single landscape. *Arctostaphylos uva-ursi* [Bearberry] and *Juniperus sabina procumbens* [Savin Juniper] are dune-formers within moderate limits. Both of these shrubs are procumbent creepers, and hence unable to rise above the sand to any considerable height, probably never as much as a meter above their original position. It is for this reason that such hardy plants as these cannot grow successfully on an upper beach that is exposed to extensive sand drifting. The above three species are the most prominent dune-formers in protected places. Arctostaphylos dunes occur throughout, and are not confined to fossil beaches, but are also common on exposed heaths. The Andropogon dunes were not seen except on fossil beaches, although this grass is common along the entire coast. The Juniperus dunes occur chiefly northward.

The dune formation seen on east coasts was chiefly of this small, slow-growing, secondary type. The dunes at Waukegan, in part at least, are formed by Juniperus. On the east shore of Beaver and North Manitou islands, there are a number of low dunes formed conjointly by Juniperus and Arctostaphylos. There are low slow-growing Juniperus dunes on the shore of Fount lake on Beaver island; in addition to the procumbent juniper, *Juniperus communis* [Common Juniper] and *Gaylussacia resinosa* [Black Huckleberry] assist in dune building here. The Andropogon dunes are better developed on the fossil beaches of North Manitou island than at any other point visited. On these same fossil beaches, *Hudsonia tomentosa* serves in a small degree to collect the wind-blown sand. On the east shore of North Manitou island, the pasture grass [Canada Blue Grass], *Poa compressa*, forms miniature dunes.

Near the beach at South Chicago there are swampy depressions tenanted by *Potentilla anserina* and *Polygonum amphibium var. stipulaceum* [Water Knotweed], plants which are best developed in low grounds but which often creep up to higher levels. On these higher levels near the beach they collect the drifting sand and are able to form low dunes, similar to Arctostaphylos. These plants show a most surprising plasticity, since a single individual developed in a swamp is able to adapt itself to a mild type of dune existence. Another swamp plant *Cephalanthus occidentalis* [Buttonbush], occurs near the same beach and in a similar way helps to build these low slow-growing dunes. The conversion of swamp plants to dune plants will be discussed more at length in another place.

The most extensive area of dune formation on the beach was seen on the west shore of Beaver island. *Fig. 6* shows a small portion of this area. This place is of peculiar interest because there is a perfect series of gradations between the rapidly growing dunes first described and those of the slower growing type. Toward the beach proper (foreground, *fig. 6*) there are dunes formed by Salix, Prunus, and other high-grade dune-builders. Farther back, toward the taller and older dunes of a previous epoch, there may be seen low dunes built by Arctostaphylos, Juniperus, and *Potentilla fruticosa* [Shrubby Cinquefoil], small dune excrescences on a general dune substratum. The life-history of these dunes appears to have been as follows. First a stage of dune formation by such plants as Salix, then, as vegetative propagation allowed these plants to encroach more and more lakeward upon the broad beach, new dunes were formed nearer and nearer the lake. Or, perhaps, there was a recession of the lake and a consequent extension of the beach into new territory; these new dunes may have thus been formed farther and farther lakeward, keeping pace with the advancing shoreline. In any event, the interposition of a new row of dunes between the lake and those first formed essentially changed the life conditions on the latter. The row of dunes nearest the lake serves as a windbreak. The first row catches most of the drifting sand, and the second catches most of what remains. This fact makes it possible for the slow dune-formers to inhabit the more inland of the ridges. Expressed in other words, the high-grade or primary embryonic dunes encroach upon the lake, not by the actual advance of an individual dune in that direction, but by the formation of new ones; in like manner the low-grade or secondary embryonic dunes encroach upon the former type, using the topographic form of the primary dune as a base of operations, and building new dunes as low excrescences upon the old.

The advance of a dune area toward the lake, as just described, shows how the coastal belt of dunes may grow wider as the years pass by. In another place it will be shown how they may also grow wider by the actual advance of an individual dune upon the land. In concluding the section on the embryonic dunes, it may be well emphasize in another way the radical difference between the two types that have been discussed. Their intimate gradation, as shown at Beaver island, is by no means the universal fact. Perhaps it is even more common for one of the primary type to leave its original habitat and wander across the country as an active dune. The secondary type never has that history; an Arctostaphylos dune almost always grows into a heath.

C. THE ACTIVE OR WANDERING DUNES. THE DUNES-COMPLEX.

1. *Transformation of stationary into wandering dunes.*

The symbiotic growth of the beach dunes and their builders may go on for years, but a prolonged existence of these relations is unlikely. As the mounds get larger and higher the conditions for further accumulation of sand become, if anything, more favorable. It is not so with the plant tenants, for each year they are raised farther from their chief base of supplies, the water level. It is probable, also, that the desiccating influence of radiant energy and wind upon the aerial organs becomes greater and greater as the years go on, because of greater exposure at the higher levels. Again, the dune-formers, although perennials, do not have an indefinite duration. The life cycle of the cottonwood is relatively short for a tree. All of the other prominent dune-formers spread more or less by vegetative propagation, so that it is difficult to determine a definite life cycle. Even though an existence of indefinite duration might be secured through vegetative propagation, many individual shoots must die in the course of time.

In one way or another, then, dune formation ceases and another phase of dune history begins. There is here an end of the stationary beach dunes, a beginning of the wandering dunes. When the plants are no longer able to oppose its progress, the first effect of the untrammeled action of the wind is seen in a tendency to reshape the topographic forms. The beach dunes heretofore described are more or less symmetrical, because of the tendency toward symmetrical plant growth. A dune fashioned entirely by the winds without the assistance of plants is never symmetrical. The windward slope has a very gentle gradient, usually about 5°, and because of the destructive action of the wind, this slope is topographically rough and uneven. The leeward slope, however, is much steeper, averaging about 30°, and is very smooth and even, because determined by gravity instead of wind. The wind sweeps up the gentle windward slopes, blowing or rolling the sand along until the crest is reached; here the sand is deposited by the wind and it rolls down the steep slope, spreading itself quite evenly. *Fig. 17* shows an average gentle windward slope, *figs. 13–15* steep leeward slopes.

The Prunus dunes are particularly favorable for a study of the origin of an active dune, since their form is most at variance with that of the wind-shaped dune, as described above. A Prunus dune is commonly a low cone more or less rounded at the top. As soon as the plants are dead, and sometimes long before that event occurs, the wind endeavors to reduce the windward gradient by removing the sand toward the top and blowing it over on the other side. In this way the roots are exposed and existence made less endurable, if the plant is still living. Prunus dunes with roots exposed on the windward side are common at Dune Park, Beaver island, and elsewhere. On the terrace at Glen Haven, some dunes have been carried beyond their former resting place, leaving the scraggy clumps of Prunus roots at the rear.

What has been said of the Prunus dunes holds more or less for the other types. The cottonwood dunes especially are peculiarly subject to the destructive attacks of the wind, since their shape also notably fails to correspond with that of a normal wind-made topographic form. The lower Ammophila, Salix and Agropyron dunes are less likely to suffer destruction, and yet small Ammophila dunes were seen on the dune-complex at Glen Haven that had been blown away from their first abode, leaving the Ammophila stranded at the rear. Even while living, these dune-formers were unable to hold the dunes which they had helped the wind to build; much more when dead are they likely to have the dune swept on beyond them.

The destructive action of the wind and the transformation of a stationary into an active dune are very much retarded by the tenacity with which the stems and roots retain their place, even when dead. A plant which thus has the power to hold its position and keep the sand from being blown away is commonly called a sand-binder. In this connection it may also be called a dune-holder, as it has been already called a dune-former. Perhaps the most tenacious of all the dune-holders on the coast of Lake Michigan is *Calamagrostis longifolia var. longifolia*. This grass, as has been seen, is not of first importance as a dune-builder, but when it has once built up a dune it seems almost impossible to dislodge it. At the left of the basswood trees in *fig. 23*, there is shown a clump of Cala-magrostis directly facing the prevailing wind at the summit of a mound, and stubbornly holding its position. The leaves, stems, and roots are all stiff and wiry, almost perfectly resisting the mechanical action of the wind. The roots in the sand form a network so dense that it is almost impossible for the wind to remove the sand from among them.

From an economic standpoint, *Ammophila brevigulata* is a more suc-cessful dune-holder than is Calamagrostis, but its greater success is due to its extensive vegetative propagation. The dense social growths of Ammophila make it difficult for the wind to get a start in the process of sand removal, whereas the sand can be readily picked up from be-tween the more scattered tufts of Calamagrostis. An individual tuft of the latter, however, seems to be much more resistant than a tuft of Am-mophila. Calamagrostis, too, grows in more exposed situations than does the other grass, and hence is a valuable dune-holder in places where Ammophila might not thrive at all.

Another noteworthy dune-holder is *Prunus pumila*. A very common sight on the upper beach is a truncated cone literally covered at the summit and sometimes on the sides with a dense tangle of dead stems and roots of the sand cherry. The wind has removed all the sand which it can reach and is obliged to wait until the stems and roots decay suf-ficiently to allow the wind to blow them away and get at the sand be-neath. Prunus is one of the first plants to succumb before the dune in the process of dune formation; perhaps its life cycle is normally short, but more probably the process of drawing up water a greater and greater distance each year compels the plant to give up the unequal struggle.

Sooner or later the dead roots and stems of the dune-holders are all removed, and the wind becomes the undisputed master of the situa-tion. If there is a sufficient amount of sand still remaining, the once sta-tionary dune begins to move, not bodily, of course, but none the less steadily and surely. The sand is swept up the low gradient of the wind-ward side, deposited at the crest, and carried down the steep leeward slope by gravitation. In this manner successive parallel layers of the windward slope are carried over the crest, and the dune as a whole ad-vances inland. The simple life-history just outlined is the exception, not the rule. Much more commonly the sand is scattered in many direc-tions, collecting wherever new lodging places can be found. These processes of deposition and removal, dune formation and dune destruc-tion, are constantly going on with seeming lawlessness. However, in the district as a whole the sand is constantly increasing in quantity, what-ever may be true of the individual dunes here and there. The outcome is certain to be a wandering dune in the process of time, unless the actions of the wind and wave are checked. Because of the complexity of the conditions when the movement across the country becomes a conspicuous fact, it seems well to apply the term dune-complex to the totality of topographic forms which make up the moving landscape as a whole.

2. *Physical and biological features of the dune-complex.*

It will not be necessary to trace farther the changes involved in the transformation of simple beach dunes into a dune-complex, although the coast of Lake Michigan shows all of the intervening stages. Inasmuch as a single dune-complex illustrates almost all conceivable conditions of a dune's life history, a careful description of a typical dune-complex will involve all of the essential points. The dune-complex is best developed at Glen Haven, Mich., and Dune Park, Ind. All of the essential features are present in both areas, though developed on a grander scale at Glen Haven. The Dune Park area has been most carefully studied, and most of my photographs were taken there.

The dune-complex is a restless maze. It is a maze because all things that a dune ever does are accomplished there. While there is a general advance of the complex as a whole in the direction of the prevailing winds, individual portions are advancing in all directions in which winds ever blow. It is not at all uncommon to find small dunes advancing over the dune-complex back toward the lake. At Dune Park the main line of advance is southeast, yet some small dunes advance toward the northwest, because taller dunes are situated between them and the lake. These little dunes in the lee of large ones are protected from the westerly and northerly winds but feel the full force of the easterly and southerly winds, and hence advance contrary to the prevailing direction. It is thus a common sight to see two dunes advancing to meet each other; when they come together, of course the two dunes become one and move in the direction of the prevailing winds. From this account it is easy to see that small dunes on the complex may advance in any direction, provided only that the are protected from winds blowing in other directions.

The dune-complex, however, is much more than a maze of little dunes wandering in all directions. At many points there are to be found the stationary embryonic dunes that have been previously described. All stages of their life-history may be seen; the beginning, the climax, the destruction. Here and there the wind sweeps out great hollows, which reach down almost to the water level. Great troughs are carved out by the wind, chiefly at right angles to the lake, but also at all other angles. Here and there vegetation has obtained a foothold on the complex, thus converting portions of it into an established dune. These established dunes may become rejuvenated, or the vegetation may spread until it covers large portions of the complex. The most striking feature of the dune-complex, then is its topographic diversity.

To one who visits a dune-complex season after season, another feature comes to be as striking as its diversity, and that is its restlessness. From a distance the complex seems always the same, a barren scene of monotony, but the details are never twice alike. A little dune arising on the complex has become enlarged, another has passed from existence without leaving a trace behind. Where a dune was advancing last year, there is now, perhaps, a hollow swept out by the wind. Where last year was a hollow there may now be seen the beginnings of a flora, or again the flora of a former year may have been buried out of sight. The dune-complex, then, is not only a maze, but also a restless maze.

It might seem impossible to unravel the tangled threads of the dune-complex; it is, indeed, impossible to write the details of its history. There is, however, a simplicity in the complexity. While little dunes advance in all directions, the complex as a whole advances in the direction of the prevailing wind. While there are troughs at all angles, the main troughs are likewise in the direction of the wind. The complex is like a river with its side currents and eddies at many points, but with the main current in one direction.

It has already been stated that the windward slope of an advancing dune is very gentle, averaging perhaps about 5°. That portion of the windward slope up which the main wind currents pass is also trough-shaped and may be called a wind-sweep. *Fig. 7* shows a small trough-shaped wind-sweep at Beaver island; the direction of advance is from the foreground to the background. In the path of the wind there may be seen dead branches, the remnants of a vegetation that has been swept away. In the background are small dunes which have been formed by sand carried along the trough by the wind. A wind-sweep more characteristic of the dune-complex is shown in *fig. 17*. Here, likewise, the prevailing wind direction is up the gentle slope away from the foreground. At this particular place there is in reality much more of a trough than is shown in the photograph, since there is a conspicuous rise both at the right and at the left. Just beyond the pines in the background there is a steep pitch downward, the advancing lee slope.

The most remarkable wind-sweep at Dune Park reaches down almost to the water level, appearing like a cañon, by reason of its steep sides from ten to twenty meters in height. This sweep, unlike most of the troughs, is curved so that a wind entering it as a northwest wind becomes a west and finally a southwest wind, and actually contributes to the advance of a dune toward the lake, as will be discussed more fully at another place in connection with *fig. 10*. The concentration of the wind energy which these gorge-like wind-sweeps permit is something remarkable. At no place is the destructive power of the wind upon the vegetation felt more keenly than along the sides of these deeper wind-sweeps. The foreground of *fig. 22* shows the upper part of one of these troughs, and gives a vivid impression of the wind's destructiveness.

The advancing lee slopes, as has been previously mentioned, have a gradient in the neighborhood of 30°. The slope is exactly that at which sand, whose grains have the size and cohesiveness there found, will lie. *Figs 9, 13, 14*, and *15* give some conception of the striking features presented by a landscape of which an advancing dune forms a part. Nowhere can there be a sharper line in nature, nowhere a more abrupt transition. The height of these slopes above the country on which they are advancing varies from almost nothing up to thirty meters at Dune Park. The Glen Haven dunes are far more imposing, since there is an almost unbroken line of advance for four kilometers, while the average height is from thirty to sixty meters above the territory on which they are encroaching.

The vegetation of the complex proper is exceedingly sparse. In the winter it appears almost a barren waste. The one plant which seems to be at home in all locations, whether wind-sweeps, exposed summits, or protected lees, is the bugseed, *Corispermum hyssopifolium*. This plant is an annual, and has been previously mentioned as a tenant of the beach and the beach dunes. The bugseed is shown in several of the photographs, but best in the left foreground of *fig. 12*. The seeds are winged and readily dispersed by the wind. Furthermore they germinate rapidly during wet spring weather. This power of rapid germination is a necessary condition of success, since the surface layers of sand dry off very quickly after the wet weather has ceased. The plants are obliged not only to germinate rapidly but also to send roots deep enough to reach beyond the surface desiccation. Even this perfectly successful plant species is often absent from large areas on the dune-complex, probably because of the difficulty which the seeds meet in finding lodgment. It is only an exceptional seed which is allowed to remain stranded on the complex, and many of the seeds which succeed in finding lodgment are likely to be buried too far below the surface to permit germination.

Another plant which deserves especial mention is the cottonwood, *Populus deltoides monilifera*. The plasticity of this species is remarkable. Normally at home along protected river bottoms, it is yet able to endure almost all of the severe conditions of the dune-complex. Mention has been made of its importance as a dune-former, and *fig. 5* shows a group of cottonwoods on an embryonic dune partially buried by the sand. Photographs might have been secured showing trees, presumably fifteen meters in height, buried up to the topmost branches and yet alive and vigorous. *Fig. 8* (taken in the winter) shows a vigorous clump of trees, high up on the dune-complex, with their roots exposed by reason of the removal of the sand from around them. Much more striking examples than this have been seen of living trees standing high up in the air, and yet with no apparent injury. In one respect the cottonwood is a hardier plant than Corispermum; it is a perennial and hence passes the winter on the dunes. In the summer the winds are much more moderate, and the chances of being covered or uncovered are more remote.

Two grasses are more or less at home at many places on the complex, *Ammophila brevigulata* and *Calamagrostis longifolia var. longifolia*. Of these the latter is the hardiest and most typical of exposed positions, such as shown at the left in *fig. 23*. The tenacity with which Calamagrostis holds its ground has already been mentioned. On the Glen Haven complex, Ammophila is particularly abundant. In some places it is so thick and green as to look almost like a field of grain from a distance; yet even here, the luxuriant growth is only in the protected places, and none at all is found in the most exposed situations.

The reasons for the scanty plant life on the exposed portions of the dune-complex are not far to seek. First of all it is not due to the scarcity of water in the soil. Even after a long period of drought in summer, the sand is cool and moist at a short distance below the surface. The upper dry layers of sand act as a non-conductor of heat and prevent the evaporation of the water that lies beneath. The height of the underground water level beneath the dunes was not ascertained. Indeed it is not at all necessary to determine where this level actually resides, since there is enough water far above it to support a luxuriant vegetation, if that were the only factor concerned.

In spite of the water supply in the dune sand, the scanty flora of the complex is characterized by the possession of the most pronounced xerophytic adaptations to be found in this latitude. These xerophytic structures will be discussed in the second part of this paper. At this point it is necessary only to state that in the main they are to guard against excessive transpiration, such as is induced by the unusual exposure to wind, heat, and cold. In a certain measure one might attribute these xerophytic adaptations to an insufficient amount of water in the soil, since, were they absent, the soil water would soon be used up. But it is much more important to discriminate, as ecologists are now coming to do, between conditions in the soil and those in the air. A plant may have its roots in the water and yet be exposed to a xerophytic air;

in that case the aerial organs will be provided with xerophytic adaptations, as is the bulrush. Schimper, in his recent plant geography, goes still farther and calls some plants hydrophytic at one season and xerophytic at another. Perhaps the ultimate definition of a xerophyte will be a plant that is endeavoring to reduce its transpiration.

Directly or indirectly, the wind is the factor primarily responsible for the scarcity of vegetation on the dune-complex. Incidentally, as has been stated, the wind dries up the soil and increases transpiration. Incidentally, too, the mechanical action of the wind in connection with the sand-blast is destructive to vegetation. The cardinal destructive influence of the wind, however, consists in its power to cover and uncover the dune plants. Two plants have been referred to as peculiarly well adapted to dune life, Corispermum and Populus. The former is a small herb, and unable to endure either covering or uncovering to any great extent. This plant, however, is an annual of shortest duration and does not exist during the periods of the greatest wind activity.

The cottonwood, which has been shown to be best fitted to withstand the instability of dune conditions, might be expected at first to grow in abundance there. It has almost unlimited powers of endurance in all conditions of exposure; it may be covered to the upper branches, or may have its roots uncovered to a depth of two or three meters, and yet flourish. Its failure to make any considerable headway on the complex is due partly to its relative inability to extend its area by vegetative propagation, partly to its short life cycle, and partly to the impossibility of germination. Thus a group of cottonwoods, which germinated when the conditions were more favorable and have been able to withstand the severe environment of the dune-complex, cannot appreciably extend their area, nor can they live for many years. New trees cannot take their place, because of the inability of the cottonwood seed to germinate on the higher exposed portions of the complex. These seeds sprout much more slowly than those of the bugseed, nor could the young plants withstand the winter conditions on the complex, even should they germinate. Furthermore, the likelihood of any considerable lodgment of cottonwood seeds is excluded by their light cottony appendages.

3. Encroachment on preexisting plant societies.

Those who are at all familiar with wandering dunes are acquainted with their power to destroy vegetation in the path of their advance. This, indeed, is to many people the most conspicuous feature of a sand dune area, because it often becomes a feature of the greatest economic importance. The effect of an advancing dune upon the preexisting vegetation varies greatly as conditions vary. The most important factors are the rate of advance, the height of the advancing dune above the territory in its path, and the character of the vegetation that is encroached upon.

The rate of advance is, of course, a decidedly variable factor, since all rates, from nothing up to the maximum rate, may be found along nearly all advancing lee slopes. At a given point the rate varies greatly during different seasons. An advancing portion may become checked and a checked portion may advance again, as wind-sweeps are clogged up or opened once more. The multiform changes on the complex, each and all, affect the rate of advance to a remarkable degree. Attempts have been made to measure the maxima of advance at Dune Park, but a sufficient time has not elapsed as yet to allow of any satisfactory conclusions. In November 1897 a stake was driven at the basal edge of a rapidly advancing lee slope. The height of this stake above the ground was a little more than a meter. In May 1898 the stake was nearly covered, and it could not be found at all in July. At this point, therefore, the vertical component of advance amounted to a meter in six months; the horizontal component, of course, was greater still, since the angle of the slope was about 30°. The general statement may be made for the Dune Park complex that the maxima of advance are to be measured in decimeters or meters per annum, rather than in centimeters or decameters. No estimates can be given for other localities. In all probability the Glen Haven dunes move more slowly, since the slopes have a much richer vegetation.

The height of an advancing dune above the territory in front of it is a very important factor, inasmuch as it often determines the life or death of a flora. At Glen Haven, where the advancing dunes are from thirty to sixty meters high, no preexisting vegetation can survive the burial which awaits it. At Dune Park, where the crest is never as much as thirty meters high, vegetation sometimes survives. This survival is determined chiefly by the nature of the vegetation, and the succeeding paragraphs will have to do with the struggle between dunes and floras at Dune Park.

The advancing dunes at Dune Park encroach now upon a swamp, now upon a forest. *Fig. 9* shows how these forests and swamp conditions alternate. In the right foreground is a pool surrounded by bulrushes. Toward the center of the photograph there is a ridge tenanted by pines and oaks, then another swamp and another ridge. *Fig. 10* shows a very interesting phenomenon. At the center is a deep trough, surrounded on all sides by advancing dunes. This trough has never been a wind-sweep, but was made by the piling of the sand all about it. The flora is this depression is not a typical sand-dune flora, although surrounded by such on all sides. It is a mesophytic island in a xerophytic sea. The dominant trees in this little group are the basswood, *Tilia americana*, and the [white] ash, *Fraxinus americana*. Although the basswood is common on the arrested dunes, this plant society is quite evidently a relict of a larger area developed under more genial conditions. The lake is toward the right, and the dune on that side is advancing with some degree of rapidity. The dune to the left is pushed forward in the main by the action of southerly winds, and moves quite slowly. This dune, however, is at the upper end of the curved wind-sweep previously mentioned, so that northwest winds, contribute to its advance. Thus it becomes possible for the same wind to cause the advance of two dunes toward each other and hasten the burial of a flora. The advance of all dunes at this point is relatively slow, as is shown by the comparatively abundant vegetation on the advancing slopes. This vegetation is not a relict of the past. The advancing dunes completely destroy all of the preexisting vegetation at this point. In a few more years, unless conditions change, there will be nothing left at the surface by which one may interpret the history of this dying plant society.

The encroachment of a dune upon a forest is shown in *figs. 11* and *12*. The forests in this vicinity consist principally of the scrub [or jack] pine, *Pinus banksiana*, and the black oak, *Quercus velutina*. Neither of these trees can survive any such degree of burial, as can the cottonwood. The oak, especially, succumbs long before the entire tree is buried; the dead trees along the dune margin in both pictures are oaks. *Fig. 12* shows a pine that is half buried, but apparently as vigorous as ever. The dead trees in *figs. 15* and *16* are mostly scrub pines, and they seem to show no greater adaptation to their new surroundings that do the oaks. There appears to be a wide range of individual adaptation in pine trees, some dying almost as soon as the dune reaches them at all, while others are nearly as resistant as the cottonwood. In both pines and oaks the first obvious sign that the tree is waging a losing struggle is etiolation. The living trees along the margin (as in *figs. 11* and *12*) rarely have a dark green foliage. In most cases the leaves are yellowish green, and in some cases almost white. Nor are the leaves as numerous or large as on healthy trees.

Such tree groups, as are shown in *figs. 9, 10, 13*, and *14*, are doomed to an inevitable death. The length of life allotted to them in the future depends almost entirely upon the rate of the dune's advance. There are some evidences in favor of the view that an individual pine tree can endure a deeper covering before death ensues, if the rate of advance is slow. *Fig. 12*, which represents a half buried pine that is still vigorous, was taken at a point where the advance is relatively slow. *Figs. 15* and *16*, on the other hand, where the pines were soon killed, represents one of the most rapidly advancing dunes at Dune Park. Thus the individual adaptation referred to in the preceding paragraph may be in part delusive. Perhaps the trees are able to adapt themselves more fully, and hence undergo a greater degree of covering before they die, where the advance of a dune is comparatively slow. Sometimes (as in *fig. 11*) the territory toward which the dune advances is higher than the dune itself. In such a case the advancing dune is checked. If the entire area in front is higher than the dune, the sand gradually accumulates until the altitude is great enough to permit another advance. When, however, a ridge meets the advancing dune at right angles (as in *fig. 9*), the dune's course is deflected to either side. If the ridge is high enough, some of the trees may be able to escape the fate of their associates. The pines in the background of *fig. 17* probably represent a portion of the flora at the top of one of these ridges.

At Glen Haven, as has been stated, the forest vegetation readily succumbs, because of the great height of the advancing dune. The forests are mainly of two types, the maple or the arbor vitae. The maple forests have a dominance of *Acer saccharinum* [Silver Maple], and represent the most common type of mesophytic forest in that part of Michigan. The arbor vitae forests are in reality swamp forests, and the most typical trees present there are *Thuya occidentalis* [Eastern White Cedar], *Betula papyrifera* [Paper Birch], and *Fraxinus americana*. The line of dead trees along the margin of the advancing dune (as shown to a slight extent in *figs. 11* and *12*) is particularly striking where there is an encroachment upon a maple forest. Sometimes the hemlock, *Tsuga canadensis*, grows with the maple and shares its fate. At one point the dune encroaches upon a forest of *Pinus banksiana*, and the results are precisely as at Dune Park.

Dunes that are encroaching upon forests may be found along the entire coast, though their best development is in association with an extensive dune-complex, as at Dune Park or Glen Haven. The burial of forests was observed at Frankfort, Muskegon, and elsewhere, and is a relatively common phenomenon. In closing up the treatment of the forests, the general statement may be made that an advancing dune destroys the entire forest vegetation. Where this rule meets with any exception, it is an exception that in no real sense invalidates the main proposition.

The encroachment of a dune upon a swamp is of less common occurrence than encroachment upon forests, because forests are so much more common than swamps along the lake shore. The best examples of dunes advancing on swamps were seen at Dune Park, where there are a number of swamps that run more or less parallel with the lake shore. *Fig. 9* gives a good impression of the general appearance of things in the vicinity of Dune Park. In the foreground is a pool and bulrush swamp upon which the dune is encroaching. Beyond the wooded ridge at the center is another swamp of the same type, which is suffering the same fate. In the distance there can be seen the crest of a dune, which is advancing upon a chain of forest-clad hills.

The dune which is shown in the foreground of *fig. 9* encroaches upon a pool in which there is an abundance of aquatic plants, such as *Nymphaea tuberosa* [White Water Lily] , *Nuphar advena* [Yellow Pond Lily], and *Pontederia cordata* [Pickerel Weed]. These plants are soon destroyed, of course, but it is surprising how long it is before they die. Leaves of Nymphaea and Nuphar have often been seen raised above the sand, a meter back of the present margin of the pond. These plants must have been partially buried for some weeks, and yet the leaves were scarcely blanched at all. Indeed, an oak tree buried to an equal relative depth would have succumbed entirely. Around the margin of the pool is a luxuriant growth of the bulrush, *Scirpus lacustris*. This plant soon gives up the struggle, etiolation being present when only the basal portion of a stem is buried. The appearance of the bulrush is often striking by reason of the fact that there are etiolated rings alternating with green rings of stem tissue.

Fig. 13 shows the encroachment of a low dune upon a sedge swamp. The beachlike fringe of sand at the base of the dune is peculiar to dunes that encroach on swamps. Considerable sand rolls or is blown beyond the base of the steep slope. Under ordinary conditions this sand is blown away, but as soon as it reaches the wet, swampy ground, it becomes moist, and hence remains for a time as a fringe to the dune. The plants of a sedge swamp are unable to adapt themselves to a dune environment, and quickly succumb. *Fig. 14* shows a dune advancing on a more mesophytic flora and on a group of pines. The effect here is also destructive, in the main. An interesting pocket in the dune, in which there is a group of pine trees, appears in this figure.

One of the most remarkable phenomena seen in the dune region is shown in *fig. 15*. A dune about twenty five meters in height is advancing with considerable rapidity upon a bulrush swamp. This swamp is more or less continuously surrounded by a marginal fringe of willows and dogwoods. The bulrushes are quickly destroyed, but the dogwoods and willows have thus far been able to remain not only alive but luxuriant. In order to keep above the sand, these plants are obliged to lengthen their stems far more than is ever the case under normal conditions. Already some of these plants have twice and three times their normal stem height. The buried portions of the stems, particularly of the willows, send out roots almost as soon as they are buried. These plants, therefore, become more and more independent of the deeper soil in which they first grew, thus escaping one of the greatest dangers that was mentioned in connection with many tenants of the embryonic dunes.

Three species have been found that are able to adapt themselves almost immediately to a dune environment, *Salix glaucophylloides, S. adenophylla*, and *Cornus stolonifera*.[3] The taller shrubs in *fig. 15*, as at the left of the center, are *Salix syrticola*. The lower shrubs are dogwoods or glaucous willows. *Fig. 16* shows a group of the latter two species growing together. How long these plants will be able to endure is a question that cannot now be answered. The conditions become severer each year, because of the necessity for increased stem elongation, and also because the plants are constantly rising above the protected position in the lee of the dune. At no place is the destructive action of the wind greater than at the summit of an advancing lee slope.

The encroachment of a dune upon an open swamp or a body of water is seen occasionally along the Michigan shore, as at Grand Haven. In no case, however, were any facts obtained that added anything essential to those given above. In concluding the section on dune encroachment, it may be said that the only conspicuous case of the survival of members of a preexisting flora is furnished by the swamps. It may at first seem a surprising fact that the plants which are able to adapt themselves to the intensely severe conditions of an advancing dune are hydrophytic willows and dogwoods, rather than mesophytic oaks, basswoods, and maples, or xerophytic pines. Such a view as this comes from a misconception of the change that is needed in the life-habits of the plant. The relation to the soil water is not conspicuously altered, or at least not rapidly altered. It is true that the elongating stem makes it more and more difficult for the plant to draw water from the original root system; but in the case of the willow, at any rate, this is counterbalanced by the development of new roots along the buried stem, which allow the plant to utilize the moisture in the sand. The trees mentioned above are unable to send out such roots, and here, at least, is one possible source of their failure.

---

[3] Some of the *Cornus stolonifera* may prove to be *C. Baileyi*. These two species certainly intergrade in the dune region. The pubescence character is largely a question of habitat. The best determinative character is the stone, and, judged by this, nearly all specimens examined, whether from the swamps or from the dunes, were *C, stolonifera*. See BOT. GAZ. 15:38, 86–88. 1890.

There is another line along which the solution of this problem of adaptation may be sought. A number of ecologists in later years have commented on the xerophytic structures of many swamp plants. These structures are not to be found in all swamp plants, but are particularly well-marked in plants of undrained swamps, *e. g.*, peat bogs. Schimper even goes so far as to regard peat bog plants as xerophytes, because the humus acids in the soil make it difficult for plants to obtain the requisite amount of water. Consequently peat bog plants have worked out xerophytic structures to reduce the transpiration. All of the swamps at Dune Park are undrained swamps, and may be called potential peat bogs. The chemical nature of the soil is such that the plants have doubtless adapted themselves to all of the essential conditions of a xerophytic life. The partial burial of these plants by a dune results, as has been seen, in no rapid change of relations with the water in the soil. The aerial organs, however, are exposed to a greater degree of light and heat by reason of their proximity to the sand. Thus the tendency to transpiration is increased, but the plants may be able to keep it within bounds through the xerophytic structures that have already been worked out in a swamp environment. It is likely, too, that these structures become more and more xerophytic as a result of life on and in the dune.

The theories that have been exploited in the preceding paragraph find, at least, a partial confirmation. The leaves of the three successful species have more or less pronounced xerophytic structure. The leaves of the dogwood are quite strongly pubescent. The willows, however, are more decidedly xerophytic. The leaves of *Salix syrticola* are very hairy, and the cuticle is thick. *Salix glaucophylloides* has leaves with a very thick cuticle, and coated on the under surface with a dense layer of bloom. In the dune form of this latter species the leaves are notably thicker and the bloom more dense. It is the author's intention to make a careful comparative study of the anatomical characters of these plants, and make report in the second part of this paper. All three of the species named above have a remarkably wide range of habitat, occurring on embryonic dunes, arrested dunes and heaths, as well as in swamps and on lee slopes. These shrubs may grow at almost any altitude and show a surprising independence of the water level in the soil. There seems to be scarcely any doubt, therefore, but that these species are naturally adapted to a xerophytic life, and that, when the occasion arises, still further xerophytic conditions can be met successfully.

The success of the willows and dogwoods on the dunes may be due, in part, to yet another characteristic. It is well known that swamp plants are provided with extensive adaptations to promote aeration. This need is especially apparent in undrained swamps, where the gases necessary for the underground tissues and organs have to be almost entirely supplied from above the surface of the soil. It is in these undrained swamps, too, that the accumulation of peat is so rapid. It seems rational, then, to suppose that tenants of undrained swamps by adapting themselves to prevent suffocation, have also adapted themselves to withstand burial by sand without injury. Just what is the cause of death, when plants are partially buried by the soil is, so far as the author knows, an unanswered question. A wide field for anatomical study and physiological experiment lies open along this line. In the meantime the notion that plants of undrained swamps are better fitted to suffer partial burial than are other plants may remain as a tentative theory.

In considering the formation of secondary embryonic dunes, mention was made of *Potentilla anserina, Cephalanthus occidentalis,* and *Polygonum amphibium var. stipulaceum* as dune-formers under certain conditions. Potentilla and Polygonum are extensively creeping herbs, while Cephalanthus is an erect shrub. All three are swamp plants naturally, and yet able, as has been said, to build low dunes of a slow growth. In like manner they sometimes remain living for a time when a wandering dune encroaches upon them. They are especially plastic where the advance of a dune is relatively slow. Among these plants Potentilla seems to be the most adaptable to dune conditions. Another swamp plant that shows a surprising degree of plasticity is *Hypericum kalmianum* [Kalm's St. John's Wort]. This shrub is very common in the undrained swamps of the dune region, and very often finds itself in the path of an advancing dune. Hypericum, like Salix, often forms a marginal fringe about a swamp, and miniature lines of this shrub are frequently to be seen toward the base of an encroaching dune, resembling the line of willows and dogwoods shown in *fig. 15.* Of course, Hypericum has nothing like the plasticity and endurance of Salix; nevertheless it may live for many years if the dune advances slowly. Its capacity for vertical elongation is much less than that of Salix or Cornus, so that a rapid advance would soon cover the plants and cause their death. Near the South Chicago beach is a pool with a dense vegetation of *Scirpus pungens* [Three-Square Bulrush, Chair Maker's Rush] about its margin. This plant has served to collect a small amount of sand, and is forming a low secondary dune. Although a large portion of each shoot is covered by the sand, there is as yet no sign of etiolation on the aerial parts of the plant.

Since the highest portion of a wandering dune is close to its advancing front, it is evident that a buried forest will gradually become uncovered, as the dune passes on beyond. No scene in all the dune area is more desolate that such a place. It is a veritable graveyard, where the

146

corpses once buried are exposed again. *Fig. 17* shows a pine graveyard which has had a history like this. In the background are several living pines, presumably members of the same forest with the others. Their position at the summit of a hill permitted them to survive, while those at lower levels were buried by the sand. The uncovered pine trunks are directly in the path of the main wind currents, and hence are subjected to the severest action of the sand-blast. The trunks are carved and battered away until the last remnant of the old vegetation passes away forever.

Graveyards similar to those at Dune Park occur on the extensive dune-complex at Glen Haven. The commonest dead tree there appears to be the arbor vitae, thought there are occasional dead trees of birch and ash. In addition to the trunks of trees, there is an abundance of res-urrected soil lines at all altitudes on the complex. These black streaks in the sand vary greatly in depth and persistence. Doubtless the organic matter thus exposed is sometimes utilized by the scanty vegetation on the complex, but more commonly it is rapidly scattered by the winds.

4. *Capture of the dune-complex by vegetation.*

The capture of a dune by plants may begin within the dune-complex itself or along its margin. In either case the first appearance of the ad-vancing vegetation is commonly in the lower places toward the water level. The reasons for this fact are obvious. These low places are well protected from the wind; there is no danger, therefore, of any sand-blast action on the plant organs nor any removal of soil from around the roots. When the growth begins at the foot of an advancing lee slope, there is, however, considerable likelihood that the plants will be cov-ered by the sand. It is this fact which prevents the capture of a rapidly advancing dune; the vertical growth of the plant must be greater than the vertical component of the dune's advance.

The most important reason for the first appearance of plants at lower levels is the soil moisture. It is the moisture at the surface of the soil which causes to a large degree the lodgment of seeds, and especially light cottony seeds like those of the cotton wood and willow. At the base of the dune shown in *fig. 9*, where it is encroaching on a swamp pool, there is a line of young cottonwoods and willows several inches above the level of the pool. The seeds were blown across the complex by the wind; when they reached the crest of the advancing lee slope, they rolled down to the base together with the sand. The base of the dune is always moist several inches above the surface of the water be-cause of capillarity. As soon as the sand and seeds reached the moist soil near the base, the movement was checked and both found lodgment.

The moisture necessary for the germination of the cottonwood and willow seeds is also furnished at these low places near the water level. The danger of being covered by the drifting sand is much less at this place because moist sand is more compact than dry sand, and because moist sand does not collect about the growing plants. The dune shown in the foreground of *fig. 9*, however, is advancing very rapidly, and it is not likely that the growth of the young plants will be rapid enough to prevent their being covered. In the moist sand at the base of the dune shown in *fig. 9* patches of algae have been seen, presumably Chlamydomonas, such as have been described in connection with the lower beach. It is doubtful if these algae are of any significance in the capture of dunes.

If the vegetation gets a foothold at the base of an advancing slope, it tends to creep up the slope by means of vegetative propagation. At the base of the cottonwood dune shown in *fig. 5*, there may be seen grasses which appear to be creeping up the slope in this manner. It should be borne in mind that such appearances are often deceptive. In this particular instance the appearance would be the same if the dune were advancing and the grasses rising to keep above the sand. In like manner there is doubt with regard to *fig. 16*, as to which vegetation antedates the dune and which is subsequent. As has been already stated, the clump of dogwoods and willows at the center beyond all question antedates the dune; so too, the dead half-buried pines. The annual bugseeds toward the base, of course, are subsequent.

The greatest doubt is as to the frost grape, *Vitis vulpina*[4]. At the upper right hand there is a luxuriant grapevine climbing over a dead pine. The clumps back of the willows and the trailing vines in front of them are also Vitis. *Fig. 15* shows several large grapevines back of the row of willows. The coarse-leaved vines at the lower right hand of *fig. 10* are also Vitis. It seems incredible that the vines in this last picture should be anything else than subsequent, since the height of the sand above the wooded hollow is more than twenty meters. Then too the Vitis vines are very abundant all along the coast on the naked dunes, but are rarely found elsewhere. On the dune shown in *fig. 15*, for instance, there are two willows, a dogwood, and the grape growing together. The dogwood and one of the willows are very common in the adjoining swamp, while the grape was not found there at all. On the other hand, no grape seedlings have as yet been found in any such

---

[4] The identification here may be question; fruiting specimens are rather rare, but prove to be this species so far as examined.

location. While much further study is needed in this connection, it seems likely that Vitis is subsequent to the dune.

A little above the center to the left in *fig. 16* is a young [red] cedar, *Juniperus virginiana*. This little plant is several meters up the slope and is unquestionably subsequent. In the left foreground of *fig. 10* is a shrub of the chokecherry, *Prunus virginiana*, which is certainly subsequent to the dune. In fact this shrub is rather frequent in such locations. The author does not feel clear as to the conditions which permit the germination and development of these plants in such unstable situations, for it must be remembered that the advance is rather rapid in all cases. No seedlings of the cherry, grape, or cedar have been seen in any such location. It may be that the germination and early growth took place when there was a temporary lull in the advance or during extremely moist seasons. The question cannot be fully solved without a careful study of marked plants for several seasons.

So far as the capture of the dune is concerned, it is a matter of no moment whether the vegetation is antecedent or subsequent. All contribute together to the common end. Of the plants mentioned thus far, Corispermum (shown in the left foreground of *fig. 12*) is of no value in dune capture, because of its annual habit. *Prunus virginiana* and *Populus deltoides monilifera* are rarely abundant enough on lee slopes to be of much value, especially because they have little or no vegetative propagation. The only plants which seem to thrive and increase their area of control on rapidly advancing lee slopes are *Salix syrticola* and *glaucophylla*, *Cornus stolonifera*, and *Vitis vulpina*. None of these, however, flourish except on the protected slopes. They are unable to grow along the crest, and hence unable to check the constant advance of the sand.

Vegetation seems to be unable, then, to capture a rapidly moving dune. No such dune has been seen where the vegetation has secured a greater foothold than is represented in *figs. 15* and *16*. This dune is in no sense captured; indeed, its progress is scarcely checked. The more vigorous plants may retain an uncertain foothold for a long time, and again they may not. So long as the crest is unoccupied by plants, the advance will continue almost without hindrance. The life conditions at the crest are so much more severe than on the slope that vegetation is almost certain to be excluded until the advance is checked by physical agencies. For the capture of a rapidly moving dune, a plant species should have the power of rapid germination possessed by the bugseed, the power of vegetative propagation possessed by the willows, the capacity for growth in height possessed by the cottonwood, or even more than that. The growth of the young plant during the first season should be greater than any of the above, so as to more than counterbalance the vertical component of advance during the period of rest. The life cycle should be of very great length. The plant should be able to endure all extremes of heat, cold, and drought, and all degrees of covering by the sand. No plant species in the Lake Michigan region begins to meet all of these requirements, and, as a consequence, the dunes would advance indefinitely so far as vegetation is concerned.

Various physical conditions tend to check the progress of many dunes. As a dune advances farther and farther from the lake, the effective power of the wind which moves it becomes reduced. The energy is largely spent before the crest of the advancing dune is reached, because of inequalities in its path. The wind commonly builds up other dunes between the lake and the main crest; these dunes serve as barriers, and of course check the advance. Occasionally there are hills in front of the advancing dunes; these check the advance temporarily, at least. The primary cause for a permanent decrease or cessation of movement is the decrease or entire loss of available wind energy. Many wandering dunes never advance rapidly at any period of their life-history. This is because their movement is in some other direction than that of the prevailing wind, or because the full force of the prevailing wind is not directed toward their advance, because of physical reasons. Dunes of this slowly moving type are much more common than the other, and may be seen at almost any point along the entire southern and eastern shore.

Whatever the cause, a slowly advancing lee slope is soon captured by vegetation. The process begins just as described above. Vegetation gets a foothold at the base and creeps up the slope. Antecedent plants, like dogwoods and willows, increase their area by vegetative propagation. Annuals, biennials, and even the hardier perennials germinate and successfully develop at all points. There are many plant species whose power of vertical growth is greater than the vertical component of a slow dune's advance. This latter condition is always the chief test which determines the vegetation of a lee slope. As the advance becomes slower, more and more plant species are able to get and retain a foothold on the dune.

The capture of lee slopes by vegetation was well seen in all its stages at Glen Haven and Grand Haven. At first the vegetation may be dominantly antecedent, as in the case at Dune Park. More commonly, however, the vegetation is chiefly subsequent from the start, chiefly because the area that is encroached upon contains no plants that are fitted for a dune life. Where there is no antecedent vegetation, the first plant to get a foothold is commonly *Ammophila brevigulata*. Plants that follow in quick succession are *Asclepias syriaca, Equisetum hyemale,* [and] *Calamagrostis longifolia var. longifolia.* Some dunes are almost completely covered with a dense growth of Ammophila. All of these plants are perennial herbs and all but Calamagrostis have very extensive vegetative propagation, so that the capture of a slowly moving dune is a relatively quick process. With these plants there may grow annuals and biennials, but they are of little or no value in dune capture. The commonest of these is *Corispermum hyssopifolium.*

Before many years have passed, shrubs and small trees find an entrance and gradually drive out the herbaceous vegetation described in the preceding paragraph. These herbs are all fitted to grow in the most exposed situations, but are not adapted to shade. The shrub vegetation of arrested lee slopes may be partly antecedent, but not largely so. The most common species of shrubs on recently captured slopes are *Cornus stolonifera* (or *C. baileyi), Salix syrticola* and *glaucophylla, Vitis vulpina,* and *Prunus virginiana.* With these shrubs young trees of *Tilia americana* are common. A lee slope thicket of Cornus, Tilia, and others of the above plant species is shown at the upper left hand of *fig. 10.*

All of the species named above occur on arrested lee slopes along the entire coast. The species which are peculiarly characteristic of such habitats are Cornus, Prunus, Equisetum, and Asclepias. These four species are found in other associations, but reach a decided climax here. Ammophila, Calamagrostis, Corispermum, Salix (both species), Vitis, and Tilia are almost as common, but have a much wider habitat range. Ammophila, Calamagrostis, and Corispermum are also found in nearly all plant societies thus far discussed, but they disappear entirely as soon as the vegetation becomes dense. The willows are common in many places on the beach and complex, but they too are ruled out as soon as a real forest vegetation gets a start. Vitis grows also on rapidly moving lee slopes, and remains after the forest has begun. Tilia more than all others looks to the future; as will soon be shown, it is the dominant tree of the first forests that form on the old lee slopes. With the entrance of the basswood the true dune conditions and the true dune plants are obliged to pass away.

There are other interesting plants that get an occasional foothold on the arrested lee slopes. At several such places at Glen Haven *Betula papyrifera* was seen. Near Chicago this tree does not grow on the dunes at all, although common along the margins of sloughs. It appears to become more xerophytic northward. Exactly the same is true of *Thuya occidentalis.* Possibly the climatic conditions northward are such as to permit plants that grow normally in protected situations to grow where the exposure is much greater. On an arrested dune at Glen Haven where shrubs for some reason are infrequent, *Solidago racemosa var. gill-mani, Aster laevis* [Smooth Aster], and *Achillea millefolium* grow abundantly with the herbs previously mentioned.

Before tracing the further growth of vegetation on lee slopes, something may be said of the origin and development of vegetation within the dune-complex. Of course all antecedent vegetation has been long ago destroyed. The capture of the dune must, therefore, be effected entirely by means of plants which germinate and develop on the complex itself. Speaking broadly, the complex is almost entirely composed of windward and leeward slopes. Since the windward slopes are low, it follows that they cover a much larger area than do the other. Perhaps nine tenths of an ordinary dune-complex is directly exposed to the prevailing wind. The capture of any portion of the windward slope is unlikely, because of the combination of exposure and instability of soil. In the summer a somewhat extensive vegetation may develop, made up largely of annuals and biennials. The most abundant of these plants is *Corispermum hyssopifolium*. Other species are *Artemisia canadensis* (or *A. caudata), Cakile americana, Euphorbia polygonifolia,* [and] *Cirsium pitcheri.* These plants are commonly more abundant in the deeper wind-sweeps than elsewhere, probably because the sand is moister and more stable in the sweeps than at other places. *Fig. 7* shows a very characteristic wind-sweep with its vegetation composed of the bugseed and other short-lived plants.

Although the summer winds are much less severe than those of winter, the effects on the vegetation of the wind-sweeps are often conspicuous. Artemisia and Corispermum plants frequently have the sand blown away from their roots and they are thus obliged to lean over on the sand. The stems become much twisted and the whole plant is shorter and more compact than when developed in more protected habitats. Occasional perennials that may germinate in such places rarely live over the winter. The vegetation develops anew each year and no steps toward capture are taken. The conditions on the lee slopes of the complex are much like those on the main advancing slopes. Of course all of the vegetation is subsequent. The conditions are, perhaps, more severe because more uncertain. Large slopes covered with Ammophila are common on the Glen Haven complex. Permanent capture may sometimes result on such slopes, but it is much rarer than at the slowly advancing edges of the complex.

The most important development of vegetation on the complex is in the "blowouts," or hollows produced by the wind. These depressions sometimes reach down almost to the water level and may be as much as thirty meters below the general level of the complex about them. In these depressions the sand is moist and protected from the severest actions of the wind, so that seeds find ready lodgment and a favorable opportunity for germination and growth. The commonest plants observed are the annuals and biennials mentioned just above, and the following perennials: *Populus deltoides monilifera, Salix interior, syrticola,* and *glaucophylloides,*[and] *Juncus balticus littoralis.* Seedlings of the cottonwood and the three willows appear by the thousand, and a large number survive the rigors of the winter. This is the one dune habitat where Juncus and *Salix interior* are at all abundant. These two species are marvelously well adapted to inaugurate dune capture. Both of these plants have very extensive powers of vegetative propagation. Rootstocks of this last-named willow often trail along in the sand for ten, twenty, or thirty meters. Thus the plants extend their area up the slopes of the depression on all sides by means of this vegetative increase. *Fig. 18* shows a lee slope on the complex, which has been almost entirely captured in this way. The dense clump of narrow-leaved shrubs at the center is *Salix interior,* probably all coming from one or two plants that have spread vegetatively. The broad-leaved shrubs and trees are *Populus deltoides monilifera.*

D. THE ESTABLISHED DUNES.

1. The basswood-maple series.

It was shown in another place how the steep lee slopes of the slowly advancing dune-complex are first captured by social perennial herbs like the Ammophila and Asclepias. Then shrubs like Cornus, Salix, and Prunus grow up and gradually drive out the herbs which grew there first, because they are ill-adapted to the shade. With these shrubs there often develop many young trees of the basswood, *Tilia americana.* As these trees grow rapidly, it is not long before the thicket becomes a little forest, in which the dominant tree is the basswood. The basswood dune, more than any other type of established dune, is *sui generis* [unique]. It is to be found along the entire coast between Dune Park and Glen Haven.

The conditions that determine the development of the wonderfully characteristic flora are very obscure. The basswood dunes are always very steep and relatively near the lake. Unlike all other established dunes there is no approach to a vegetation carpet; the sandy soil is loose and bare and evidently more or less shifting. The movement of the sand is due directly to gravity and only indirectly to the wind. The only obvious condition which favors the rich development of plants is the almost complete protection from the wind.

The trees of the basswood dunes grow as thickly together as trees ever grow and much more thickly than in any other dune forests. Everywhere the basswood is the dominant tree; no other tree begins to approach it in importance, although *Populus deltoides monilifera* is often common. At the south end of the lake *Sassafras albidum* [Sassafras] grows with the basswood in abundance. Trees that occur occasionally along the coast in this association are *Quercus velutina, Fraxinus americana, Juglans cinerea* [Butternut], *Ulmus rubra* [Slippery Elm], *Ostrya virginiana* [Hop Hornbeam], *Acer saccharinum, Betula papyrifera, Abies balsamea* [Balsam Fir], *Pinus strobus* [White Pine], *Tsuga canadensis,* [and] *Thuya occidentalis.*

One of the remarkable features of the basswood dunes is the luxuriant development of lianas. Scarcely anywhere away from the river bottom forests is there such a development of climbers in this region. *Celastrus scandens* [Climbing Bittersweet], *Vitis vulpina,* and *Rhus radicans* [Poison Ivy] occur almost everywhere. *Parthenocnissus quinquefolia* [Virginia creeper] and *Smilax tamnoides var. hispida* [Bristly Green Brier] are not infrequent. The great liana development may be correlated, perhaps, with the dense growth of trees.

Shrubs are abundant about the margins of the miniature forests and in the more open places. Often these may be regarded as relics of a former exclusive shrub vegetation. *Prunus virginiana* and *Cornus stolonifera* are the most common tall shrubs, *Rosa engelmanni* the most common low shrub. At the south end of the lake *Hamamelis virginiana* [Witch Hazel], *Ptelea trifoliata* [Downy Wafer Ash], *Rhus canadensis* [Fragrant Sumac], and *Celtis occidentalis pumila* [Common Hackberry] are common and very characteristic. The only herb that can be regarded as characteristic of this association is *Smilacina stellata* [Starry False Solomon's Seal]. *Elymus canadensis* occurs in the open places. Many other herbs are occasionally present, but there is no necessity for mentioning them. The slopes of the crateriform depression in *fig. 22* have most of the typical plants of a basswood dune. The bare trees are chiefly basswoods, the others pines.

By all odds the most remarkable feature of the flora on the basswood dunes is its decided mesophytic flavor. The majority of the above-named species are usually pronounced mesophytes. Indeed, along the wooded bottoms of the Des Plaines river far from dunes and dune influences, the following of the above plants may be found growing together: Tilia, Fraxinus, *Ulmus rubra*, Populus, Celastrus, Vitis, *Rhus radicans, Parthenocnissus quinquefolia*, Smilax, Prunus, Cornus, Hamamelis, Ptelea, and Celtis. Thus half of the entire number recorded above are found in a single river bottom forest. Of the fifteen most characteristic plants of the basswood dunes at the south end of the lake, eleven are found along the Des Plaines bottoms; two of the remaining four, Sassafras and Smilacina, are common as mesophytes. Only two of the fifteen, *Rhus canadensis*, and Rosa, are commonly xerophytic.

Apparently the life conditions on the basswood dunes are anything but similar to those of the river bottoms. The former appear to be xerophytic, the latter mesophytic and inclining to hydrophytic. The soil of the dunes is sand with scarcely any humus at all, and the slight water content is made less by the steepness of the slope. In the river bottom there is a deep alluvial soil rich with humus and with an abundance of water. Nor is the river bottom flora on the dunes the vanguard or the relict of a river bottom flora. At the south end of the lake, at least, the basswood dunes and river bottoms are separated from each other by many kilometers. The likeness of the floras suggests a likeness of conditions in the two apparently very dissimilar habitats. What this likeness is, if it exists at all, cannot easily be seen.

It is this river bottom flora on the dunes that furnishes the best examples of anatomical variation due to habitat conditions. Most remarkable gross variations are found in the leaves of nearly all the species. Celtis, a tall tree on the bottoms, is a thorny shrub on the dunes. The tissues, also, are highly modified so as to meet the requirements of the dune conditions. These great variations, not alone in a single species, but in a plant society transported, as it were, from the river bottoms to the dunes, will supply a large part of the material for the second or anatomical portion of this paper. It is also the author's intention to experiment with the river bottom and dune forms of the various species, and endeavor to determine whether or not these changes can take place within a single plant generation.

The development of an undergrowth of shrubs and herbs on the steep basswood dunes tends more and more to stop the sifting of the sand between the plants. The partial decay of the leaves which fall year after year gradually produces a humus. The conditions approach more and more those of the typical mesophytic forest, even though xerophytic dune societies may surround on every side. The growth of the humus permits the development of a low vegetation, consisting of lichens, mosses and forest herbs. The vegetation, shade, and humus conserve the water and cause a mesophytic soil in spite of the slope and sand. Seedlings of other trees, yet more indicative of the shady mesophytic forests than the basswood, make their appearance. The most prominent of these is the sugar maple, *Acer saccharinum*. Scarcely less important are the beech, *Fagus ferruginea*, and the hemlock, *Tsuga canadensis*. These trees produce the densest shade and cause the extermination of the basswood and its associates. Each vegetation from the original Ammophila to the maple forest, therefore, gives a denser shade than the one preceding.

Accompanying the above-named trees are such typical mesophytic forest herbs as *Hepatica americana* [Round-leafed Hepatica], *Trillium grandiflorum* [Large Flowered Trillium], *Epifagus virginiana* [Beech Drop], and *Arisaema triphyllum* [Jack-in-the-Pulpit]. That the conditions not only in the soil but even in the air are less xerophytic than when the basswood was the dominant tree is shown by the great luxuriance of the vegetation. The trees are just as large as in inland forests and the xerophytic structures that were present in the basswoods and their associates are quite absent in the maples, beeches, and hemlocks. The air seems to be almost as mesophytic as in the inland forests. The maple and beech forests are not frequent on old dunes at the south end of the lake, but, for that matter, they are not so well-developed anywhere in this region as they are in Michigan. Mesophytic forests on old dunes were seen at Saugatuck, Grand Haven, Frankfort, and Charlevoix. At Frankfort there is a maple forest on the steep slope of an old dune which is as luxuriantly developed as in an inland location. At Charlevoix a hemlock was seen which had over 200 rings, showing the minimum length of time that the mesophytic flora could have existed on the dune. The mesophytic forest is the most permanent of plant societies in the lake region. It may be regarded as the culmination of the series which began with the lower beach.

2. The evergreen series.

a. The heath.—The life-history of a windward slope is vastly different from that which has just been described. If one views a region of established dunes from the lake side, he sees a landscape in which evergreens predominate, whereas a view from the land side often shows a decided dominance of deciduous trees. Not only the windward slopes but the summits have an evergreen flora. The key to these facts is exposure to desiccating factors, especially heat, cold, and winds. So far as the soil is concerned, there is but little difference between the conditions on the windward and leeward slopes. In both cases there is a vegetation carpet and a covering of humus. The more gentle slope favors the retention of moisture, though this factor is counterbalanced by the desiccating influence of the wind on the soil. At the south end of the lake the soil of the leeward slopes is drier than that of the windward slopes, because of the southern exposure and consequent drying influences of the sun. Even in this latter instance, the contrast between the floras of the two slopes is tremendous. It is the condition in the air, not the condition in the soil, which determines the difference here found. Both slopes have a mesophytic soil; the leeward slope also has a mesophytic air, but the windward slope has a xerophytic air.

The heath has several origins but one destiny. It may arise on the slow-growing embryonic dunes, in depressions on the upper beach, on the fossil beach, on gravel terraces, or in pastures. In all cases the dominant plant species come to be one or more of the following: *Arctostaphylos uva-ursi, Juniperus communis* ,and *Juniperus sabina procumbens.* The first two are common along the entire coast, the latter only northward. The term heath has been but little used in America, perhaps because we do not have the peculiar Calluna heaths of Europe. The term heath, as here used, may be defined as a xerophytic flora in which there is a dominance of low evergreen shrubs. Warming and Graebner use the term heath much more comprehensively speaking of moss and lichen heaths and coniferous heaths. Along Lake Michigan the heath formation becomes more and more prominent northward. A well-marked juniper or bearberry heath is rare at the south end of the lake, while extensive areas are covered by the heath on Beaver and North Manitou islands and on the neighboring mainland.

During the development of a heath, the vegetation partakes of the nature of the formation which preceded it, whether dune or beach or terrace. Before the true heath plants cover the soil, the open places are inhabited more or less abundantly by such plants as *Prunus pumila, Salix glaucophylloides* and *adenophylla, Solidago racemosa var. gillmani* and *S. nemoralis, Aster laevis, Calamagrostis longifolia var.longifolia, Smilacina stellata, Lithospermum croceum, Artemisia canadensis, Rhus radicans,* [and] *Rosa acicularis* [Bristly Rose]. On fossil beaches and terraces, embryonic heaths often have *Hudsonia tomentosa, Andropogon scoparius,* and *Campanula rotundifolia arctica* in addition to the above.

At the center of *fig. 6* there is shown a heath developing on a substratum of embryonic dunes; the bearberry has already covered a large portion of this area with a low heath carpet. *Fig. 24* shows the development of a heath on a fossil beach. In the foreground is a typical fossil beach flora, consisting of scattered grasses, sand cherries, etc. The small scattered tufts are Hudsonia. At the center is a low Ammophila dune, while back of this are patches of embryonic heath, composed of the bearberry and the procumbent juniper. Along the edge of the forest the heath forms a continuous carpet. *Fig. 25* shows a typical juniper heath when fully developed. At the left background the heath is younger and still made up of disconnected patches. *Fig. 26* shows the formation of a *Juniperus communis* heath in a pasture. Since this latter species is more or less erect, while the bearberry and procumbent juniper are creepers, the aspect of the heath shown in *fig. 26* is very different from those shown in *figs. 6* and *24*.

b. The coniferous forests.—Whatever the origin of the heath, it is rarely a climax type along the Lake Michigan shore. It almost uniformly develops into a coniferous forest sooner or later. The most conspicuous and extensive forests of this type are on the lakeward slopes, at the summit of these slopes, or at the summit of the taller inland dunes. These forests, like the heath, become more abundant and the growth more luxuriant as one passes northward along the lake shore.

The development of a forest from a heath is easy to understand and can be observed at almost all points. The heath vegetation is dense enough to prevent the tearing up of the soil by the wind, but not too dense for seedlings of various trees to get a start. The dense tangle of junipers and bearberries close to the soil is peculiarly well fitted to protect the trees while small and tender. In a very short time small and scattered trees become conspicuous on the heath. The transformation of a heath into a forest is illustrated by *figs 24* and *25*. In each case the heath is encroaching on a beach and is being followed up *pari passu* by the forest. The advance of the heath is secured mainly by vegetative propagation, that of the forest by germination of seeds. This fact, together with the need for protection to the seedlings, prevents the forest from overtaking the heath in the struggle for more territory. So far as observed, the heath always precedes the forest, when the latter is developed in an exposed situation.

In the region as a whole, the pines are by all odds the character trees of the coniferous forests, and especially the white pine, *Pinus strobus*. This tree is found at all places along the coast. At the south end of the lake the scrub pine, *Pinus banksiana*, is more abundant than the white pine, while at the north end the red pine, *Pinus resinosa*, is often as frequent as the white pine. The distribution of the pines is very surprising. The scrub pine is the most northern of the three pines mentioned, and its farthest known southern limit is about the south end of Lake Michigan. Peculiarly enough, it is far more abundant than all other conifers put together at the south end of the lake, while it is much less abundant to the north along the lake shore. It was not seen at all north of Glen Haven, though it is reported as common inland. The red and white pines have in general a more southern range than the scrub pine, and yet they are more abundant northward along the lake than is the latter. Furthermore, these pines become more abundant absolutely as one goes northward. The red pine was not seen south of Pentwater.

North of Grand Haven *Thuya occidentalis* becomes a frequent member of the coniferous forests; sometimes it becomes as dominant as the pines. The same may be said of *Abies balsamea*, though it was not seen south of Frankfort. *Juniperus virginiana* is frequent, especially southward. With the evergreens are occasional deciduous trees, especially at protected forest margins; among these are *Betula papyrifera, Tilia americana, Populus deltoides monilifera,* and *Ostrya virginica.*

So long as the coniferous forests remain more or less open, the three dominant heath plants, *Arctostaphylos uva-ursi, Juniperus communis,* and *J. sabina procumbens,* retain their prominence. Of these Arctostaphylos is the most persistent, and may be regarded as the most characteristic plant of the forest undergrowth. There are occasional shrubs in the open places, such as *Shepherdia canadensis* [Buffalo Berry], *Diervilla trifida* [Bush Honeysuckle], *Rosa acicularis,* [and] *Prunus pumila.* Among the herbs in open places are *Calamagrostis longifolia var. longifolia, Aster laevis, Smilacina stellata, Arabis lyrata,* [and] *Lithospermum croceum.* Many mosses occur more or less shaded by the evergreens, especially Thuidium and other trailing varieties. *Fig. 19* shows a coniferous society at the summit of a dune. The trees are white pines; the shrubs in front of them, *Juniperus communis;* those at the left, *J. virginiana.* The grass in the foreground is *Andropogon scoparius.* Coniferous forests on exposed slopes are shown in *figs. 6* and *21.*

The coniferous forests heretofore considered are chiefly on exposed slopes and summits. Sometimes there are coniferous forests farther inland developed on older and lower dunes. The protection here is greater and the air is less xerophytic. Extensive forests of this type were found between Frankfort and Empire and on Beaver island. The trees are chiefly pines or balsams just as before, but the evergreen undergrowth of junipers and bearberries is largely replaced by such plants as *Vaccinium augustifolium* [Early Low Blueberry], *V. myrtilloides* [Canada Blueberry], *Epigaea repens* [Trailing Arbutus], *Gaultheria procumbens* [Wintergreen], *Linnaea borealis* [Twin Flower], *Melampyrum lineare* [American Cow Wheat], [and] *Pteris aquilina* [Common Brake]. In the more open and sterile places there is often a moss or lichen carpet, consisting largely of *Cladonia rangiferina* [Reindeer Lichen] (or other Cladonia species) or *Polytrichum commune* [Hair Cap Moss]. At the south end of the lake plant societies of this type become more like pine barrens. On the east coast of Beaver island there is a beautiful gradation series from the heath on the beach through a pine forest like that described in this paragraph into a pine forest in which there is almost no undergrowth at all. The scarcity of herbaceous or shrub vegetation is due to the dense shade and the carpet of pine needles. This last type is the summit of the evergreen series, and is in all probability a climax type, at least in certain situations.

A very distinct type of coniferous forest is especially well developed at the south end of the lake. Since it is not developed in exposed situations, or even on old dunes, but in low depressions between dunes, it may be called a pine bottom. These societies are developed where the soil is almost hydrophytic. A common location for these miniature pine forests is about the gently sloping margins of an undrained swamp. *Figs. 9, 13, 14,* and *20* show them in such a situation. The line of demarcation between the sedge swamp and the pines is usually quite sharp. The surface of the soil where the pines grow may be less than a meter above the water level.

The character tree of the pine bottoms is always *Pinus banksiana.* This species is, perhaps, less common than the white pine at the higher levels, but the white pine is rarely, if ever present on the bottoms. No growth of trees anywhere in the dune region is so pure as the pine growth here. The most common shrubs in these locations are *Hypericum kalmianum, Salix glaucophylloides, Arctostaphylos uva-ursi,* and *Juniperus communis, Linnaea borealis, Arabis lyrata, Fragaria virginiana* [Wild Strawberry], and species of Pyrola [Shinleaf] are frequent. The development of the pine bottom flora was seen at several points. One of the most interesting cases was in a region of oak dunes, where a railroad company had removed considerable sand and lowered the level several meters. Although surrounded on all sides by oaks and at some distance from a pine flora, the new flora at the lower level is developing into that of a pine bottom.

c. The rejuvenated dunes.—The instability of dune conditions is not confined to the dune-complex. The capture or establishment of a dune is liable to be stopped at any point and retrogression toward the active dune conditions instituted. Even a dune that has long been completely established may have its vegetation destroyed and pass again into a state of activity. This process may be called rejuvenation. Any dune may become rejuvenated if the physical conditions are favorable, but the great majority of rejuvenated dunes are developed from established coniferous dunes; hence this type is discussed in connection with the evergreen series. The coniferous forests that develop on the windward slopes near the lake are peculiarly subject to destruction. The slightest change in the physical conditions is often sufficient to bring about the destruction of a coniferous society. The removal of a comparatively slight barrier may be enough to direct the entire wind energy against a pine forest.

The formation of a wind-sweep is, perhaps, the most common way for rejuvenation to begin. *Fig. 6* shows a windward slope tenanted by conifers that has become rejuvenated at three points. One of these wind-sweeps is seen at closer range in *fig. 21.* This latter sweep is forty-five meters in height, and the angle of slope varies from twenty to thirty degrees. When once a sweep is formed the tendency to self-perpetuation becomes greater and greater, since the wind becomes more and more concentrated as the sweep grows deeper. The destruction of the forest vegetation is very soon accomplished at such a place. The desiccating influence of the wind becomes increased and makes it difficult even for the xerophytic conifers to survive. At no place is the destructive action of the sand-blast seen so well as in these rejuvenated sweeps. The branches and even the trunks of the trees have the softer parts carved away, while the more resistant portions stand out in conspicuous relief. The leaves, especially of deciduous trees, are torn or withered or even altogether destroyed.

These destructive agencies are aided by another force that is altogether irresistible when the sweeps grow deeper, the force of gravity. *Fig. 22* shows a plant society that is being destroyed mainly by gravity. The view is taken looking at the side of a deep gorge-like wind-sweep which the wind has cut. As the wind blows along, its energy increased by concentration, a large amount of sand is picked up along the base of the steep sides. The sand is as steep as it will lie, so that each removal causes a movement of the sand down the slope. The fallen trees shown in the photograph have been overturned and carried down the slope in just this way. That the direct action of the wind is also powerful enough to destroy without the assistance of gravity is proven by the dead but standing trees at the left, where the action of gravity happens to be much less.

Many plant species resist the process of dune rejuvenation to a surprisingly successful extent. *Fig. 23* shows the last remnant of a plant society that may have been somewhat extensive. The tree at the center is a basswood, a tree which could never develop in such an exposed situation. In all probability this mound is a fragment of a protected lee slope, on which the basswood grew and flourished for a time. The grass at the left is Calamagrostis; the tenacity with which it holds its ground has already been mentioned. Sometimes a group of cedars, *Juniperus virginiana*, remain at the apex of a conical mound of sand, their associates having been swept away with the sand in which they grew. On the beach at Charlevoix there is a stranded clump of stunted trees of Thuja; they are probably the remnant of a society which has been otherwise destroyed.

As a wind-sweep is developed, and the evergreen vegetation destroyed, many plants that have been previously mentioned as characteristic of bare and exposed situations again make their appearance. The most prominent of these are *Artemisia canadensis* (or *A. caudata*), *Elymus canadensis, Solidago racemosa var. gillmani, Asclepias syriaca, Oenothera biennis, Rosa acicularis, Calamagrostis longifolia var longifolia,* [and] *Prunus virginiana*. In addition to these there come in, of course, the annuals and biennials mentioned in connection with the wind-sweeps on the dune-complex.

While rejuvenated dunes are to be found along the entire coast, they reach their highest development northward, especially at the summit of the terraces and bluffs. Perched dunes, it would seem, are favorably located for destruction by the wind. At Frankfort and Empire the perched dunes are in the earlier stages of rejuvenation. At Glen Haven these dunes have been rejuvenated, the vegetation entirely destroyed, and the sand removed inland to form the gigantic moving dunes previously mentioned. The substratum on which the dunes rested remains as a bare gravel mesa, with only the Sleeping Bear left to tell the tale of its former occupation by coniferous dunes. It is barely possible that some of these so-called rejuvenated dunes have never been established, and that they have grown slowly to their present height *pari passu* with the vegetation. This is purely a theory without any facts whatever to support it. The evidence seems to point unmistakably to an establishment followed by rejuvenation. Evergreen vegetation is very poorly adapted for any *pari passu* growth, such as is found on the embryonic dunes.

3. The oak dunes.

At the south end of the lake, and as far up the eastern shore as Manistee, there may be seen old dunes covered over with rather open and scrubby oak forests. These dunes have long been established and are entirely free from the destructive sand-laden winds which are so influential in determining the character of the other dune societies. As a rule the oak dunes are low and are separated from the lake by several series of dunes on which the vegetation is less stable.

The dominant tree on the oak dunes is the black oak, *Quercus velutina*.[5] This tree is far more abundant than all others combined. The only other tree that may be called characteristic in the Dune Park region is *Quercus alba* [White Oak]. On some oak dunes there are low trees or tall shrubs of *Sassafras albidum*, *Cornus florida* [Flowering Dogwood], *Amelanchier arborea* [Juneberry], and *Hamamelis virginiana*. The characteristic shrubs are comparatively few except along the lower margins toward the swamp level, or on shaded northern slopes. The most abundant shrubs are *Vaccinium palladium* [Late Low Blueberry] and *V. angustifolium*, *Salix humilis* [Prairie Willow], *Viburnum*

---

[5] The closely related *Quercus rubra* and *Q. coccinea* occur commonly in neighboring plant societies and may be present on the dunes, as may hybrids between any of the three forms here mentioned.

acerifolium [Maple-leafed Arrowwood], *Rosa blanda* [Early Wild Rose] and *R. carolina* [Pasture Rose], and *Rhus copallina* [Shining Sumac].

The herbaceous vegetation of the oak dunes is very diversified and interesting. The trees are always far enough apart to permit an extensive undergrowth of relatively light-loving plants. On the southern slopes, where there is considerable exposure to the sun, there is rarely a continuous vegetation carpet, but a more or less tufted vegetation with intervening patches of naked sand. A large number of herbs are characteristic of such places, for example: *Pteris aquilina, Koeleria cristata, Cyperus schweinitzii* [Rough Sand Sedge], *Carex pennsylvanica* [Common Oak Sedge], *C. umbellata* [Early Oak Sedge], *C. muhlenbergii* [Sand Bracted Sedge], *Tradescantia virginiana* [Virginia Spiderwort], *Arabis lyrata, Lupinus perennis* [Wild Lupine], *Tephrosia virginiana* [Goat's Rue], *Lespedeza capitata* [Round-headed Bush Clover], *Euphorbia corollata* [Flowering Spurge], *Helianthemum canadense* [Common Rock Rose], *Viola pedata* Birdsfoot Violet], *Opuntia humifusa* [Eastern Prickly Pear], *Oenothera rhombipetala* [Western Sand Evening Primrose], *Monarda punctata* [Horse Mint], *Aster linariifolius* [Flax-Leaved Aster, and] *Helianthus divaricatus* [Woodland Sunflower]. In very open places there are various species of Geaster [Mushroom] and Lycoperdon [Puff Ball], *Vulpia octoflora* [Six Weeks Fescue], *Polygonum tenue* [Slender Knotweed], *Polygonella articulata* [Jointweed], *Talinum teretifolium* [Appalachian Fameflower], *Mollugo verticillata* [Carpet Weed], *Draba reptans* [Common Whitlow Grass], *Linaria canadensis* [Blue Toadflax, and] *Krigia virginica* [Dwarf Dandelion].

On the shaded northern slopes *Pinus banksiana* and *Pinus strobus* often occur with the oaks (see *fig. 20*). The undergrowth is often a complete vegetation carpet, and consists of Vaccinium, Viburnum, and others of the above plants, together with many different forms. Among the plants here there may be mentioned various species of Cladonia and Peltigera [lichens], several mosses, *Aquilegia canadensis* [Wild Columbine], *Epigaea repens*, [and] *Phlox pilosa* [Sand Prairie Phlox].

In the background of *fig. 9* there may be seen several oak dunes. The view was taken in the winter and shows a dominance of oaks, but the scrub pines are scattered here and there on northern slopes or in exposed situations. *Fig. 11* shows the advance of an active dune on the north slope of an oak dune with a wealth of oaks and a few scattered pines. *Fig. 20* is a view looking upon the north slope of an oak dune (taken in winter). The pines are abundant at the base and scattered on the slope. A view of the south slope would show no pines at all.

The conditions for the origin and development of an oak dune flora are obscure. At Grand Haven and Ludington the oak flora appears to follow the basswood flora. Remnants of the basswood flora are conspicuous in both places: Sassafras, Hamamelis, Vitis, Smilacina, *Rhus radicans*, Smilax, [and] Celastrus. It may be that where the conditions are most favorable a maple forest develops after the basswood, but the oak forest elsewhere. At any rate the maple forests are more prevalent northward and the oak forests southward. While the oak forests at Grand Haven , Ludington, and Manistee are on steep, long-established lee slopes, the oak forests at the south end of the lake are often on rather low ridges, where the basswood may never have prevailed.

Quite probably the pine is the normal predecessor of the oak. The scattered pine trees shown in *figs. 9* and *20* may be the relics of a more extensive pine flora that has been succeeded by the oaks. The oak cannot get a foothold until the dune has become well established and protected from the lake winds. If the pines are scattered, there is opportunity for the oak seedlings to develop successfully. Forest fires are more destructive to the pines than to the oaks; the former are more readily burned, and basal sprouts are less likely to appear afterward than in the case of the oaks. Near Dune Park there is a tract on which the pines have been burned and replaced by the oaks.

One of the most striking landscape features of the Dune Park region is the appearance of the pines at the lower levels (pine bottoms), and again on the highest summits. The oaks occupy an intermediate position as to altitude. The reason for this distribution seems to be that the pines have a much wider range of life conditions than the oaks. The oaks are excluded from the summits because of the extreme exposure to wind and cold; they are not xerophytic enough for such a habitat. They are excluded from the bottoms, because the conditions are too hydrophytic for them there. The pines are excluded from the intermediate positions not because of lack of adaptation, but because the oaks are better adapted for that position than are the pines. Where the oaks can live at all, they seem able to drive out the pines, while the pines occupy areas that are not adapted to the oaks.

The flora of the oak dunes, especially that found on sunny southern slopes, is a true xerophytic flora, but a xerophytic flora resembling that of the more southern type, where the adaptations are developed to protect against heat and the excessive transpiration which it causes. The flora on northern and windward slopes is predominantly evergreen, developing into a heath or a coniferous forest. This flora, too, is xerophytic, but of an arctic or alpine type, where the adaptations are developed to protect against the wind and cold and the dangers of excessive transpiration which they bring. The correctness of this view is shown by studying the floras of the oak and pine dunes. The former has a flora related to those farther south, containing Opuntia, Euphorbia, and many other plants of southern range. The pine dunes, on the other hand, show the farthest southern limits of many northern plants—for example, the scrub pine itself. Linnaea, the bearberry, and many others have a northern range.

V. Conclusion.

No attempt will be made to summarize the results of this study, but a few of the more striking phenomena of the Lake Michigan dunes and their vegetation will be given. The dunes have been determined in the main by westerly winds. The great majority of the dunes are established, and many of them are perched high up on bluffs. The vegetation is xerophytic, belonging either to the arctic or desert type.

The xerophytic beaches are subdivided into three zones: the lower beach which is washed by summer waves and is essentially devoid of life; the middle beach which is washed by winter waves and is inhabited only by succulent annuals; the upper beach which is beyond present wave action and is inhabited also by biennials and perennials. There are also fossil beaches and gravel terraces with a flora resembling that of the upper beach, but less xerophytic.

Perennial plants are necessary for any extensive dune formation on the beach, since they alone furnish growing obstacles. Such plants must be pronounced xerophytes and be able to endure covering or uncovering. The most successful dune-formers are *Ammophila brevigulata, Agropyron smithii, Elymus canadensis, Salix glaucophylloides* and *S. adenophylla, Prunus pumila,* [and] *Populus deltoides monilifera.* Ammophila and Agropyron form low dunes that have a large area, because of their extensive rhizome propagation. The Elymus dunes do not increase in area since rhizome propagation is absent. The Salix dunes increase both in area and height, because of extensive horizontal and vertical growth. The Populus dunes are the highest and steepest, since the cottonwoods grow quite tall, but do not spread horizontally.

Small dunes are formed in more protected places by plants that are unable to exist on the beach, or where there is rapid dune formation. Among these secondary dune-formers are Andropogon, Arctostaphylos, [and] Juniperus. Primary embryonic dunes may pass gradually into this second type, as this latter passes into the heath.

The stationary embryonic dunes on the beach begin to wander as soon as the conditions become too severe for the dune-forming plants. The first result of this change is seen in the reshaping of the dune to correspond with the contour of a purely wind-made form. The rapidity of this process is largely determined by the success or failure of the dune-formers as dune-holders. The best dune-holders are Calamagrostis, Ammophila, and Prunus.

There are all gradations between a simple moving dune and a moving landscape; the latter may be called a dune-complex. The complex is a restless maze, advancing as a whole in one direction, but with individual portions advancing in all directions. It shows all stages of dune development and is forever changing. The windward slopes are gentle and are furrowed by the wind, as it sweeps along; the lee slopes are much steeper. The only plant that flourishes everywhere on the complex is the succulent annual, *Corispermum hyssopifolium*, although *Populus deltoides monilifera* is frequent. The scanty flora is not due to the lack of water in the soil, but to the instability of the soil and to the xerophytic air.

The influence of an encroaching dune upon a preexisting flora varies with the rate of advance, the height of the dune above the country on which it encroaches, and the nature of the vegetation. The burial of forests is a common phenomenon. The dominant forest trees in the path of advancing dunes are *Pinus banksiana*, *Quercus velutina*, and *Acer saccharinum*. All of these trees are destroyed long before they are completely buried. The dead trees may be uncovered later, as the dune passes on beyond.

In the Dune Park region there are a number of swamps upon which dunes are advancing. While most of the vegetation is destroyed at once, *Salix glaucophylloides*, *S. adenophylla*, and *Cornus stolonifera* are able to adapt themselves to the new conditions, by elongating their stems and sending out roots from the buried portions. Thus hydrophytic shrubs are better able to meet the dune's advance successfully than any other plants. The water relations of these plants, however, are not rapidly altered in the new conditions. It may be, too, that these shrubs have adapted themselves to an essentially xerophytic life through living in undrained swamps. Again it may be true that inhabitants of undrained swamps are better able to withstand a partial burial than are other plants.

Vegetation appears to be unable to capture a rapidly moving dune. While many plants can grow even on rapidly advancing slopes, they do not succeed in stopping the dune. The movement of a dune is checked chiefly by a decrease in the available wind energy, due to increasing distance from the lake or to barriers. A slowly advancing slope is soon captured by plants because they have a power of vertical growth greater than the vertical component of advance. Vegetation commonly gets its first foothold at the base of lee slopes about the outer margin of the complex, because of soil moisture and protection from the wind. The plants tend to creep up the slopes by vegetative propagation. Antecedent and subsequent vegetation work together toward the common end. Where there is no antecedent vegetation, Ammophila and other herbs first appear, and then a dense shrub growth of Cornus, Salix, *Vitis vulpina*, and *Prunus virginiana*. Capture may also begin within the complex, especially in protected depressions, where *Salix interior* is often abundant.

Tilia americana develops rapidly on the captured lee slopes, and the thicket is transformed into a forest. The trees grow densely, and there is little or no vegetation carpet. Associated with Tilia is a remarkable collection of river bottom plants, so that the flora as a whole has a decided mesophytic cast. These plants have developed xerophytic structures that are not present in the river bottoms. Acer and Fagus succeed Tilia and represent the normal climax type of the lake region, the deciduous forest.

On the established windward slopes the development is quite different from that described above. There is a dominance of evergreens instead of deciduous vegetation. The soil conditions are nearly alike on the two slopes, but the air is more xerophytic on the windward slopes. The evergreen flora starts as a heath formed of Arctostaphylos, *Juniperus communis*, and *J. Sabina procumbens*. The heath arises on fossil beaches, secondary embryonic dunes, or wherever the wind is relatively inactive and where the conditions are too xerophytic for the development of a deciduous flora. Before long the heath passes into a coniferous forest, in which *Pinus banksiana*, *P. strobus*, or *P. resinosa* dominate. Coniferous forests also occur on sterile barrens and in bottoms, where the conditions are also unfavorable for deciduous forests. A slight change in the physical conditions may bring about the rejuvenation of the coniferous dunes, because of their exposed situation. Rejuvenation commonly begins by the formation of a wind-sweep; the vegetation on either hand is forced to succumb to sand-blast action and gravity.

The evergreen floras are more and more common northward, while to the south there are developed forests in which *Quercus velutina* prevails. The oak forests are more common on inland dunes and on southern slopes. The oaks may follow the pines, when the areas occupied by pines become sufficiently protected from cold winds. The pines have a much wider range of life conditions than the oaks, since they appear at lower levels, higher levels, and on northern or windward slopes. The oaks flourish best on southern slopes. The flora of the oak dunes is xerophytic, but of the desert type, while that of the pine dunes is of the arctic xerophytic type. The pine dunes have a northern flora, the oak dunes a southern flora.

VI. Previous studies of sand dune floras.

A great deal of physiographic work has been done in sand dune areas in total disregard of the plant life, although the results obtained from this study show that the vegetation profoundly modifies the topography. In like manner the flora has often been studied from a purely taxonomic standpoint, little attention being paid to the striking effects of the environment upon plant structures. More recently the ecological standpoint has been taken by a number of investigators, particularly to show the influence of the extreme environment upon plant organs and tissues. The second part of this paper will treat this phase of the subject in some detail. Very little previous work has been done on the geographic phase of the subject from the standpoint of historical development and the order of genetic succession of the various dune types. Still less has there been any adequate study of the modifying influence of vegetation upon topography. These latter phases of the subject have given color to the work which has resulted in this paper.

Warming's work on the sand dune vegetation of Denmark stands in the front rank. In his separate publications and in his text-book of ecology, the conditions on the Danish dunes are quite fully stated. The order of succession, speaking broadly, seems to be quite similar to that along Lake Michigan, but there appears to be less diversity of conditions, and the features appear to be developed on a smaller scale. The strand is succeeded by the wandering or white dunes, and these by the established or gray dunes. Beyond these are sandy fields. Just as along Lake Michigan, the dune floras may pass into the heath and these latter into coniferous forests.

There is a remarkable similarity in the flora of the Danish and Lake Michigan dunes. The same genera and often the same species occur in the two regions. *Cakile maritime* [Sea Kale] and *Lathyrus japonicus glaber* grow on the strand. *Ammophila brevigulata* (=*Psamma arenaria*), *Elymus arenarius* [Lyme Grass], and *Agropyrum junceum* [Sand Couch] grow on the wandering dunes. Where the genera are not common or even nearly related, there are to be found in the two regions plants that have the same life habits. There is thus a striking similarity in the two regions in almost every respect, and that too in spite of the marine conditions in Denmark, as contrasted with the inland fresh-water area in the United States. The life conditions appear to be essentially alike on all dunes, whether marine or not, and there are found not only identical life habits, but even identical plant species.

Warming reports Chlamydomonas on the strand in the same relations as along Lake Michigan. Among the sand-binding plants, Warming and Graebner give an important place to mosses. Along the Lake Michigan dunes, mosses do not appear to any great extent until establishment is nearly complete. On the Denmark coast, the Agropyrum dunes are lower than those formed by Ammophila, just as along Lake Michigan. The Danish dunes have also been studied by Raunkiaer, Paulsen, and Feilberg. Erikson has studied the similar dunes of southern Sweden, Giltay and Massart those of Holland and Belgium.

The dunes on the islands along the German coast have been carefully studied by Buchenau and to some extent by Knuth. Graebner, in his exhaustive work on the North German heath, discusses the origin of the heath on naked dune sand. He gives an important place to algae and moss protonema, since they precede other vegetation, forming the first humus and causing the sand grains to cohere. It is doubtful if these lower plants are so important as sand-binders along Lake Michigan. Rothert and Klinge have studied the coast vegetation of Russia.

The French dunes have been very carefully studied by Flahault alone and also in association with Combres. Some work has also been done in France by Constantin and Masclef. Willkomm's work in Spain and Portugal, covering a period of nearly fifty years, is very complete and satisfactory. Daveau has worked out the conditions along the coast of Portugal. On these more southern dunes, the plant species resemble those along Lake Michigan less than do those in northern Europe, but the life habits are the same.

The dune flora of South Africa has been touched upon by Thode, that of Chile by Kurtz and Reiche, that of northern Siberia by Kjellman, that of New Zealand by Diels. The tropical dunes of Indo-Malaysia have been studied in detail by Schimper, and are fully discussed in his work on the Indo-Malay strand flora and also in his recent Plant Geography. In the latter work there are several excellent discussions of sand dune vegetation, accompanied by photographs from a number of regions. The tropical dunes have totally different species, but even there the dominant dune-formers are grasses with the same life habits as Ammophila.

Dunes may be formed in deserts and inland regions apart form large bodies of water. Those in the Sahara and in the deserts to the northeastward have been more or less studied. Brackebusch has described dunes in Argentina.

In the United States dunes are common along the Atlantic coast, especially in Massachusetts, New Jersey, North Carolina, and Florida. On the Pacific coast they also occur extensively. None of these marine dunes have been exhaustively studied from the ecological standpoint. One of the best works that has ever appeared on strand floras is that by

MacMillan on the shores at the Lake of the Woods. The dune formation is not extensive there, but is most admirably treated. As would be
expected, there are many species common to Lake Michigan and the
Lake of the Woods. The sand hills in the interior have been studied by
Rydberg, Hitchcock, and Pound and Clements. Hill has studied the
dune floras about Lake Michigan for many years, and although he has
not written a great deal along ecological lines, he has had the ecological standpoint thoroughly in mind and the author has received from
him a number of valuable suggestions.

THE PLANT SOCIETIES OF CHICAGO AND VICINITY (1901)

I. Introduction.

In recent years a great impulse has been given to the study of plants in their environment by the works of Warming, Schimper, and other European botanists. The subject that deals with this part of the botanical field is now called plant ecology—the science of plant housekeeping, or, as some would say, plant sociology. One phase of ecology deals with the meaning of plant structures, such as leaves, roots, [and] flowers; the variation of these organs is investigated in relation to the influence of external agents, and attempts are made to work out the causes which determine plant forms. This phase of the subject is presented in Kerner and Oliver's Natural History of Plants and in Dr. Coulter's Plant Relations.

A second phase of ecology, and the one that concerns us here, has to do with plants not as individuals, but as grouped in societies. Very superficial observation shows that certain plants grow in swamps, others in forests, and still others on sand dunes. Warming, in his Ecological Plant Geography, published at Copenhagen in 1895, gave the results of a long series of investigations as to the causes determining these diversities in the distribution of plants. He divided the plants of the world into four great groups: hydrophytes, or plants which grow in water or wet places; xerophytes, or plants which grow in dry habitats; mesophytes, or plants which grow in places of medium moisture, such as ordinary forests and meadows; and halophytes, or plants which grow in salt-water or alkaline soil. It will be seen that all of these groups except the last are related to water, which is commonly regarded as the most important factor in determining local differences in plant societies. Most botanists have accepted Warming's classification of plant societies as a more or less complete organization of this part of the ecological field.

The present paper attempts to relate the plant societies not only to water, but also to soil, and more especially to the physiography. The geographic and physiographic features of the Chicago region have been admirably presented in papers by Leverett,[1] and Blatchley,[2] and more

---

[1] Leverett, F.: The Pleistocene features and deposits of the Chicago area. Chicago. 1897.

[2] Blatchley, W.S.: The geology of Lake and Porter counties, Indiana. Reprint from the Twenty-second Annual Report of the Department of Geology and Natural Resources of Indiana. Indianapolis. 1897.

recently in a bulletin of the Chicago Geographic Society by Salisbury and Alden.[3] As the map shown in *Fig. 39* indicates, the topographic and soil areas in the vicinity of Chicago are of three types: morainic deposits, chiefly boulder clay; the Chicago plain, representing the area covered by the glacial Lake Chicago; and beach or dune sands, connected with the present or former beach lines. Speaking generally, the Chicago district has three great vegetation types connected with these three soil and topographic types; the mesophytic upland forests of the morainic clays, the hydrophytic lakes and swamps or mesophytic prairies of the Chicago plain, and the xerophytic forests of the dunes and beaches.

A close analysis shows that the types of plant societies are numerous in each of the three general areas named above. In the morainic areas there are several forest types, as will be shown in the body of the paper, and it is here that the various phases of stream activity with their characteristic plant societies are best seen. The types of vegetation on the plain are fewer, including in the main only the various transitions between ponds, swamps, and prairies. The ancient beach lines present some, but not much variety, but the dune area of the present beach line presents a rich diversity of plant societies.

The keynote of this paper is that each particular topographic form has its own peculiar vegetation. This is due to the fact that the soil conditions upon which plants depend are determined by the surface geology and the topography. From the standpoint of the vegetation the topographic relations are more important than the geological. As will be shown later, all kinds of soils may have the same vegetation when placed in similar topographic conditions, whereas the same soil may show many diverse types of vegetation. The topographic conditions determine the exposure, the presence or absence of drainage, and the humus content of the soil, and are thus of overshadowing importance.

Having related the vegetation largely to topography, we must recognize that topography changes, not in a haphazard manner, but according to well-defined laws. The processes of erosion ultimately cause the wearing down of the hills and the filling up of the hollows. These two processes, denudation and deposition, working in harmony produce planation; the inequalities are brought down to a base level. The chief agent in all these activities is water, and no fact is better established than the gradual eating back of the rivers into the land and the wear-

---

[3] Salisbury, R.D., and A.Den, W.C.: The geography of Chicago and its environs. Chicago. 1899.

ing away of coast lines; the material thus gathered fills up lakes, forms the alluvium of flood plains, or is taken to the sea. Vegetation plays a part in all these processes, the peat deposits adding greatly to the rapidity with which lakes and swamps are filled, while the plant covering of the hills, on the contrary, greatly retards the erosive processes. Thus the hollows are filled more rapidly than the hills are worn away. As a consequence of all these changes, the slopes and soils must change; so, too, the plant societies, which are replaced in turn by others that are adapted to the new conditions.

There must be, then, an order of succession of plant societies, just as there is an order of succession of topographic forms in the changing landscape. As the years pass by, one plant society must necessarily be supplanted by another, though the one passes into the other by imperceptible gradations. One thing more must be recognized, and that is that environmental influences are normally cumulative. A plant society is not a product of present conditions alone, but the past is involved as well. For example, a hydrophytic plant society may be seen growing in a mesophytic soil; the author has seen a mesophytic tamarack swamp which can be explained only in this way. We have in this phenomenon a lagging of effects behind their cumulative causes, just as the climax of the heat in summer comes long after the solstice.

In a classification like this great emphasis is placed on border lines or zones of tension, for here, rather than at the center of the society, one can best interpret the changes that are taking place. Of course the order of succession referred to above is a vertical or historical one. One plant society is said to follow another if it is actually superimposed upon the one preceding. In many cases, if not in most, there is a horizontal order of succession at the present time that resembles the vertical succession of which we now have only the topmost member. Instances of similarity between vertical and horizontal orders of succession are well shown in peat swamps and along shores and flood plains. Along a sandy shore it is only by studying the horizontal succession that one can get any idea of the vertical, since all fossil traces of preceding plant societies have passed away. In peat swamps one can sometimes verify the results of a horizontal zonal study by investigating the fossil remains beneath.

We may now outline the main features of a physiographic classification of plant societies. Speaking in the large, the tendency of the erosive processes is to reduce the inequalities of the topography and produce a base level. This base level may not soon be reached, though geological history furnishes instances of extensive base leveling. Crustal movements interfere with the erosive agencies, and a mature base level topography may become rejuvenated by a great uplift of the land, or sinking, on the other hand, may check the rapid action of erosion. Yet even with the crustal movements there go these topographic changes, and with them the plant societies must change. Putting the facts of physiography in the terms of ecology, the conditions become more and more mesophytic as the centuries pass. In a young topography such as the recently glaciated areas of Michigan, Wisconsin, and Minnesota, there is a great variety of topographic conditions and of plant societies. Among these are many hydrophytic lakes and swamps and many xerophytic hills. The hills are being denuded and the swamps and lakes are being filled, so that the hydrophytic and xerophytic areas are becoming more and more restricted, while the mesophytic areas are becoming more and more enlarged. In passing from youth to old age, then, a region gradually loses its hydrophytic areas, and also its xerophytic areas, though in the latter case there is usually at first an increase in the xerophytic areas, which is due to the working back of the young streams into the hills. These latter conditions are well shown in Iowa; in the comparatively recent Wisconsin drift of northern central Iowa the topography is much less diversified and there are fewer xerophytic areas than in the older Iowan drift farther south, which has been greatly dissected by stream erosion. Later, however, the inequalities are removed and we find great mesophytic flood plain areas, such as are seen along the lower Mississippi.

From what has been stated it will be seen that the ultimate stage of a region is mesophytic. The various plant societies pass in a series of successive types from their original condition to the mesophytic forest, which may be regarded as the climax or culminating type. These stages may be slow or rapid; some habitats may be mesophytic from the start; undrained lakes and swamps fill up and become mesophytic with great rapidity, whereas granite hills might take many centuries, or even geological epochs, in being reduced to the mesophytic level. Again, the stages may be direct or tortuous; we have already seen how the first consequences of stream erosion may be to make mesophytic areas xerophytic. So, too, in flood plains, the meanderings of the river may cause retrogressions to the hydrophytic condition as are seen in oxbow lakes, or the river may lower its bed and the mesophytic flood plain become a xerophytic terrace. But through all these changes and counterchanges the great mesophytic tendency is clearly seen; mesophytic areas may be lost here and there, but many more are gained, so that the approach to the mesophytic base level is unmistakable. Moreover, the retrogressive phases are relatively ephemeral, while the progressive phases often take long periods of time for their full development, especially in their later stages. The statements made in this paragraph have reference only to such regions as the one in which Chicago is located. In desert regions, and also in arctic or alpine districts, the ultimate stage cannot, of course, be mesophytic under the present climatic conditions.

II. The Plant Societies.

A. THE INLAND GROUP.

1. The River Series.

a. The ravine.—No topographic forms lend themselves so well to a physiographic sketch of the vegetation as do those that are connected with the life history of a river. Beginning with the ravines, which are deep and narrow, because of the dominance of vertical cutting, we pass to the broader valleys, where lateral cutting becomes more pronounced. From this stage on we have to deal with two phases of river action, the destructive, which is concerned with the life history of the bluff, and the constructive, which has to do with the development of the flood plain.

Wherever there is an elevated stretch of land adjoining a body of water, such as a lake bluff, one is apt to find excellent illustrations of the beginning of a ravine. *Fig.1* shows an embryonic ravine of a type that may be seen frequently along the clay bluffs between Evanston and Waukegan. A ravine of this type is essentially a desert, so far as plant life is concerned. The exposure to wind and to alternations of temperature and moisture is excessive. The lack of vegetation, however, is due chiefly to the instability of the soil; this instability is particularly great in the case of clay bluffs such as these, where the seepage of water causes extensive landslide action. No plants can get a foothold in such a place, unless it be a few species that may be able to make their appearance between periods of landslide action; among these plants annuals particularly predominate. The perennials that may be found in such places are almost entirely plants which have slid down the bank. Near the center of *fig. 1* is a clump of shrubs that have slid down in this way. Ravines of a similar type may also be seen at many places inland, and wherever found the poverty of vegetation on the slopes is the most striking character.

As a ravine extends itself inland the conditions outlined above may be always seen about its head, but toward the mouth of the ravine the slopes are less precipitous. Torrents cut down the bed of the ravine until a depth is reached approaching the water level at its mouth. From this time on the slopes become reduced and the ravine widens more than it deepens, by reason of lateral cutting, landslide action, and side gullies. After a time a sufficient stability is reached to permit a considerable growth of vegetation. If the erosion is light enough to allow a vegetation carpet to develop, a high degree of luxuriance may be attained. In fact, ravine conditions are usually extremely favorable for plants, after the initial stages have passed. In a comparatively few years the vegetation leaps, as it were, by bounds through the herbaceous and shrubby stages into a mesophytic forest, and [then] a maple forest, the highest type found in our region. Nothing shows so well as this the brief period necessary for a vegetation cycle in a favored situation as compared with an erosion cycle.

Of such interest are the facts just noted that it is worth while to mention some of the characteristic ravine plants. Perhaps the most characteristic trees of the Glencoe ravines are the basswood (*Tilia americana*) and the sugar maple (*Acer saccharium*), though the ash, elm, and other trees are frequent. The most characteristic undershrub is the witch hazel (*Hamamelis virginiana*). The herbaceous plants are notoriously vernal forms, such as Hepatica, Thalictrum [Meadow Rue], Trillium, Mitella [Bishop's Cap], Dicentra [Dutchman's Breeches], [and] Sanguinaria (Bloodroot); mosses abound and liverworts are frequent. A ravine with the above vegetation is shown in *fig. 2*. We can explain this flora only by regarding it as having reached a temporary climax. Ravine conditions are more favorable for plants than those that precede or follow. The instability and exposure of the gully have gone; in their place there is protection from wind and exposure. The shade and topography favor the collection and conservation of moisture, and as a result there is rapid development into a high-grade forest, as outlined above.

Rock ravines are much less common in the Chicago area than are those of clay, since the underlying limestone rarely comes near the surface. Excellent illustrations of stream gorges are to be seen at Lockport, and also in various tributaries of the Illinois river near Starved Rock. A striking difference between these rock gorges or canyons and the clay ravines is in the slope of the sides. The physical nature of the rock excludes landslide action, hence the sides are often nearly vertical for a long time. Lateral cutting is also relatively slow as compared with clay. Thus the conditions for vegetation at the outset are much more favorable than in a clay ravine. Rock-bound gorges are very shady and often dripping with moisture, hence liverworts and many mosses find here a habitat even more congenial than in the clay. Among the higher forms are found the most extreme shade plants that we have, such as Impatiens [Jewelweed], Pilea [Clearweed], and shade-loving ferns, plants whose leaves are broad and remarkably thin. *Figs. 3* and *4* represent canyons of the above description, whose rocks drip with moisture.

The stages of development pass much more slowly in canyons than in clay ravines, largely because the primitive conditions of shade and moisture remain for along period of time. Nor do the steep slopes permit the development of a wealth of trees and shrubs, since a secure foothold is not easily found. However, as the canyon broadens out and the slopes become less steep, shrubs and trees come in, though a typical mesophytic forest is rarely seen. The Starved Rock ravines are cut in St. Peters sandstone, those at Lockport in the Niagara limestone, yet the vegetation in the two places is essentially alike; at any rate, the resemblances are greater than the differences. Much has been written on the physical and chemical influences of rocks upon the vegetation. The facts seen here seem to show that the physiographic stage of a region is more important than either. The flora of a youthful topography in limestone, so far as the author has observed, more closely resembles the flora of a similar stage in sandstone than a young limestone topography resembles an old limestone topography. A limestone ravine resembles a sandstone ravine far more than a limestone ravine resembles an exposed limestone bluff, or a sandstone ravine resembles an exposed sandstone bluff. We may make the above statements in another form. Rock as such, or even the soil which comes from it, is of less importance in determining vegetation than are the aerial conditions, especially exposure. And it is the stage in the topography which determines the exposure.

All of the preceding statements as to topographic stages, whether young or old, refer not to times but to constructional forms. Two ravines, equally youthful from the topographic standpoint, may differ widely as to actual age in years or centuries, since erosion is more rapid in one rock than in another. In our region, however, elements of actual time are not very important, except as between rock and clay, since the limestone is less soluble and the sandstone is more easily eroded than is often the case.

b. The river bluff.—As a valley deepens and widens, the conditions outlined above undergo radical changes. From this point it will be necessary to discuss two phases in the growing river, the bluff phase and the bottom phase. We have left the clay ravine bluffs in a state of temporary climax, clothed with luxuriant mesophytic forest trees and with a rich undergrowth of vernal herbs. More and more the erosive processes are conspicuous laterally, and widening processes prevail over the more primitive deepening. As a result, the exposure to wind, sunlight, and changes of temperature increases; the moisture content of the slopes becomes less and less. The rich mesophytic herbs, including the liverworts and mosses, dry up and die. The humus oxidizes more rapidly, and a xerophytic undergrowth comes in. In place of Hepatica and its associates, we find Antennaria [Pussy Toes], *Poa compressa* (Wire grass), *Equisetum hyemale* (Scouring Rush), and other xerophytic herbs; Polytrichum [Haircap Moss] also replaces the mesophytic mosses. The first signs of the new xerophytic flora are seen at the top of the ravine slope; indeed, the original xerophytic plants may never have been displaced here by the ravine mesophytes. As the ravine widens, the xerophytic plants creep down the slope, often almost to the water's edge. Some of the young ravines between Evanston and Waukegan show xerophytes at the summits of the slopes. *Fig 5* shows a widening ravine at Beverly Hills; the vegetation is much less luxuriant than that shown in the young ravine of *fig. 2*.

After a few years have passed, xerophytic shrubs appear on the bluff in place of the witch hazel and its associates. And it is not long until xerophytic or semi-xerophytic thickets prevail, in place of the former mesophytic undershrubs. Among the more characteristic of these shrubs are the hop tree (*Ptelea trifoliata).* bittersweet (*Celastrus scandens)*, sumacs (*Rhus typhina* and *R. glabra)* [Staghorn Sumac and Smooth Sumac], chokecherry (*Prunus virginiana)*, nine-bark (*Physocarpus opulifolius)*, [and] wild crab (*Pyrus coronaria)*. Two small trees are common on stream bluffs, the service berry (*Amelanchier arborea)* and the hop hornbeam *(Ostrya virginica);* this last species is perhaps the chief character tree of river bluffs, and is rarely absent. Perhaps the best examples of xerophytic stream bluffs near Chicago are along Thorn creek. One of the most interesting things about these bluff societies is the frequent presence of basswoods and sugar maples. Doubtless these trees look back to the mesophytic associations that have otherwise disappeared. As would be expected, the last of the mesophytes to die are trees, because they are longer-lived than herbs and shrubs, and also because their roots reach down to the moisture. But they cannot be succeeded by their own kind, inasmuch as the critical seedling stages cannot be passed successfully.

The life history of the rock ravines, or canyons, is somewhat different. When the ravine vegetation is at its height, the moisture and shade are greater here than in the clay, hence the high development of liverworts and their associates. As the ravine widens, these extreme shade forms are doubtless driven out almost immediately by xerophytes, since intermediate or mesophytic conditions are seldom seen where the soil is rock. Furthermore, the xerophytic conditions become much more extreme on rock bluffs than on clay bluffs. This is well illustrated at Starved Rock (see *fig. 6)*, where the dominant tree vegetation is coniferous, consisting especially of the white pine (*Pinus strobus)* and the arbor vitae (*Thuya occidentalis)*. The herbs and undershrubs here are also pronouncedly xerophilous, resembling the vegetation of the sand dunes, *e.g.*, *Selaginella rupestris* [Sand Club Moss], *Campanula rotundifolia* [Harebell], *Pellaea atropurpurea* [Purple Cliff Brake], *Talinum teretifolium* [Appalachian Fame Flower], *Opuntia humifusa* [Eastern Prickly Pear], etc. The entire bluff flora down to the river's edge is xerophytic, except in shaded situations.

When a stream in its meanderings ceases to erode at the base of a bluff, increased opportunity is given for plant life. Through surface wash the slopes become more and more gentle. Mesophytic vegetation comes in at the foot of the bluff and creeps up as the slopes decrease. Finally the xerophytes are driven from their last stronghold, the top of the slope, and the mesophytes have come to stay, at least until the river returns and enters upon another stage of cliff erosion. The growth of a ravine into a valley with xerophytic bluffs is rapid, when expressed in terms of geology, but far less rapid when expressed in terms of vegetation. A ravine in the vigor of youth may develop so slowly that forest trees may grow to a considerable size without any perceptible change in the erectness of their trunks. Thus, in *figs.* 2 and 5 it will be seen that most of the trees stand approximately vertical. But the activity of the erosive forces, slow as it may be, is nevertheless revealed by occasional leaning, or even falling, trees. From the above it is easy to understand that cycles of vegetation often pass much more rapidly than cycles of erosion, but never more slowly. During one erosion cycle the mesophytic forest develops at least twice—once on the ravine slopes, and then finally on the gentler slopes that betoken approach toward base level.

c. *The flood plain.*—We may now follow the successive stages in the development of the flood plain vegetation. While the ravine is still young, as in *fig.* 2, there is no permanent stream, but merely torrents, which remain but a short time. As the ravine deepens, widens, and lengthens, thus approaching the underground water level and increasing the drainage area, the water remains for a longer and longer time after each rainfall. As the ravine conditions thus become more and more hydrophytic, the original flora, perhaps of shade mesophytes (as Impatiens), becomes replaced by amphibious shade plants, such as the common buttercup (*Ranunculus septentrionalis*), *Plantago cordata* [Heart-Leafed Plantain], various mosses, etc. Together with these forms algae of short vegetative period may be found in the wet seasons. When a ravine at last is sufficiently developed to have a permanent stream, a definite hydrophytic flora appears, consisting largely of algae (*e.g.*, Batrachospermum) aquatic mosses, and seed plants with finely dissected leaves and strong holdfast roots (such as Myriophyllum [Milfoil]), though these latter plants are more characteristic of ponds. In the early phases of a stream the currents are rapid and the vegetation (apart from lower forms) is sparse, by reason of the difficulty which plants have in securing and retaining a foothold on the stream bed. This difficulty is due to the rapid erosion and consequent instability of the substratum, as well as to the direct destructive action of the currents. *Fig. 7* shows one of these young streams whose flora is sparse.

Springs and spring brooks may be classed with ravine streams, but differ from them in the relative absence of erosion phenomena. This type of stream is uncommon in the Chicago area, though there are a few spring brooks near Chesterton. The water supply is much more constant than in ravine streams, and the shade of the ravines is often lacking. Besides the aquatics, there may be mentioned a characteristic brookside flora, including such plants as *Symplocarpus foetidus* (Skunk Cabbage), *Asclepias incarnata* (Swamp Milkweed), *Chelone glabra* [Turtlehead], *Polygonum sagittatum* [Arrow-Leafed Tearthumb], and two or more species each of Eupatorium [Boneset], Lobelia, Mentha [Mint], Lycopus [Horehound], and Bidens [Marigold]. The most characteristic spring book shrub is the alder (*Alnus incana*), though the extensive northern development of alder thickets has no parallel here.

As the energy of the developing stream is checked, the conditions for plant life become more favorable. In the quiet pond-like waters of an older stream there may be found many of the aquatics that frequent the ponds and lakes. In fact, the flora that is given later as characteristic of half-drained ponds and lakes (such as Calumet lake) may be transferred almost bodily to sluggish streams, such as the Calumet and Desplaines rivers.

When streams are old enough, and therefore slow enough, to support a pond vegetation, they have become essentially depositing rather than eroding streams, and we find there the development of a flood plain. While the river is still confined within narrow walls, and may thus be called young, there may be embryonic patches of flood plain, representing alternations of erosion and deposition in the stream. *Fig. 7* shows such a condition of affairs; though the stream is young and more destructive than constructive at that point, there are to be seen small flood plain areas with their typical tree inhabitants.

There is no place where flood plain development can be better studied than on growing islands in relatively rapid and yet essentially depositing streams, such as the Illinois river at Starved Rock. *Fig. 8* gives a general view of the Illinois islands and flood plain. In *figs. 9* and *10* the lower island (foreground of *fig. 8*) is seen close at hand. Any obstacle, such as a partially submerged tree trunk, serves to check the river current and cause a deposition of sand or silt, and before long a sand bar originates. As in the case of a sand dune, the bar itself becomes an obstacle to the currents, and hence continually grows larger.

The first vegetation, as on the lake beach, consists largely of annuals, especially the giant ragweed (*Ambrosia trifida*); rushes and sedges, some annual and some not, are also present, but are less conspicuous. The perennials that manage to survive one season are largely washed away in the winter and spring, so that in reality the vegetation is almost exclusively annual. The first woody plants to get a more or less permanent foothold here are willows (*Salix nigra* [Black Willow] and *S. interior* [Sandbar Willow]).

While islands of the above type gain more soil than they lose, a comparison of *figs. 9* and *10* shows that the river erodes above and deposits below. As a consequence, these islands migrate down the river, as well as grow in area year by year. Hence the upper part of the island is the oldest, as the vegetation well shows. *Figs. 8* and *10* show at the lower end of the sand bar, which comes to a point, and is so young or so exposed to submergence as to be barren of vegetation. Next comes the Ambrosia [Ragweed], then the willows, and finally a characteristic flood plain forest (background of *fig. 8*). The asymmetry of the river island vegetation is in striking contrast with the zonal symmetry of pond islands, as will be shown later (see *fig. 19*). The cause is evident, viz., the relative lack of symmetry in river currents as compared with pond currents.

The gradual encroachment of the land upon a stream through continuous deposition is well shown along the Desplaines river, and to a less complete degree along the Chicago river and Thorn creek. In the Desplaines bottoms the sand bar and island formations of the Illinois are largely absent, the currents being much less rapid. In the shallow water near the margin of the river are various hydrophytes, such as Sagittaria (Arrowhead), *Rumex verticillatus* (Swamp Dock), etc. The outermost fringe of land at ordinary low water is often almost as barren of vegetation as are the islands, but the soil is fine, and hence makes a mud flat instead of a sand bar. Immediately after the spring freshets have gone, an alga vegetation is frequently found on these flats, consisting especially of Botrydium and Vaucheria. Later in the season, annuals, or even scattered perennials, may occur here, though the winter and spring floods uproot or bury most of this vegetation. The Ambrosia and willow vegetation soon appears, as described above. The river [Silver] maple (*Acer dasycarpum)* usually appears with or soon after the willows. After the willows the cottonwood (*Populus deltoides monilifera*) and the ash (*Fraxinus americana*) soon come in. *Fig. 11* shows an advancing flood plain of this type; willows are seen on the margin and cottonwoods farther back.

Gradually the growing flood plain becomes dry enough to permit the germination and development of a true mesophytic flora. The trees named above, especially the willows, are largely replaced by others that seem better adapted to the changed conditions; among these are the elms *(Ulmus americana* [American Elm] and *U. rubra* [Slippery Elm]*)*, the basswood *(Tilia americana)*, the walnut and butternut *(Juglans nigra* and *J. cinerea)*, [and] the pig-nut *(Carya porcina)*. In this rich flood plain forest there are many lianas climbing over the trees, *e.g.,* greenbrier *(Smilax tamnoides var.hispida)*, grape *(Vitis*—various species), Virginia creeper *(Parthenocnissus quinquefolia)*, and poison ivy *(Rhus radicans)*.

The undergrowth in these river woods is very dense and luxuriant, the alluvial character of the soil making it very fertile. Among the shrubs are the thorns (various species of Crataegus), the gooseberry *(Ribes cynosbati)*, and many others. The herbaceous vegetation is dominantly vernal, the shade being too dense for a typical estival flora. Prominent among the spring flowering herbs are *Trillium recurvatum* [Red Trillium], *Phlox divaricata* [Blue Phlox], *Polemonium reptans* [Jacob's Ladder], *Hydrophyllum virginianum* (Waterleaf), *Mertensia virginica* (Virginia Bluebells), *Collinsia verna* [Blue-Eyed Mary], *Claytonia virginica* (Spring Beauty), *Erythronium albidum* (Dogtooth violet), *Arisaema triphyllum* and *A. dracontium* (Jack-in-the-Pulpit and Green Dragon), *Glechoma hederacea* (Ground ivy), *Isopyrum biternatum* [False Rue Anemone], *Caulophyllum thalictroides*, ([Blue] Cohosh), *Viola cucullata* [Hooded Violet], [and] *Galium aparine* [Annual Bedstraw]. Other characteristic herbs are the [stinging] nettles *(Urtica gracilis, Laportea canadensis)*, various umbellifers (Heracleum [Parsnip], Cryptotaenia [Honewort], Sanicula [Snakeroot], Osmorrhiza [Sweet Cicely]), and the parasitic dodder *(Cuscuta gronovii)*. *Fig. 12* shows a characteristic mesophytic flood plain forest along the Desplaines river; underneath the elms and basswoods is seen a rich herbaceous flora, consisting largely of Phlox, which the picture shows in full bloom.

In some of the bottom lands there is a rather striking collection of trees, whose chief range is mainly southward. *Fig. 13* shows a flood plain tree group near Lockport, most of whose members are largely southern, viz., the coffee tree *(Gymnocladus dioica)*, seen in the foreground; the pawpaw *(Asimina triloba)*, the sycamore *(Platanus occidentalis)*, and the hackberry *(Celtis occidentalis)*. In other flood plains there may be found the [red] mulberry *(Morus rubra)*, the red bud *(Cercis canadensis)*, the buckeye *(Aesculus glabra)*, and the tulip [tree] *(Liriodendron tulipifera)*.

None of these trees are common in our district, and only Celtis may be regarded as frequent. These relatively southern trees are found not only along the Desplaines and its tributaries, where there is supplied a continuous habitat along the river southward, but also along the Calumet and its tributary, Thorn creek. The occurrence of the tulip is full of interest, since it has been found thus far chiefly (perhaps only) in the vicinity of the dunes. Its occurrence has been noted especially at Chesterton along a small stream which empties into Lake Michigan at that point; the tulip has also been found away from present streams, but apparently in old valleys whose streams have been diverted by dune activity. The confinement of these southern trees to flood plains is not strange, since in such habitats are given the most congenial conditions that can be found in our area.

The vegetation on flood plains is not always as described above. Sometimes meadows are found instead of forests; this condition is particularly well shown along Thorn creek. *Fig. 18* shows a stretch of meadow of this type. Besides various grasses, such as *Poa pratensis* (Kentucky Bluegrass) and *Agrostis alba* (Red Top), there are often other plants in abundance, *e.g., Thalictrum purpurascens* (Meadow Rue), *Fragaria virginiana* (Strawberry), and *Anemone dichotoma* [Forked Anemone]. The ecological meaning of the meadow is not clear. Probably mowing or grazing is responsible for the failure of a mesophytic forest to develop. Extensive [haw]thorn (Crataegus) thickets sometimes occur in these meadows, and probably betoken the beginning of a mesophytic forest. Extensive and apparently natural meadows are found in the Calumet valley.

As we have seen, the climax type of vegetation on the flood plain is the mesophytic forest; but here, as well as on the river bluffs, the climax may be but temporary. Retrogression is almost sure to come in connection with terrace formation. While it is true that deposition is the main feature of flood plains, it is also true that erosion has not ceased; the downward cutting of the river once more causes vertical banks, though this time in its own flood plain. This action is seen in *fig. 14*, which shows the beginning of the new erosive phase, and its indication in the falling elm. There has doubtless been lateral erosion here also, since the elms are not usually marginal trees. *Fig. 15* shows the erosion of the flood plain still farther advanced; this bank is just opposite the willow vegetation shown in *Fig. 11*, hence there is deposition on one side and cutting on the other. A river may thus swing quite across its flood plain, destroying all that it has built, including the mesophytic forest. Not only is the vegetation destroyed directly, as shown in *fig. 14*, but also indirectly, since the lowering of the river causes the banks to become more xerophytic. In place of the herbaceous mesophytes, Equisetum and other relatively xerophytic forms may appear, though the trees usually live until directly overthrown by the river.

One more phase of river activity may be briefly sketched. In meandering over a flood plain, serpentine curves, or oxbows, are frequently formed. In time the river breaks across the peninsula, and the oxbow remains as a crescentic lake. The conditions radically change almost immediately, and the river life is replaced by pond life. The change is even more striking on the margins, where the old plants pass away and the forms of undrained swamps come in. *Fig. 16* shows the remnant of one of these oxbows; on the farther side are old and dying willows, trees that look back to the well-drained river margin. On either side of the pond are seen clumps of the button bush (*Cephalanthus occidentalis*), one of the most characteristic plants of undrained swamps. Thus the willows are antecedent and the button bush subsequent to the formation of the cut-off. *Fig. 17* shows a portion of the same, in which the willows, and even the pond itself, have gone, and only the marginal button bush is left, though in this case the margin occupies the center of the original pond. Near Starved Rock an extinct oxbow lake on the flood plain of the Illinois river contains an extensive patch of Sphagnum [Peat Moss] and Osmunda [Flowering Fern], among the most characteristic plants of undrained swamps. There are many undrained swamps, some with tamaracks, in the Calumet valley. The future of these swamps is like that of other swamps, and will be described in the next section. *Fig. 18* shows a morainic island in the Thorn creek flood plain; the stream has meandered, but has thus far left this detached fragment of the morainic mainland with a large part of its original flora.

In closing the section on rivers, all that is needed is to emphasize again the idea that the life history of a river shows retrogression at many points, but that the progressions outnumber the retrogressions. Not only this, but retrogressive phases are relatively ephemeral. Thus a river system, viewed as a whole, is progressive, and through all its vicissitudes there is an ever-increasing area of mesophytic forest. When the theoretical base level is reached, there seems to be no apparent reason why mesophytic forests should not be developed throughout most of the great plain.

2. The Pond-Swamp-Prairie Series.

a. The pond.—There are all gradations between rapid streams and completely undrained ponds, and corresponding with these various gradations are characteristic plant species. It will be convenient to sub-divide the series under discussion into two parts, the first dealing with undrained ponds and swamps, the second with half-drained ponds and swamps.

No two floras can be more unlike in species or in adaptations than are the typical brookside and swamp floras. Though each type may be called hydrophytic, so far as the water is concerned, the vegetation is really hydrophilous in the first case, but pronouncedly xerophilous in the second. Peat bogs, which may be taken as the type of undrained swamps, have a remarkable assemblage of xerophytic adaptations, such as leathery or hairy leaves, and special structures for water absorption. Schimper believes that these structures are due to the difficult absorption in peaty soil, the humus acids and the lack of oxygen being detrimental to normal root activities. For similar reasons the normal soil activities of bacteria and fungi are lessened, and as a result of this relative lack of decay great quantities of peat accumulate. All of these peculiarities of peat bogs may be referred to the lack of drainage, since the stagnant conditions prevent oxidation and the removal of the humus acids. The lack of drainage is of course due to topographic conditions. Peat bogs and undrained lakes, therefore, are features of a young topography, since several agencies combine to cause their rapid destruction. Rivers may work back and tap the undrained lakes or inlets may fill them up. Probably the most important agent in the death of undrained lakes, however, is the vegetation, as will be seen later. The great abundance of lakes and ponds in the young glaciated regions as compared with older regions to the south is a striking proof of their short life.

In the immediate neighborhood of Chicago typical peat bogs are scarce. They find their best development in the depressions of the dune region, where they may be called abundant. Wherever a sag between two dunes is low enough to retain moisture for the greater part of the season, the conditions favor the development of an undrained swamp flora. If the depression is so low that the water level outcrops throughout the year, then there is an undrained pond or lake. The first flora in this latter case consists of plants that are able to exist with little or no change in the water of the pond except through rain and evaporation. Among these plants the alga Chara takes a prominent place. The water lilies (Nymphaea and Nuphar) are an exceedingly important constituent of this first vegetation, as is also Utricularia [Bladderworts], which is represented by several species. The above species, together with others, play a great part in filling up lakes, since their remains accumulate with almost no decay. Chara in particular is a soil former of great importance. The rapidity with which these filling processes are carried on is striking; in pools of known age among the rubbish heaps of Jackson park the author has noticed accumulations of Chara peat amounting to none or two inches per year.

b. The undrained swamp.—It is obvious that the processes outlined in the preceding paragraph must eventuate in the death of the lake or pond involved and its replacement by a marsh, entirely apart from ordinary erosive activities. Indeed, as has been stated, these activities are relatively unimportant here; this fact is shown by the absence of ordinary sediments from most peat beds. As the aquatics make the pond shallower and shallower, they make it more and more unfit for themselves and fit for their successors, viz., those plants which grow along pond margins. Among the first plants of this type are various sedges (Carex), also the bulrush (*Scirpus lacustris*), though this latter species is more characteristic of the half-drained margins than of those under discussion here. Other marginal plants of our peat bogs are *Menyanthes trifoliata* (Buckbean) and *Potentilla palustris* (Swamp Cinquefoil).

The vegetation that follows may be called typical of peat bogs. The dominant plants are usually shrubs, especially the leather leaf (*Chamaedaphne calyculata);* this plant may be so abundant as to give tone to the landscape. *Fig. 19* shows some Chamaedaphne islands in a sedge swamp. It is clear that the islands represent places where in the original lake the water was shallow. The present remnant of the lake is shown at the left. Not only have the sedge zones advanced upon it from all sides, but centers of sedge growth appear also in shallow places in the lake itself. Just as the sedge zone encroaches upon the lake, when conditions become favorable, so the Chamaedaphne zone advances on the sedges. Again, a tree zone advances on the shrubs, as will be seen farther on. The zonal arrangement of plant societies that has just been seen is a feature of most peat bogs, and is due to the symmetry of lake and bog conditions. It will be observed that along the lake margin the zones advance toward a common center, while on the islands the advance is from a center. Eventually, of course, the marginal and island zones will merge.

Besides Chamaedaphne many other plants are commonly found in the shrub zone. Other shrubs are the swamp [highbush] blueberry (*Vaccinium corymbosum),* the [large]cranberry *(Vaccinium macrocarpon),* the dwarf birch (*Betula pumila),* the alder (*Alnus rugosa),* the hoary willow (*Salix candida),* and the poison sumac (*Rhus vernix).* Characteristic herbs, especially in the open places, are the pitcher plant (*Sarracenia purpurea),* the [round-leafed] sundew (*Drosera rotundifolia),* various orchids, as *Calopogon tuberosus* [Grass Pink], Pogonia , and

Cypripedium [Lady's Slipper Orchid]; sedges, as Eriophorum [Cotton Grass] and Dulichium [Three Way Sedge]; *Woodwardia virginica* [Virginia Chain Fern], and *Elodes campanulata* [Marsh St. John's Wort]. One of the most typical plants of these places is the peat moss, Sphagnum.

The flora just mentioned has many interesting features which are well known and may be passed over briefly. The highly xerophytic character of this plant society has already been noticed, and the reasons for it briefly given. The xerophytic structures are well illustrated in the leathery leaves of Chamaedaphne and the absorption and storage adaptations of Sphagnum. Many bogs of this type are very spongy and unstable, whence the name quaking bogs; this feature is due to the rapid growth of the vegetation and the absence of ordinary inorganic soils for a considerable depth. The similarity of the peat bog vegetation throughout the northern hemisphere is one of its most striking features. Not only the adaptations but the species themselves are similar over vast areas; the conditions are unique and the flora also. None of our plant societies, not even the lakeward dune slopes, have such a pronounced northern flora as do the peat bogs. No contrast could be more striking than that between the southern vegetation of the flood plains and the northern flora of the bogs.

Fig. 19 shows that a coniferous vegetation, now represented by but two or three small trees at the centers of the islands, is to follow the Chamaedaphne. Such an advance of conifers on Chamaedaphne is shown in the background at the right. The most typical conifer in such cases is the tamarack (*Larix laricina*); with this the arbor vitae (*Thuya occidentalis*) is sometimes found. Larix and Thuya swamps reach but an imperfect development in our region, and little need be said about them. The shade in these forest swamps is so dense that bare patches of soil are often seen. The vegetation consists largely of shade plants, among which may be mentioned Mnium and other similar mosses, *Coptis trifolia* (Goldthread), *Cornus canadensis* [Bunchberry], *Viola incognita* (Hairy White Violet), and Impatiens. The tamaracks appear to be succeeded by the pines (*Pinus strobus* or *P. banksiana*), and they in turn by oaks, as the soil becomes drier and better drained, and thus more adapted to deciduous trees. *Fig. 20* shows a tamarack swamp near Miller, Ind.

Not all peat bogs have a history like the above. Just as some flood plains are forested and others not, so some peat bogs grow up to shrubs and trees, while others are dominated, for a long time at least, by herbs and grasses. *Fig. 21* shows a swamp of this character. Bulrushes are seen to be encroaching upon the water lily vegetation, while back of the bulrushes, instead of Chamaedaphne, is a zone with sedges and grasses and scattered willows. Among the species other than sedges and grasses in a plant society like this are *Viola sagittata* [Arrow-Leafed Violet] and *V. lanceolata* [Lance-Leafed Violet], *Potentilla anserina* [Silverweed], *Fragaria virginiana* ([Wild] Strawberry), *Parnassia glauca* [Grass of Parnassus], *Sabatia angularis* [Rose Gentian], *Gentiana crinita* [Fringed Gentian], *Gerardia purpurea* [Purple Gerardia], *Castilleja coccinea* (Indian Paint Brush), *Aletris farinosa* [Colic Root], *Iris virginiana* [Blue Flag Iris], *Sisyrinchium angustifolium* ([Stout] Blue-eyed Grass), *Hypoxis erecta* (Star Grass), *Xyris torta* [Yellow-eyed Grass], [and] *Triglochin maritima* [Common Bog Arrow Grass]. The shrubs in such places are chiefly *Salix glaucophylloides* (Blue-Leafed Willow), *Cornus stolonifera* ([Red] Osier Dogwood), *Potentilla fruticosa* (Shrubby Cinquefoil), [and] *Hypericum kalmianum* [Kalm's St. John's Wort]. The conditions that determine this type of bog, as contrasted with the Chamaedaphne type, are not clear. The soil is hard, compact, shallow, and usually sandy; it may be that this type develops in shallow depressions, while the type with spongy, quaking ground develops in deeper depressions. This second type much more closely resembles the half-drained swamps in its flora than does the Chamaedaphne type, although so far as drainage is concerned it agrees with the Chamaedaphne bogs.

There is yet a third type of swamp which still more closely resembles the half-drained swamp in its flora. It is found along the edge of the Calumet valley near Dune Park, also at West Pullman. In this case the soil is rather deep and rich, in which respects there is agreement with the first type rather than the second. Grasses and sedges, but of a more luxuriant type, dominate here also, and with them are found such plants as *Cephalanthus occidentalis* (Button Bush), *Aspidium thelypteris* [Marsh Fern], *Onoclea sensibilis* (Sensitive Fern), *Saxifraga pennsylvanica* [Swamp Saxifrage], *Caltha palustris* (Marsh Marigold), *Viola incognita*, [and] *Polygala sanguinea* [Field Milkwort]. Sphagnum occasionally occurs here, as it never does in the second type. Here again there is doubt as to the determining conditions, but it may be that things can be explained by the difference in the drainage. The ultimate fate of the second and third swamp types is not known. The relative absence of trees and shrubs is certainly natural and in no wise due to man. Possibly local prairies will be the final type, or it may be that the forest will come in. *Fig. 21*, which shows pines encroaching upon the grassy areas, favors the latter view. So do some of the facts seen in the Calumet valley.

All of the peat bog types have a characteristic marginal flora, *i.e.*, the vegetation at the margin of the original lake is essentially alike in all cases. These plants, as well as those of Chamaedaphne bogs, are the same over wide areas. The most common members of the bog margin flora are the sour gum (*Nyssa sylvatica*), the [quaking] aspen (*Populus tremuloides)*, *Ilex verticillata* [Winterberry], *Pyrus arbutifolia* (including var. *melanocarpa)* [Red Chokeberry], *Spiraea salicifolia* [Bridewort] and *S. tomentosa* [Steeplebush], *Rubus hispidus* [Swamp Dewberry], *Gaultheria procumbens* (Wintergreen), *Osmunda cinnamomea* [Cinnamon Fern], *O. claytoniana* [Interrupted Fern], *O. regalis* [Royal Fern], *Betula papyrifera* (Paper birch), and *Polytrichum commune* [Moss]. This vegetation originates outside the swamp, and may be regarded as xerophytic; however, it often encroaches upon the swamp as the latter develops. At Thornton there is a dead swamp which is now almost entirely occupied by this xerophytic bog margin flora, only a few of the original swamp plants now remaining. Near Morgan Park is a bog margin flora without a bog; a shallow trench has been dug and in this trench there have appeared various peat bog plants, *e.g.*, Sphagnum. These considerations show that bog margin floras, though associated with most bogs, are not necessarily genetically connected with them.

A word may be said about undrained swamps among the active dunes. The conditions here, of course, are far more severe than in ordinary peat bogs and only a few species are able to endure in such a habitat. The most typical herb is *Juncus balticus littoralis* [Lake Shore Rush]. Seedlings of the cottonwood, as well as the long-leaved and glaucous willows, germinate in these wet depressions. Reference will be made to these plants in connection with the dunes.

In the morainic portions of our territory there are few if any peat bogs as described above, although they are usually more typical of moraines than of other topographic areas. On account of the clay soil which characterizes the morainic uplands there are many patches of swampy woods throughout the district. Shallow depressions of this type in sandy soil would not have a swamp developed. Morainic forest swamps are characterized by several trees, viz.: the bur oak, swamp white oak, and scarlet oak (*Quercus macrocrapa, Q. bicolor,* and *Q. coccinea)*, the red maple (*Acer rubrum)*, the [American] elm (*Ulmus americana)*, and the [White] ash (*Fraxinus americana)*. Other species are *Cephalanthus occidentalis* (Button Bush), *Salix discolor* [Pussy Willow], *Ribes floridum* (Wild Currant), *Cardamine bulbosa* (Bulbous Cress), [and] *Ranunculus septentrionalis* (Buttercup). This vegetation is ultimately supplanted by the mesophytic forest. A vegetation allied with that of swamps is the amphibious ditch flora with such plants as *Nasturtium palustre* (Ditch Cress), *Penthorum sedoides* (Ditch Stonecrop), *Proserpinaca palustris* (Mermaid Weed), *Ludwigia palustris* [Marsh Purslane], *Polygonum hydropiper* (Water Pepper), etc.

Calumet lake and Grand Calumet river may be taken as types of half-drained waters. We have here conditions that are midway between those of peat bogs and those of ordinary rivers. The vegetation is subject neither to the currents of the rivers nor to the stagnant conditions of the peaty lakes, and hence the luxuriance of the flora is far greater than in either of the other instances. The aquatic vegetation is rich both in species and individuals. Here is to be found a great wealth of alga vegetation, including such forms as Cladophora, Spirogyra, Oedogonium, [and] Hydrodictyon. Among the floating plants are Riccia, Ricciocarpus [Purple-Fringed Riccia], [and] the duckweeds (Spirodela, Lemna, and Wolffia). There are also a large number of attached plants, including many species of Potamogeton (Pondweed), *Ranunculus longirostris* (White Buttercup [also called White Water Crowfoot]), Brasenia [Water Lily], Nelumbo (Lotus), Myriophyllum (Water Milfoil), Ceratophyllum (Hornwort), Elodea (Waterweed), Vallisneria (Tape Grass), and Naias [Naiads]. This rank growth of vegetation fills the lake up rapidly, since the currents are not sufficient to carry off the plant remains. There is a rapid advance of marginal plants upon the lake, a phenomenon that is shown in *fig. 22*, where the scattered bulrushes *(Scirpus lacustris)* are seen to be soon followed by a dense bulrush society. With or soon after the bulrushes are a number of marginal plants, especially *Typha latifolia* ([Common] Cattail), *Pontederia cordata* (Pickerel Weed), *Sparganium eurycarpum* [Common Bur Reed], *Sagittaria variabilis* and *S. rigida* (Arrowheads), *Zizania aquatica* (Wild Rice), *Phragmites australis* (Reed), *Acorus calamus* (Sweet Flag), and *Eriophorum cyperinum* [Wool Grass]. *Fig. 23* shows a stage in which a lake has been all but destroyed by a rank bulrush vegetation.

c. The prairie.—Sedges encroach rapidly upon the bulrushes as the new soil becomes raised more and more above the lake, and grasses in turn encroach upon the sedges, forming a prairie. *Fig. 24* shows an expanse of grassy prairie which has developed through these successive stages from Calumet lake. Skokie marsh and Hog marsh are undergoing transformations of this character also. Sometimes with the prairie are a number of coarse xerophytic herbs, largely composites, as *Silphium laciniatum* (Compass Plant), *S. terebinthinaceum* (Prairie Dock), *S. integrifolium* (Rosin Weed), Lepachys [Coneflower], *Solidago rigida* [Stiff Goldenrod] Aster, Liatris (Blazing Star), and some legumes, as *Amorpha canescens* (Lead Plant), Petalostemon (Prairie Clover), Melilotus (Sweet Clover), and Baptisia [Wild Indigo], Eryngium [Rattlesnake Master], Dodecatheon (Shooting Star), Phlox, [and] *Allium cernuum* (Wild Onion). A Silphium (Compass Plant) prairie is shown in *fig. 25*.

The prairies of our area are in the basin of the glacial Lake Chicago, and hence all may be referred to a lake or swamp origin, exactly as prairies are developing from Calumet lake today. This explanation of the prairie, an undoubted explanation for the cases in hand, must not be applied to the great climatic prairies farther west. Whether the Chicago prairies will ever become forested is a question not easily answered. There are signs of it in some places, as at Stony Island, but this topic needs more detailed treatment than can be given here.

The processes outlined in this section are rapid. The mesophytic prairie or forest develops from the lake or marsh, while the region as a whole still retains a young topography. Thus this mesophytic assemblage, like that of the ravine slope, is bound to pass away, though its life tenure is much longer. Sooner or later river action will enter; there will be developed ravines, xerophytic bluffs, and ultimately flood plains, again with a mesophytic flora. A broad survey then shows a rapid development to a somewhat prolonged temporary climax, and finally, after ravine and bluff vicissitudes, there appears the true and more enduring climax of the mesophytic flood plain.

3. The Upland Series.

a. The rock hill.—While all of the land is eventually worked over by stream activities, and can thus be referred to the river series, other activities are at work in the young topography. The swamp series which has just been discussed is one illustration. So also there are hills which are not due to erosive processes, but to other causes, notably, in our region, morainic hills and sand hills. There are rock hills, also, which are not connected with the present erosion cycle. All of these hill types have their peculiar vegetation features, and must be discussed apart from river activities, since they have an interesting history before they are attacked by stream erosion.

We may speak first of rock hills, which in the vicinity of Chicago are quite rare, and consist entirely of dolomitic Niagara (Silurian) limestone. Not only are hills of this limestone quite rare, but surface outcrops of any kind are uncommon, because of the heavy drift. Hence the rock vegetation of the Chicago area is not very important. Perhaps the most interesting outcrop is at Stony Island, where it is quite easy to trace the various stages in the development of the vegetation. This rock, like most limestone, is subject to chemical as well as mechanical erosion, but is much more resistant than most limestones, on account of its strongly dolomitic character. The first vegetation that gets a foothold is composed of lichens, but the lichen flora appears to be rather sparse, perhaps because of the chemical nature of the rock, since lichens are commonly supposed to shun calcareous soils. The relative poverty of lichens may be due, however, to the easy solution of the surface rock layers and the consequent difficulty in retaining a foothold. The limestone is considerably jointed and fractured, and there is in consequence a rich crevice vegetation, composed of several mosses, especially Ceratodon and Bryum, and also various grasses. *Fig. 26* shows a vegetation of this nature, and among the other crevice plants is an abundance of *Solidago nemoralis* [Old Field Goldenrod]. Other species growing in the crevices or on the first soil which is formed on the rock face are *Potentilla arguta* [Prairie Cinquefoil], *Verbascum thaspus* (Mullein), *Heuchera richardsonii* (Prairie Alum Root), [and] *Poa compressa* (Wire Grass), etc. At Thornton there is a rock outcrop which gradually recedes from the surface, and it is possible to tell by the vegetation where the rock surface dips considerably under the surface of the soil. Where the soil is shallow the dominant plant is *Poa compressa*, but as the soil layer deepens it becomes gradually replaced by *Poa pratensis* (Blue Grass). Similarly, at Stony Island, crevices can be distinguished in a covered horizontal rock surface by a sudden change from the xerophytic plants of the shallow soil, that hides most of the rock, to the mesophytic plants of the deeper soil which lies over the crevices.

Through rock decay and the accumulation of organic matter a considerable soil comes to be developed where there was at first an outcrop of bare rock. The opportunity for a shrubby vegetation eventually arrives, especially in the crevices. *Fig. 27* shows such a vegetation getting a foothold. Among the shrubs in such places are the chokecherry *(Prunus virginiana)*, ninebark *(Physocarpus opulifolius)*, poison ivy *(Rhus radicans)*, *Rosa carolina* [Pasture Rose], sumac, *(Rhus typhina)*, hop tree *(Ptelea trifoliata)*, [and] wild crab *(Pyrus coronaria)*. Still later the way is open for a tree vegetation, at first xerophytic, but ultimately mesophytic, as the author has frequently observed in the Alleghenies. There can be no doubt but that a temporary mesophytic climax can be reached even on rock hills, though the probability of this is much greater where the hill is composed of limestone than in the case of sandstone or granite.

b. The clay hill.—Morainic hills are common in the Chicago region, and almost without exception they are covered with a mesophytic forest, in which the dominant trees are usually the white oak (*Quercus alba*), the red oak *(Quercus rubra)*, and the shell-bark hickory (*Carya alba*). This is easily the dominant forest type of the Chicago region, and is remarkably characteristic of morainic areas. The soil in all cases is a glacial clay or till, heterogeneous in composition, but rich in food salts. Of all our plant society life histories these are about the most difficult to unravel, and it is due to the favorable conditions under which they have developed. After the continental glacier left this region for the last time, it was doubtless on these low morainic hills that the first mesophytic forests were developed. And they have been developed for so long that almost no traces of their history are left behind; we have only the completed product, the mesophytic forest.

Where these mesophytic forests are disturbed we may perhaps get some notion of what took place in the first postglacial centuries. On the clay banks along the drainage canal, and also on recent river bluffs, one may follow in rapid succession a series of plant societies leading to the forest. There is here no pronounced lichen or moss stage as on rock hills, but the first vegetation consists of xerophytic annuals and perennial herbs. Xerophytic shrubs, especially Salix and Populus, soon appear. It is not long before there is an extensive thicket formation with an herbaceous undergrowth. Humus accumulates with great rapidity, and we soon have almost a mesophytic vegetation in which the dominant thicket species are likely to be the aspen (*Populus tremuloides*), wild crab (*Pyrus coronaria*), [the] red haw [family] (*Crategeus punctata* [Dotted Hawthorn], *C. Coccinea* [Scarlet Hawthorn], etc.). Such a thicket is the immediate forerunner of the oak-hickory type of mesophytic forest. When a forest of oak and hickory is cut down or destroyed by fire, it returns after a comparatively short interval, but the first stages in the clearing are thicket stages much like those just described. Of course it takes much longer to develop a forest from naked clay soil than from a forest land that has been cleared. Whether the stages that led up to the first postglacial forests are such as have been described is very doubtful. It is much more likely that the first forests were of slow growth and were coniferous in character, such as are found farther north. *Fig. 28* shows a typical morainic hill forest of the above type. Here the dominant tree is the red oak; a white oak is seen at the right.

Among the shrubs of these morainic forests there may be mentioned, apart from the crabs and haws, the hazel (*Corylus americana*), and various species of Viburnum. Many herbaceous plants are found, among which are Podophyllum (May Apple), Claytonia (Spring Beauty), various species of Aster, Trillium, *Geranium maculatum* [Wild Geranium], *Viola pubescens* (Yellow Violet), [and] *Anemone nemorosa* [Blue Wood Anemone], etc. Sometimes the bur oak (*Quercus macrocarpa*) is the dominant tree in these morainic forests, though in such cases the habitat is usually more moist or else the drainage is less perfect. A bur oak forest is shown in *fig. 29*. The transition from this type to the morainic swamp forests, already mentioned, is an easy one, and bur oaks are often found with the swamp white oak and other species characteristic of such places.

In spite of the abundance of the type of morainic forest described above, it is scarcely probable that it is anything more than a very slowly passing forest stage. The fact that in all directions from Chicago the ultimate forest type on morainic uplands is not the oak-hickory but the maple-beech forest leads us to expect that here. This latter type seems to be of a higher order in all respects. It is found in richer soil, where the humus content is very great. Seedlings of the beech or maple can easily grow in the relatively light oak forest, whereas oaks cannot grow in the denser shade of the maple or beech. Furthermore, oak forests have been seen with a pronounced undergrowth of beech. It would seem that one of the chief factors in determining the order of succession of forests is the light need of the various tree species, the members of the culminating forest type being those whose seedlings can grow in the densest forest shade. There are evidences that the oak forests about Chicago are being succeeded by the beech or maple. The best instance of this which the author has seen is on the low moraines along the Desplaines river west of Deerfield. The sugar maple (*Acer saccharium*) has already been mentioned as a character plant of the temporary mesophytic forests of ravines. Here we see it in the more permanent forest of the morainic hills. The beech (*Fagus ferruginea*) is much rarer than the sugar maple, though it is a rather important constituent of the mesophytic forests about Chesterton. Why the beech-maple forest has lagged so far behind in the region about Chicago is a question not yet settled. If these forests elsewhere have had an oak stage it indicates that the development here is very slow.

Though the forests just described, whether of the oak-hickory or the maple-beech type, are of a high degree of permanence, it can be seen that this permanence is but relative. Sooner or later stream action will enter these districts and base leveling processes will begin on a more rapid scale. But for these activities the lowering of hills would be very slow indeed, so slow as hardly to interfere at any point with a luxuriant development of the vegetation. The destruction of these morainic forests by stream erosion is well shown near the shore north of Evanston, and also along Thorn creek. *Fig. 18* shows a morainic island in a flood plain, the sole remnant of an extensive stretch of upland mesophytic forest. We must therefore regard upland forests as temporary also, though they endure for a much longer time than do the temporary mesophytic forests of the ravines.

c. *The sand hill.*—A third type of upland is found in the sand hills, but since most of these in our district are of dune origin, their treatment will be deferred until later.

B. THE COASTAL GROUP.

1. The Lake Bluff Series.

The plant societies that have been discussed hitherto may be found in many if not in most inland districts. The societies that follow, on the other hand, are best worked out only in connection with the coasts of oceans or great lakes. Theoretically a bluff may be composed of any kind of rock or soil, but those of our area are composed of morainic clays, and the life histories that follow will not hold good in other conditions. It may be noted here that there is a short stretch of rocky shore with lithophytic algae at Cheltenham, but there is nothing that in any way approaches a rock cliff.

Wherever a sea or lake erodes rather than deposits, there is commonly developed a sea cliff of greater or less dimensions. The material which is thus gathered may be deposited elsewhere in the form of beaches, and later the wind may take up the sands from the beach and form dunes. The Chicago area gives splendid examples of these two types of sea activity; to the north of the city is an eroding coast line with its bluffs, and to the south and southeast is a depositing coast with extensive areas of beach and dune.

The lake bluffs at Glencoe give an excellent opportunity for the study of the life history of a sea-cliff vegetation. There can be almost no other habitat in our climate which imposes such severe conditions upon vegetation as an eroding clay bluff. The only possible rival in this regard is a shifting dune, and even here the dune possesses some points of advantage so far as the establishment of vegetation is concerned. In the first place, the conditions as to exposure are almost identical with those of a dune; the heat of midday and of summer and the cold of night and winter are extremely pronounced; the intensity of the light and the exposure to wind make the conditions still more severe. In other words, the only plants that can grow on these lake bluffs, at least in the earlier stages, are pronounced xerophytes. Again, the character of the soil is unfavorable, for while the clay is wet in the autumn, winter, and spring, it dries out in the summer and becomes almost as hard as rock. In the heat of summer the conditions for vegetation are no better on the hard, dry slopes of a clay bluff than on the hot, dry sands of a dune. Finally, as to instability: it is doubtless the constant shifting of the sand which in the last analysis accounts for most of the poverty of the dune vegetation. It is similar on clay bluffs, for when the waves undermine the cliff at its base, the action of gravity causes great masses of material to fall down from the entire cliff face. Furthermore, when the clay is saturated with water, great portions of the cliff face slide down, entirely apart from the action of the sea or lake. At no time, then, is an eroding bluff any more stable than a naked dune.

It becomes evident from a survey of the bluff conditions that all vegetation is impossible so long as active erosion by the lake continues. Not only this, but vegetation at the top of the bluff is soon destroyed. *Fig. 30* shows a naked cliff of this character; at the top there can be seen overhanging turf, giving evidence both of the destructive action of the lake and also of the tenacity with which a grass mat holds its place in the presence of adverse conditions. Near the center of *fig. 31* may be seen a white oak which was almost overthrown by the erosive activities, but which has been preserved through the cessation of erosion at this point. The gully shown near the center of *fig. 30* is seen in closer view in *fig. 1;* the absence of vegetation, save that which has slid down from above, is very striking.

If for any reason the lake activities at the base of the cliff are stopped, an opportunity is offered for the development of vegetation. At Glencoe the cliff erosion has been checked to some extent by artificial means, and one can see various phases of cliff life within a small area. When the erosion at the base of the bluff ceases, conditions become much more stable, though landslide action may still occur. In time the slope gradient becomes so low that the cliff soil is essentially stable; when this time arises vegetation develops with great rapidity in spite of the xerophytic conditions, which are still as pronounced as before. It is very obvious, therefore, that it is the instability of the eroding cliff and not its xerophytic character which accounts for the absence of plant life.

The first vegetation is commonly made up of xerophytic herbs, both annual and perennial. Among these are the sweet clover (*Melilotus alba*), various annual weeds, various species of Aster, especially *A. laevis* [Smooth Aster], *Equisetum hyemale* (Scouring Rush), various grasses, etc. Soon there develops a xerophytic thicket vegetation, such as is shown in *fig. 31*. This may be called the shrub stage of the captured cliff, and among the dominant species are the [common] juniper and [red] cedar (*Juniperus communis* and *J. virginiana*), *Salix glaucophylloides* [Blue-Leafed Willow], the osier dogwood (*Cornus stolonifera*), *Shepherdia canadensis,* [and] various sumacs (*Rhus typhina* and *R. glabra*). The following tree stage is dominated by various poplars (*Populus tremuloides,*

P. grandidentata [Large-Toothed Aspen], *P. deltoides monilifera)*, the hop hornbeam (*Ostrya virginica*), the white pine (*Pinus strobus*), the red cedar (*Juniperus virginiana*), and some of the oaks (probably *Quercus rubra* and *Q. coccinea*). *Fig. 32* shows a tree-clad cliff in which most of the above trees are to be found.

Whether a mesophytic forest would develop on a lake bluff is something of a question. It seems likely that semi-xerophytic trees will dominate there for a long time to come on account of the xerophytic atmospheric conditions. Particularly at the top of the bluff do the conditions remain severe, by reason of the great exposure, and also the dryness of the soil. If the lake should recede for some distance, a mesophytic forest could certainly develop on the bluff before it is reduced to anything like the common level. This is shown on the ancient lake bluff at Beverly Hills. Here there is an old cliff about forty feet above the country level, representing a lake bluff of the Glenwood stage of Lake Chicago. This bluff has long had a mesophytic forest on its slopes, and yet it will be many centuries before the erosive forces remove all traces of this ancient sea cliff. A still more striking case is to be seen north of Waukegan, where an ancient lake bluff, higher than that at Beverly Hills and only a mile back of the present lake shore, is tenanted by a high grade type of mesophytic forest.

It will be instructive to make a few comparisons between lake bluffs and other plant societies. Closest to the lake bluff in a physiographic sense is the river bluff. When a stream has banks of clay, the conditions seem decidedly similar, and yet the flora is not the same. A comparison of the lake bluffs at Glencoe with the bluffs along Thorn creek shows that some species are common, notoriously Ostrya, Rhus, Quercus, [and] Populus. Yet the differences are still more striking, for the bluffs along Thorn creek do not show *Salix glaucophylloides* nor Shepherdia; most striking of all, however, is the entire absence of conifers. When we compare the lake bluffs with the rock bluffs of the Illinois river, we find that the resemblances are greater than the differences, since the river bluffs have conifers, though even here some of the lake bluff forms are absent. When, however, we compare the Glencoe bluffs with the dunes, we find that all of the dominant shrubs and trees of the bluff are found also on the dunes; not only this—the dominant bluff forms are dominant on the dunes also.

The facts of the preceding paragraph are pregnant with significance. One obvious corollary is that, given similar soils but dissimilar conditions of atmospheric exposure, as at Glencoe and Thorn creek, the vegetation is unlike. Another and more striking corollary is that, given the most dissimilar soils possible, viz., the Glencoe clay and the dune sand, we still have similar vegetation, because the atmospheric conditions are the same in the two cases. The evidence of the Illinois river bluffs is less clear; they are more xerophytic than the bluffs along Thorn creek; but whether this is chiefly due to rock as against clay, or to greater exposure, is not certain. At all events, these facts show that it is not enough to know about chemical or physical conditions in the soil. We cannot divide plants into those of clay, rock, and sand, but must take into account that most plants have a wide range of life, so far as soil is concerned, provided the atmospheric conditions are congenial. The chief exception to this statement seems to be found, not in the original soils, but in the superimposed humus. There are many plants that require humus for their occurrence in nature, but it makes no difference whether the subsoil is rock, sand or clay, provided alone that the humus is present in sufficient quantity. It is by reason of this last fact that the mesophytic forest can appear in all conditions in this climate, since the mesophytic forest is associated to a high degree with humus.

2. The Beach-Dune-Sandhill Series.

a. The beach.—The author has previously discussed in considerable detail the dynamics of the dune societies,[4] and it will not be necessary to do more here than to summarize the chief conclusions, and add a few new data. Before long it is expected that a paper will appear giving the changes that have taken place since the first observations were made in 1896.

The beach in the Chicago area is xerophytic throughout. There is nothing analogous to the salt marshes of the Atlantic coast, nor to the hydrophytic shores farther north along Lake Michigan. The lower portion of the beach is exposed to alternate washing by the waves and desiccation in the sun, and is devoid of life. The middle beach, which is washed by winter waves, though not by those of summer, has in consequence a vegetation of xerophytic annuals, the most prominent of which is *Cakile americana* (sea rocket). The upper beach is beyond present wave action, and is tenanted by biennials and perennials in addition to the annuals. *Fig. 33* shows a beach of this type, the lower beach being smooth and even, the middle beach covered with débris, while the upper beach has a scattered perennial vegetation.

---

[4] Cowles, H.C.: The ecological relations of the vegetation on the sand dunes of Lake Michigan. BOT. GAZ. 27: 95–117; 167–202; 281–308; 361–391. 1899. Also reprinted separately.

The beach at the base of cliffs shows similar subdivision, though the zones are much narrower as a rule. The vegetation, too, is much the same, though some forms, as Strophostyles [wild beans], have not been seen as yet on the beaches of the dune district. At the foot of cliffs there often occur alluvial fans of sand, which have been deposited by the torrents during and following rain storms. These fans have a comparatively rich vegetation, and species sometimes occur here that are not found elsewhere on the beach.

b. The embryonic or stationary beach dunes.—Wherever plants occur on a beach that is swept by sand-laden winds, deposition of sand must take place, since the plants offer obstacles to the progress of the wind. If these plants are extreme xerophytes and are able to endure covering or uncovering without injury, they may cause the formation of beach dunes. Among the dune-forming plants of this type are *Ammophila brevigulata* (Sand reed; [Common Marram Grass]), *Salix glaucophylloides* and *S. adenophylla* (glaucous [Blue-leafed] and glandular [Dune] willows), *Prunus pumila* (Sand Cherry), and *Populus deltoides monilifera* (Cottonwood). The shapes of these beach dunes vary with the characteristics of these dune-forming plants. Ammophila dunes are extensive but low, because of strong horizontal rhizome propagation. Prunus and Populus dunes are smaller but higher, because of the relative lack of horizontal propagation and the presence of great vertical growth capacity. Dunes are formed more slowly in protected places, and here the dune-forming species may be plants that are ill adapted to the severest beach conditions, such as the creeping juniper. A beach dune of the type just described is shown in *fig. 34.*

c. The active or wandering dunes. The dune complex.—The stationary embryonic dunes on the beach begin to wander as soon as the conditions become too severe for the dune-forming plants. The first result of this change is seen in the reshaping of the dune to correspond with the contour of a purely wind-made form. The rapidity of this process is largely determined by the success or failure of the dune-formers as dune-holders. The best dune-holders are Calamovilfa [Prairie Sand Reed], Ammophila, and Prunus.

There are all gradations between a simple moving dune and a moving landscape; the latter may be called a dune-complex. The complex is a restless maze, advancing as a whole in one direction, but with individual portions advancing in all directions. It shows all stages of dune development and is forever changing. The windward slopes are gentle and are furrowed by the wind, as it sweeps along; the lee slopes are much steeper. The only plant that flourishes everywhere on the complex is the succulent annual, *Corispermum hyssopifolium* (Bugseed), although *Populus deltoides monilifera* (Cottonwood) is frequent. The scanty flora is not due to the lack of water in the soil, but to the instability of the soil and to the xerophytic air.

The influence of an encroaching dune upon a pre-existing flora varies with the rate of advance, the height of the dune above the country on which it encroaches, and the nature of the vegetation. The burial of forests is a common phenomenon. The dominant forest trees in the path of advancing dunes are *Pinus banksiana* (Scrub Pine) and *Quercus velutina* (Black Oak). These trees are destroyed long before they are completely buried. The dead trees may be uncovered later, as the dune passes on beyond. A pine forest upon which a dune is encroaching is shown in *fig. 35*, while such a forest after the dune has passed is shown in *fig. 36*.

In the Dune Park region there are a number of swamps upon which dunes are advancing. While most of the vegetation is destroyed at once, *Salix glaucophylloides*, *S. syrticola*, and *Cornus stolonifera* (Osier Dogwood) are able to adapt themselves to the new conditions, by elongating their stems and sending out roots from the buried portions. Thus hydrophytic shrubs are better able to meet the dune's advance successfully than any other plants. The water relations of these plants, however, are not rapidly altered in the new conditions. It may be, too, that these shrubs have adapted themselves to an essentially xerophytic life through living in undrained swamps. Again, it may be true that inhabitants of undrained swamps are better able to withstand a partial burial than are other plants. A swamp upon which a dune encroaches is shown in *fig. 35*.

Vegetation appears to be unable to capture a rapidly moving dune. While many plants can grow even on rapidly advancing slopes, they do not succeed in stopping the dune. The movement of a dune is checked chiefly by a decrease in the available wind energy, due to increasing distance from the lake or to barriers. A slowly advancing slope is soon captured by plants, because they have a power of vertical growth greater than the vertical component of advance. Vegetation commonly gets its first foothold at the base of lee slopes about the outer margin of the complex, because of soil moisture and protection from the wind. The plants tend to creep up the slopes by vegetative propagation. Antecedent and subsequent vegetation work together toward the common end. Where there is no antecedent vegetation, Ammophila and other herbs first appear, and then a dense shrub growth of Cornus, Salix, *Vitis vulpina* (Frost Grape), and *Prunus virginiana* (Chokecherry).

Capture may also begin within the complex, especially in protected depressions, where *Salix interior* is often abundant.

d. The established dunes.—No order of succession in this entire region is so hard to decipher as that of the established dunes. There are at least three types of these dunes so far as vegetation is concerned, and it is not yet possible to figure out their relationships. The continuation of the conditions as outlined in the preceding paragraph results in a forest society on the lee slope, in which is found the basswood, together with a most remarkable collection of mesophytic trees, shrubs, and climbers, which have developed xerophytic structures. These dunes are evidently but recently established, as is shown by the absence of a vegetation carpet; furthermore, the slopes are almost always steep.

Again, there are forest societies in which the pines dominate, either *Pinus banksiana* or *P. strobus* (White Pine). These arise from a heath, composed in the main of Arctostaphylos (Bearberry) and Juniperus. The heath appears to originate on fossil beaches or on secondary embryonic dunes or other places where the danger of burial is not great. It will be noted that both the heath and the pine forest are dominated by evergreens. These societies commonly occur near the lake or on lakeward slopes, which are northern slopes as well. On these coniferous dune slopes there is to be found another notable collection of northern plants, resembling ecologically the peat bog plants already mentioned. Heaths and coniferous forests also occur on sterile barren sand and in depressions where the conditions are unfavorable for deciduous forests. A slight change in the physical conditions may bring about the rejuvenation of the coniferous dunes, because of their exposed situation. This rejuvenation commonly begins by the formation of a wind sweep, and the vegetation on either hand is forced to succumb to sandblast action and gravity.

A third type of established dune is that in which the oaks predominate, and especially *Quercus velutina*. The oak dunes are more common inland and on southern slopes. Probably the oaks follow the pines, but the evidence on which this is based is not voluminous. The pines certainly have a wider range of habitat than the oaks, occurring in wetter and in drier soil, and also in more exposed situations. The mutual relations of the pines and oaks are certainly interesting and deserve some very careful study. Pine forests prevail on the north or lakeward slopes, and oak forests on the south or inland slopes. With the pines are other northern evergreen forms, such as Arctostaphylos, while with the oaks are Opuntia, Euphorbia [Spurge], and other more southern types. The density of the vegetation on the north side is also in contrast with the sparser and more open vegetation of the south side. The cause for this radical difference on the two slopes is doubtless complex, but it is obvious that the north slope has greater moisture, shade, and cold, and probably more wind. Which of these is the more important is not certain, but the presence of the northern species seems in favor of cold or wind as the chief factor.

There are a number of interesting sand hills and ridges at some distance from the lake. Some of these are fifteen miles from the present lake shore, while others are found at various intervals nearer and nearer the lake. It has been found that these can be grouped for the most part into three series, representing three beach lines of Lake Chicago, as the glacial extension of Lake Michigan has been called. The upper and oldest of these ridges has been termed the Glenwood beach, the intermediate ridge the Calumet beach, and the lower and younger ridge the Tolleston beach. The geographical relations of these beaches [are] well discussed by Leverett, and also by Salisbury and Alden, and nothing need be said here except as to the vegetation. In general these ridges and hills have a xerophytic forest flora, dominated by the bur, black, and white oaks (*Quercus macrocarpa*, *Q. velutina*, [and] *Q. alba)*. The proportions between these trees [vary] strikingly, though the bur or black oak is usually the chief character tree. No satisfactory reason can yet be given for these variations, though the bur oak appears to be more abundant on the lower and less drained ridges, while the black oak is more abundant on the higher ridges. The shrub undergrowth is commonly sparse, and the most frequent members of this stratum are the hazel (*Corylus americana)*, Rosa, the New Jersey tea (*Ceanothus americanus)*, *Salix humilis* [Prairie Willow], the low blueberry *(Vaccinium angustifolium)*, and the huckleberry (*Gaylussacia resinosa)*. Among the commoner herbs are *Silene stellata* [Starry Campion], *Antennaria plantaginifolia* [Plantain-leafed Pussy Toes], *Heuchera richardsonii*, *Rumex acetosella* (Field Sorrel), *Carex pennsylvanica* [Common Oak Sedge], *Potentilla argentea* (Silvery Cinquefoil), *Poa compressa*, *Pteris aquilina* (Brake), [and] *Ceratodon purpureus* [Fire Moss]. In open places there are often almost pure growths of Poa or Potentilla. *Figs. 34* and 35 show portions of these ancient beaches in which the oaks dominate; *fig. 34* shows, perhaps, the more common condition, *i.e.*, a rather low beach with sparse tree growth.

The future of the vegetation on the established dunes and beaches is somewhat problematical. From analogy with other plant societies in this region, and from established dunes in Michigan, we should expect a mesophytic forest, probably of the white oak-red oak-hickory type at first, and then followed by a beech-maple forest. There are evidences that some such changes are now taking place. On many of the oak dunes, especially where protected from exposure, there is already a considerable accumulation of humus. Herbaceous ravine mesophytes, like Hepatica, Arisaema, and Trillium, are already present, and with them mesophytic shrubs and trees, including the sugar maple itself, though the beech has not been found on the dunes of our area, as it has in Michigan. One might expect that the flora of the older Glenwood beach would have advanced more toward the mesophytic stage than has the flora of the younger Tolleston beach. Such, indeed, seems to be the case, especially at Glenwood, where the white oaks are more numerous, and the black oaks much larger and more luxuriant. The humus is richer, and most things look as if the age of this beach were notably greater than that of the Calumet or Tolleston beaches. This subject, however, needs much further investigation. In any event, one character of the sand hill stands out in bold relief, viz., its great resistance to physiographic change. Not only is its erosion slower than that of the clay hill, but the advance of its vegetation is vastly slower at all points along the line. The slowness of humus accumulation accounts for this, perhaps, more than all else.

THE INFLUENCE OF UNDERLYING ROCKS ON THE CHARACTER OF THE VEGETATION

Contributions from the Hull Botanical Laboratory, the University of Chicago XXXIV (1901)

Introduction: The Chemistry and Physics of Soils

It is a matter of common observation that different soils have different plants. Everyone expects to see a change in the natural forest covering, as he passes from one soil to another. For example in many parts of the United States pines and oaks are found in sandy soil, while maples and beeches are found on the clay. So true is this that in many places a bird's-eye view of the forest is sufficient to indicate the nature of the soil. One may go even farther; in many places it is possible to tell the nature of the rock by means of the trees that grow above it. This implies, of course, that the residual soil which arises through rock decay varies with the character of the rock from which it comes.

So interesting is the subject just mentioned that it is well to cite examples. East of Port Jervis, NY, the Erie railway crosses Kittatinny or Shawangunk mountain. A fault line causes the Hudson river slates (Ordovician) of the east side to abut upon the Oneida conglomerates and red Medina sandstones (Silurian) of the west side. A traveler passes suddenly from the rich farmlands overlying the Hudson river slates to the barren and rocky slopes of the red sandstones. The slates erode readily, giving a rich soil, while the reverse is true of the sandstone. Along the Louisville and Nashville railway near Lebanon, Ky., there is a striking difference shown between the fertile lands of the blue grass region toward the northeast and the hilly and rocky districts toward the southwest along Muldraugh's hill. The railway runs for miles at the base of this hill, and one can scarcely imagine a greater difference than that which is presented from the car windows on the two sides of the train. These vegetation differences are associated with rock differences analogous to those noted in connection with Kittatinny mountain. Many similar instances in Europe have long been famous; for example in the Kyffhäuser mountains the Rothliegende (Lower Permian) strata are overlain by sparse heath floras while the Zechstein (Upper Permian) is overlain by beech forests. Of course differences of this character to be significant must be in regions where the soil is derived from the underlying rocks. In the glaciated districts of the northern states the soil has commonly been deposited through the action of ice or water, and it is only where there are rock outcrops that the influence of the rock on plant life can be studied. In the southern Alleghenies, however, and in most unglaciated upland the rock is directly responsible for the overlying soil and hence for its vegetation.

Many years ago Sadebeck performed an interesting series of experiments upon some plants whose natural habitats are very limited. The European [ferns] *Asplenium serpentini* and *A. adulterinum*, grow normally on serpentine rocks. When grown for six generations in soil devoid of serpentine elements, especially magnesian silicates, these "species" changed respectively into *Asplenium adiantum nigrum* and *A. viride*, common ferns of wider life range. Hence it is likely that the species first mentioned were derived from those last named and acquired their so-called specific characters from growing on serpentine rocks. In a similar it is likely that the European zinc violet, *Viola calaminaria*, is but a special form of the common *Viola lutea* [Mountain Pansy]. Kerner has listed a large number of closely related parallel species, one growing on the calcareous Alps, the other of the pair growing on the siliceous Alps. He found that the forms of calcareous rocks differed from those of the siliceous rocks somewhat uniformly, having a greater development of hairs or glaucous coats, more divided leaves and larger corollas. Thus it may be concluded that rocks not only differ as to the character of their vegetation, but that new "species" are developed in various rock habitats.

For more than half a century plant geographers have debated as to the cause of the phenomena noted in the preceding paragraphs. Some have maintained that the facts are to be explained by the chemical nature of the soil. Others have argued for a physical explanation. It may be well to outline in brief something as to the history of this prolonged discussion. More detailed treatments of this subject may be found in the plant geographies of Warming or Schimper. One of the first sponsors for the chemical theory was the famous German botanist, Unger, who published as long ago as 1836 a paper on soil influences which must forever remain as a classic. Indeed this paper may be regarded as one of the first outlooks into the field which is now known as plant ecology, that phase of botany which deals with plants in relation to their surrounding. Unger called attention to the differences between the plants of siliceous and calcareous soils. He explained this phenomenon by supposing that plants had different chemical relations with soil elements; what is a foodstuff for one plant is a poison for another. Hence the absence of certain species from certain soils is to be explained by the absence of necessary food materials in that soil or else by the presence of deleterious substances. Of course a large number of species were found to be indifferent.

In contrast to the above theory, which has had a wide acceptance especially among the French botanists, there is the physical theory for which Thurmann contended as long ago as 1849. Thurmann and others who have espoused his views have regarded soil structure as more important than soil chemistry, and especially since it is the physical structure of the soil which in large measure determines the water and heat relations. Thurman divided rocks into eugeogenous, which weather easily, and dysgeogenous, which weather with difficulty. The first gives rise to a fine or pelogenous soil, the second class to a coarse or psammogenous soil. The fine soils hold water well and support a luxuriant vegetation, whereas coarse soils are dry and the vegetation is desert-like.

Ever since the days of Unger and Thurmann the conflict between the chemical and physical schools has waxed severe, though in recent years the subject has been debated with less ardor than of old. The chemical theory seems to be favored by the phenomena exhibited by the salt plants or halophytes, since regardless of other conditions it is found that but few species can grow in salty soils, and it is noticed that these few species resemble desert plants in structure, whether water is abundant or not. The influence of calcareous soils is less marked, and yet the European botanists have listed a number of species that are said to avoid such soils, e.g. lichens, heather, chestnuts, etc. Fertilizers have marked effects, as is well known, nitrates favoring some plants, potassium salts others, [and] phosphates still others. One of the most marked instances of the chemical effects of soils is seen in humus plants; nearly all common plants grow much better in a rich humus soil than in other conditions, because of the plentiful supply of foodstuffs. The physical theory is favored, as Warming has so ably shown, by the influence of soil water. Most of the fine gradations between plant societies, he thinks are due to fine gradations in the supply of moisture. In the successive zones about a pond, each zone has a change in the plant species following a change in the water content of the soil. The transformations that come when a dry area is irrigated are well known and this phenomenon furnishes a striking argument in favor of the physical theory. For example a dry, sandy area properly irrigated can be made to support the same plants as a clay area without much irrigation. Warming in summing up the results of the conflict in 1895 concluded that there was truth in both theories, but that the physical theory was quantitatively more important, and especially because of its influence on the water relation of the soil. As a consequence Warming has given out an essentially physical classification of plant societies, dividing them into three main groups: hydrophytes or water plants, xerophytes or plants of dry soil, and mesophytes or plants of intermediate water relations. In a fourth class, halophytes or salt plants, he recognizes the dominance of chemical influences.

In the later years, as noted above, the discussion of physical and chemical theories has become less and less acrimonious. This is doubtless due, among other things, to a growing appreciation of the fact that the line between chemical and physical influences cannot be sharply drawn. Nearly all of the study on soil influences has assumed either a physical or chemical influence where it has not been experimentally proven. The halophytes form an excellent case in point; although salt plants have been all but universally instanced as illustrations of the influence of chemical factors, it may yet be proven that it is a physical rather than a chemical property of the salts which is detrimental to the activity of so many plants. Indeed it is suggested by recent studies that the osmotic properties of the soil solutions may be found to be the chief cause of halophytic structures. This subject has been but slightly investigated, and all that can be said at present is that the halophytes as a chemical class must be distinctly challenged. Vallot and Schimper show that chemical and physical properties are mutually related to one another, and that a change in the one is accompanied by a change in the other, and that one cannot say offhand which factor dominates.

Another reason for less acrimonious debate now than formerly is the growing recognition of the fact that the contrasts between the floras of different soils have been largely overdrawn. In other words the problem is not so much to explain contrasts between calcareous and siliceous or between pelogenous and psammogenous soils as to explain resemblances. The very groundwork of the debate, then, has been or is being removed. Some lines of thought that were neglected by the earlier workers will now be recounted.

Blytt, DeCandolle and other students long ago called attention to the fact that close observation for many years in a region rich in various rock types would result in eliminating most of the so-called siliceous and calcareous plants, and that most plants would be found on most soils. Even in the few exceptions to this rule a study conducted over the entire area occupied by a species would show that it grows naturally in most soils. As an instance of this there may be cited the European beech, which is reported to be a siliceous plant in southern Europe and a calcareous plant in Denmark. Indeed, Blytt observes that a number of siliceous plants have their northernmost limit in Norway on calcareous soils.

A second neglected factor was mentioned by Nägeli in 1872, viz., the struggle for existence. It was his belief that the severe competition for place was the chief cause of the so-called preference or a particular plant for any special soil. If a pine grows naturally in the sand and a beech in the clay it is not to be inferred without experiment that either tree could not grow successfully in the other soil. As practical gardeners well know, there are plants that grow well in some soils and grow poorly in others; yet the fact that plants from all soils and many climates grow and thrive side by side in identical soil in botanical gardens shows that there are more plants indifferent as to soil than there are plants that require any particular soil. In nature these plants do not grow side by side because in the natural struggle for existence some survive while others perish. It is even true that many plants grow best in soils in which they are rarely found in nature—this is notoriously true of many of the weeds growing in the hard soil of roadsides. The common doorweed [Common Knotweed] (*Polygonum aviculare*) grows everywhere in hard soil, yet it grows much better in rich garden soil; it is all but confined to roadsides and dooryards, because the better conditions elsewhere are pre-empted by other plants. We may say that while most plants appear to be obligate, they are in reality facultative, so far as soil is concerned.

A third factor which has often been neglected is the relation between the rock and the soil which comes from it. It is often assumed that a calcareous rock gives rise to a calcareous soil, just as a siliceous rock gives rise to a siliceous soil. As a matter of fact, practically all rocks give rise to siliceous soils. This would be expected of granites, sandstones or shales, but it is equally true of limestone or dolomite. Indeed the percent of silica is sometimes greater in a soil derived from limestone or dolomite than in a soil derived from a siliceous rock. One may generalize as follows: mechanical erosion results in a soil resembling the original rock, while chemical erosion, which involves the solution and removal of the soluble ingredients, gives rise to a soil differing radically from the parent rock. These facts are well brought in a table of soil analyses, published by the State Agricultural Experiment Station at Knoxville, Tenn.

Silica %	Alumina %	Iron %	Lime %	Magnesia %
Sandstone 88.7	4.1	1.5	0.06	0.18
Shale 82.9	6.0	2.7	0.16	0.44
Dolomite 87.8	4.6	1.7	0.055	0.175
Limestone 82.3	5.7	2.5	0.27	0.31

In this table the approximate equality of the silica in widely divergent rocks is very noteworthy. The small amount of lime in the limestone soil and of lime and magnesia in the dolomite (magnesian limestone) soil is almost startling. In this connection it is important to use extreme caution in the interpretation of phenomena in glaciated regions, since much of the soil overlying rocks is likely to be drift rather than residual soil.

A fourth neglected factor, which seems to the author of greater importance than all the others combined, is the physiographic or historical factor. Whatever the kind of rock, as will be shown later, the initial plants and plant conditions will be much the same and the ultimate plants and conditions exactly the same. In other words exposed rocks of all kinds have much the same floras; so too when centuries have passed and the rocks are buried underneath a rich humus soil, the conditions will be the same everywhere and the plants, under similar climatic conditions, will be the same. If a sand hill or a clay hill, a granite hill or a limestone hill, have different floras, it is not because of differences in the rock nor of the inorganic soil which comes from it, but it is because one is farther along in its life history than is the other. The vegetation that a clay hill has today will be seen on a sand hill in the future centuries. One may sum up these facts as follows: the vegetation of all hills in a given region, of whatever chemical or physical nature, is tending toward an ultimate common destiny, which in most parts of the United States is the mesophytic forest. The succession of plant societies is sometimes slow and sometimes fast, and hence we have at any given period before the ultimate stage is reached a difference in the vegetation on different rocks and soils. Were the stages equally rapid in all cases, there would be no such differences and we should have been spared the acrimonious debates of the past half century.

The materials for this paper have been gathered by the author during the past four years in various parts of the eastern United States. The principal localities studied were (1) the Lake Superior region about Marquette [Michigan] with its magnificent outcrops of granites, schists, serpentines, diorites, quartzites, sandstones, and iron rocks; (2) the Alleghenies of eastern Tennessee with splendid outcrops of sandstones, shales, limestones, dolomites, and coal rocks; (3) northern Illinois and eastern Iowa with their sandstones, limestones, and dolomites; [and] (4) Connecticut with its granites, gneisses, basalts, and sandstones. Less satisfactory studies have been made of the limestones, shales and sandstones of northern Ohio, the limestones and sandstones of Pennsylvania, Virginia, and West Virginia, and the limestones of northeastern Wisconsin. Much of this work has been done in connection with various students to whom the author wishes to make grateful acknowledgment. The photographs with which the paper is illustrated were taken by Mr. W.B. McCallum, except in a few instances where proper credit is given in the legend.

THE ROCKS AND THEIR VEGETATION

a. Granitic rocks.
The flora of granitic rocks has been studied in the Lake Superior region and in Connecticut, and the stages in the life history of the rock vegetation have been made out with considerable ease in spite of the fact that both regions studied were glaciated. There are several good reasons for starting the discussion with granites; perhaps the best of these reasons is that all the typical stages are well developed on these rocks. On many rocks some of these stages are eliminated.

The nature and duration of the granite plant societies are due chiefly to two features connected with the erosion of granite rocks, first that it is slow, [and] second that it is differential. The resistance of granite to processes of weathering is well known, and the idea which many have of "everlasting hills" is often derived from granite. Quartz, which makes up a large part of most granites, is singularly resistant to the chemical forces of erosion. The other elements, especially the feldspars, are more easily attacked, and as a result the rock surface becomes etched; the depressions represent the position of the feldspars or other more soluble constituents, while the elevations represent the quartz or other less soluble constituents.

The first plants to get a foothold on granitic rocks are commonly lichens. These interesting plants vary exceedingly in general form; those who adhere so closely to the surface on which they grow as to appear embedded in it are called crustaceous lichens, those which are leaf-like and attached by evident root-like rhizoids are called foliaceous lichens, while those that are erect and branched are called fruticose lichens. The crustaceous lichens are the first to appear on bare rock surfaces; and hence they may be regarded as the pioneers of vegetation, although foliaceous lichens are rarely absent even in the earlier stages. Lichens are wonderfully adapted to rock life, since they can attach themselves readily to bare rock surfaces—here comes in the significance of differential erosion, for the reproductive organs find lodgment in the depressions thus created. The growing plant sends out its organs of attachment and doubtless aids chemically in rock erosion by the substances which it exudes. Again lichens require practically no soil, but are able to get all of their food from the air or from the rock itself. Finally lichens are the most pronounced of xerophytes and are able to endure long periods of drought without injury. Among the more prominent of the foliaceous lichens at Marquette are *Parmelia*, which is so common everywhere on fences and trees, and the rock tripe, *Umbilicaria. Figs. 1 and 2* show granite surfaces partially covered by crustaceous and foliaceous lichens.

The granite conditions may be summed up thus in a sentence: the lichens come early because the erosion is differential, they stay late because the erosion is slow. Therefore exposed granitic rocks are usually well covered with lichens, perhaps more than in most rock types, because of the long time which they can enjoy for their development.

The continuation of differential erosion more and more accentuates the differences between the elevations and depressions. Dust and sand collect in the hollows; and lichens, by their decay, contribute to the formation of a soil. An opportunity is now given for a higher type of life than the crustaceous or foliaceous lichens, viz., a type whose members are rooted in the soil. Most commonly surface rocks are fissured and jointed so that crevice plants can make their appearance contemporaneously with the lichens above mentioned. However the crevice stage may be regarded as the second phase in the development of rock vegetation. Among the pioneer crevice plants are such mosses as *Ceratodon, Polytrichum*, and *Funaria* and fruticose lichens, especially the reindeer lichen, *Cladonia rangiferina* (see *fig. 4*). With or soon after these forms are some plants higher in the scale, such as the harebell (*Campanula rotundifolia*), the mouse-ear everlasting [Pussy Toes] *(Antennaria plantaginifolia)*, one of the cinquefoils [Three-toothed Cinquefoil] (*Potentilla tridentata*), and xerophytic ferns (*Woodsia, Ilvensis, Polypodium vulgare,* [and] *Selaginella rupestris)*. This list was made out at Marquette, and yet nearly all the plants mentioned except the cinquefoil would be found in rock crevices over most of the eastern United States. In comparing this second stage with the first rock stage the most striking difference is found in the addition of a soil to furnish food materials to the vegetation. Again the opportunities for the development of holdfast organs are much better in crevices than on bare rock. The xerophytic character of the habitat, however, is scarcely less striking than on the bare rock itself. *Fig. 1* shows crevice plants, especially mosses; the lines of moss plants are quite in contrast to the irregular patches of lichens.

The first and second stages show an interesting variation when the rocks are near the water level. For example, in *Fig. 1*, the stages are as noted above on the parts of the island above the reach of the waves. Within the reach of the waves, however, there are to be found zones, reminding of the zones on a beach. Just above the water line where waves wash frequently there are no plants, the habitat being too often exposed to allow water plants, and too often washed by waves to allow land plants. This first zone is the exact equivalent of the plantless lower beach. Then comes a zone in which mosses grow in the crevices; and finally there is a third zone in which the normal conditions are found, viz., lichens on the bare rock, mosses and other plants in the crevices. It is thus seen that within the reach of waves, mosses are the pioneers rather than lichens—mosses may be almost as xerophytic as lichens, but lichens are less hydrophytic than mosses.

The continuation of differential erosion and the increased development of crevice plants cause constant additions to the crevice soil. Opportunities are thus given to those plants that require more soil for food materials and more place for holdfast organs—among these plants, shrubs and small trees play the most important part. With the advent of shade-giving plants there enter essentially new conditions; moisture is conserved and humus is more rapidly accumulated. As a result not only in the crevices but also where the rock was bare a soil comes to be built up. This phenomenon is illustrated in the accompanying cuts. *Fig. 1* shows crevice shrubs; *Fig. 2* illustrates an older stage with crevice trees (Norway [Red] pines); while *Fig. 4* represents a stage in which bare rock can be no longer seen, and yet the reindeer lichen shows where the rock was bare while the trees locate the crevices. *Fig. 3* indicates another way in which these processes are hastened, showing a Norway pine growing in a crevice and causing its enlargement year by year. When one considers that the roots penetrate into every nook and cranny, it can be seen that the rock-splitting function of roots is no inconsequential matter. When the more favorable conditions appear as outlined above, a change takes place in the dominating tree species for two reasons. In the first place the shade may be too dense to permit the germination and development of the seedlings of the tree species present. For example, pines are often the first crevice trees, but pine seedlings cannot develop in the shade created by a dense growth of pines. Again, increasing shade and moisture make conditions that favor new tree species, such as maples. So for one reason or another there is a succession of tree stages on the rock hills, the first forms being xerophytic, while those which follow become more and more mesophytic as the centuries pass. There is a natural culmination of these processes, and perhaps the beech comes as near as any to the final species in many parts of the United States.

The development of successive forest stages on granite hills is finely shown near Marquette, both on Sugar Loaf peak and on various islands. Perhaps the dominant member of the xerophytic tree stage is the Norway pine, *Pinus resinosa*, shown in *Figs. 2 and 3*. Other trees of this stage are the scrub pine (*Pinus banksiana*), the arbor vitae (*Thuya occidentalis*), the [Quaking and Large-toothed] aspens (*Populus tremuloides* and *grandidentata*), the wild red cherry [Pin Cherry] (*Prunus pennsylvanica*), the paper birch (*Betula papyrifera*), and the service berry

(Amelanchier arborea). Characteristic shrubs are the dwarf blueberry *(Vaccinium angustifolium)*, the bearberry *(Arctostaphylos)*, *Diervilla* [Bush Honeysuckle], *Rosa acicularis* [Bristly Rose], *Cornus rugosa* [Round-leafed Dogwood], the juniper *(Juniperus communis)*, and nine-bark *(Physocarpus)*. On one of the islands there was found the beginning of a mesophytic forest. Some of the plants that indicated this were the sugar maple *(Acer saccharium)*, which is the surest sign of mesophytic conditions in the Marquette region; the flowering raspberry *(Rubus odoratus)*, and *Clintonia borealis* [Bluebead]. The soil here may have been morainic in part, but it nevertheless shows the possibilities on granitic rocks.

Very interesting successive stages were seen along the coast near Norwalk, Conn., where granitic islands rise out of salt marshes. On the younger islands the rock is bare and shrubs or trees are found only in the crevices—among these early forms are the red cedar *(Juniperus virginiana)*, and the bayberry [Wax Myrtle] *(Myrica cerifera)*. Other crevice plants are the silvery cinquefoil *(Potentilla argentea)*, the poison ivy *(Rhus radicans)*, and the Virginia creeper *(Parthenocnissus quinquefolia)*. Older islands showed a dominance of oaks and pines; the pitch pine *(Pinus rigida)*, [and] the white, post, and scarlet oaks *(Quercus alba, stellata,* and *tinctoria)*. Junipers and bayberries are still present, but the bearberry and huckleberry *(Gaylussacia resinosa)* are added. The oldest island seen showed a marked change in the flora; the pines were all but gone, the white oak was still present, but the hickory *(Carya)* equaled it in dominance. The chestnut *(Castanea)* was also present. This flora is less mesophytic than the maple forests of Marquette but it marks a great change from the original bare rock conditions. Here as at Marquette some of the soil may be glacial drift, yet the stages are the same as if the soil were residual.

From the instances cited, it may be seen that granite hills, slow as the progress may be, nevertheless furnish a favorable position for the development of all the stages in the life history of a mesophytic forest; given time enough, one may then confidently predict that where granite hills now are, there will sometime be a mesophytic forest, if the climate is such as to favor it.

b. Gneisses, syenites, schists, diorites, basalts, diabases, serpentines, etc.

With the granites there may be associated the other compound crystalline silicates. These various rock types differ more or less widely in the percentage composition of silica and also lime, soda, magnesia, iron, and other elements. Again there are differences in the physical makeup of these rocks, some being of coarse texture and others fine. It is probable, however, that the differences, whether physical or chemical, are insufficient to cause any marked variations in the vegetation. Dioritic rocks at Marquette, in texture like the granites, but with less quartz and more of various feldspar elements, have essentially the flora of the granite. The same lichens appear at the outset, the same crevice herbs and shrubs in later years, the same tree stages as the conditions become more mesophytic. Furthermore the duration of these stages approximates what has been described above for the granites, since the erosion of diorite is also very slow. At Marquette the plants of the early stages are even more similar on the above two rocks than are the trees that follow. Since rocks are more unlike than the soils that come from them, and since soils become more and more alike until they ultimately become similar, it is obvious that the first stages, if any, would be the ones to show differences. Since, however, these stages are the same, it may be concluded that the life history of granites and diorites is the same from start to finish.

What is true of diorite is in general true of the remaining compound silicates. The basaltic hills of Connecticut have essentially the flora of the neighboring granite hills, although basalt differs from granite physically as well as chemically. The percentage of silica is still less than in diorite, while various basic minerals, rich in iron, magnesia, etc., increase. The texture is much finer grained than in granite or diorite. Some floral differences have been noticed; for example the lichen stages seem to be more fully represented on the granite than on the basalt. This may be due to the more rapid and more uniform erosion of the basalt; the lichens thus get a foothold with some difficulty but do not retain their place so long as on the granite. Basaltic rocks break up with ease mechanically, showing a conchoidal fracture. In Connecticut, talus slopes are thus developed at the base of the basalt ridges. The flora of these talus slopes is of great interest in a study of this kind, since the development is extremely rapid. Though the rock character is, of course, precisely that of the ridges, the flora soon becomes mesophytic, since humus accumulates readily and since moisture is conserved. As a consequence one may commonly see a xerophytic basalt ridge with mesophytic talus slopes. At times the ridge possesses conifers, while deciduous trees occur on the talus; in this event the difference is very sharp indeed.

Gneisses and schists differ from granites, diorites, etc., chiefly in their physical properties. Schistose rocks erode more readily than do granitic rocks, and hence furnish a less secure footing for lichens. The crevice herbs and shrubs and finally the trees appear in relatively rapid succession. Serpentines are decomposition products from other rocks and are rather resistant to the processes of erosion. Serpentines derived from basalt were studied in Marquette and showed some floral differences from the granites. Lichens were abundant, but the vegetation in general seemed sparse, though the tree stages resembled those of the granite. The occurrence of ferns peculiar to the serpentine rocks of Europe has already been noted. The fact that the cultivation of these ferns in other soils destroys their specific characters is a strong argument in favor of the idea that the physical or chemical character of serpentine influences plant development. The Marquette studies were too superficial to permit any observations of the kind just noted, but an interesting line for further study is here suggested.

c. Quartzites.

These rocks present vegetation conditions that are of much interest. Chemically, quartzites are very close to the sandstones and may be regarded as having arisen from them through metamorphic processes. In each case quartz is the chief constituent, but in quartzite the rock is homogeneous, compact and shows a lustrous surface on fracture, characters that are not true of sandstone. As a consequence of its chemical insolubility, and its physical homogeneity, quartzite erodes with the greatest of difficulty. Other things being equal, quartzites will be among the last rocks to show a lichen coating, and among the last to display mesophytic vegetation. Observations made at Marquette gave support to this idea, but the general drift covering greatly interfered with any satisfactory study. An exhaustive study should be made of quartzite outcrops in some driftless area. It seems almost certain, however, that the ultimate fate of the quartzite vegetation will be that which has already been recounted for granite, diorite, and basalt, but the passing of the stages will be vastly slower.

One of the remarkable results brought out by a study of rock vegetation in Montana during this past summer is that many species are identical with those of the east, when grown in similar conditions. For example, the harebell (*Campanula*), *Selaginella rupestris* [Sand Club Moss], the juniper (*Juniperus communis*), and the yarrow (*Achillea*), all of which have been found to be characteristic members of the early stages of eastern rocks, are also characteristic of the quartzites of the Rocky mountains, in the alpine regions as well as on the lowlands.

d. Sandstones.

These well-known rocks are composed chiefly of quartz grains, held together by ferruginous, calcareous, or siliceous cements. Chemically, then, sandstones are much alike so far as the dominating constituent is concerned; for that matter they also resemble quartzite, as has been previously indicated. Physically speaking, sandstones differ as the cements differ; where the cement is calcareous, decomposition is easy, where it is siliceous, decomposition is difficult. When alteration takes place so that the granular sandstone passes into the lustrous quartzite, decomposition becomes all but impossible.

A special comparative study of the vegetation of sandstone exposures was made in northern Michigan, northern Illinois, and eastern Tennessee, and some very instructive results were obtained. In Illinois the sandstone studied was of the St. Peters (Ordovician) formation. The rock in general decomposes very readily, giving rise to extensive sand deposits, through the loss of the cement; it is even possible to crumble exposed portions of the rock in the fingers, except where an iron oxide cement makes the rock much more resistant.

The Carboniferous sandstones of Tennessee are much more resistant because the cement is less soluble. The Lake Superior (Cambrian) sandstones of Michigan occupy an intermediate position between those of Illinois and Tennessee.

The primitive vegetation of the sandstone was found to vary in harmony with the variations in physical character of the rock. The resistant rocks of Tennessee showed well developed lichen stages, whereas the friable St. Peters sandstone of Illinois in many places was entirely without a lichen covering. Where the latter rock has resistant portions cemented by iron oxide, the lichens are abundant. On the other hand the crevice herbs and shrubs start readily in the more friable rock, but much less readily in the harder rock. As a result of these conditions it will be seen that the areas of St. Peters sandstone must soon be decomposed quite generally and carpeted with a more or less rich vegetation. The areas of more durable rock, such as those noted in Tennessee, must remain much longer in a xerophytic condition. A very casual observation shows that these conclusions are correct; the contrast is very sharp between the great sandstone hills of eastern Tennessee (See *Fig. 7*) and the sandstone areas of northern Illinois (See *Fig. 6*) which are flat and soil-covered, except where exposed to recent river action. These sharp topographic differences may be due in part, but only in part, to glacial influences; differential erosion is certainly a large element in the case. The sandstones of Marquette agree closely with those of Illinois and are largely clothed with forests even to the shore of Lake Superior (see *figs. 8 and 9*).

One of the remarkable results of the study in Tennessee was that the flora of the exposed sandstone crags bore a strikingly close floristic resemblance to the flora of the granite hills of northern Michigan, 700

216

miles further north. The lichen aspect is much the same, since forms of *Parmelia, Umbilicaria* and *Cladonia* (including the reindeer lichen) predominate. Among the xerophytic mosses, *Polytrichum* and *Leucobryum* are found. Other forms found also in the north are the lichens, *Usnea* and *Ramalina calicaris;* the red maple *(Acer rubrum),* the trailing arbutus *Epigaea repens,* the huckleberry *(Gaylussacia resinosa),* the sweet birch [Yellow Birch] *(Betula alleghaniensis),* and the ground pine *(Lycopodium obscurum).* Thus the first rock stages are very similar indeed in places which are separated by ten degrees of latitude; it must be borne in mind in this connection that the altitudes involved in Tennessee are but slightly greater than those involved at Marquette. Places of equal altitude could easily be found in Michigan and Tennessee, which would show the resemblances noted above.

The later stages on the sandstone rocks vary somewhat widely in the regions studied. The first character tree on the Cumberland mountains of Tennessee was frequently the table mountain pine *(Pinus pungens),* which may be compared with the somewhat similar scrub pine of the north *(Pinus banksiana),* which occupies similar habitats. After this, however, the order of succession is divergent in the two regions. Oaks of various species follow the pines in Tennessee, at first the more xerophytic forms, such as the black jack [Water Oak] *(Quercus nigra)* and the chestnut oak *(Quercus prinus),* and later the more mesophytic red oak *(Quercus rubra)* and white oak *(Quercus alba).* In many cases the xerophytic oaks are followed by the chestnut *(Castanea sativa americana);* after these comes a luxuriant mesophytic forest made up of many species, among which may be mentioned the tulip *(Liriodendron),* the buckeye *(Aesculus),* the hickory *(Carya tomentosa),* the walnut *(Juglans nigra),* the magnolia, the beech *(Fagus),* the sugar maple *(Acer saccharinum),* and the hemlock *(Tsuga).* While, as stated above, the oak and chestnut stages have no counterpart in northern Michigan, it is interesting to observe that the last stage is found there in a perfect development, and is dominated by the hemlock, beech, and sugar maple, three prominent constituents of the mesophytic forests of Tennessee. Thus in Michigan and Tennessee the beginning and the end are alike, or in other words the intermediate stages are eliminated in Michigan. No sure reason for this can now be given, though it is likely that the northern Michigan climate is unfavorable for the development of oaks and chestnuts, hence the pines can remain until the conditions favorable to the beech and maple appear. As already noted, the oak and chestnut stages are to be found on the granitic hills of Connecticut; it may be added here that they also occur on the morainic hills of Long Island. Hence the stages outlined above, like all other stages, are general and not peculiar to the sandstone.

e. Shales.

More than all other rocks, not excluding even limestone, shales are subject to rapid erosion. So true is this that shale hills are almost never seen, and one finds outcrops commonly only along eroding streams or underlying exposures of more resistant rock. Thus, as can be readily seen, the xerophytic phases of shales are extremely ephemeral. Lichen and crevice stages are seldom seen, and the other stages pass so rapidly that most shale areas are covered with mesophytic forests. In the region of the Cumberland mountains of Tennessee, the shale areas are indicated by valleys, just as the sandstone areas already noted are indicated by hills.

f. Limestones and dolomites.

Limestones differ chemically from all the rocks considered heretofore. Hence here it is that those who hold to the chemical importance of soil factors would largely look for data. Pure limestone is ordinarily regarded as made up of calcium carbonate, but since limestones give rise upon decay to siliceous soils, it follows that there must be silicates and other mineral substances present also. In the case of other rocks considered in this paper the residual soils are much like the parent rocks, since the latter are largely insoluble and broken chiefly by physical means. But in limestones the larger part of the rock is dissolved and removed, and only the insoluble residue, largely siliceous, remains to make a soil. Many of the red residual soils of the southern states have arisen in this way, through the decay of limestone. Dolomites differ from limestones largely in the presence of magnesium. Like limestones they decay largely by chemical agencies, but they are on the whole more resistant. Dolomite hills are more likely to remain xerophytic for a long time, and the final stages will, of course come more slowly. In both limestone and dolomite siliceous material in the form of flint or chert nodules is likely to be abundant; as the hill wears down, these accumulate in greater and greater numbers and in many cases cause a serious retardation of the erosive forces.

Lichens are commonly said to shun calcareous districts. An observation of this character is due to the most superficial study. In the first place xerophytic limestone outcrops are much less common than sandstone or granite in proportion to their total area. In the second place limestone when exposed is subject to constant superficial erosion to a degree that is not true of most other rocks, hence it is difficult for lichens to get and keep a foothold there. The limestones and dolomites of Illinois, however, show a wealth of lichen carpeting wherever xerophytic exposures are found. The cliffs along the Mississippi river in Iowa and Minnesota for miles are yellow with the lichen, *Theloschistes*.

Whatever may be said of the lichen stage, all subsequent stages are quite normal. The crevice stages (see *Fig. 10*) are well developed, and such forms as the harebell (*Campanula*), the cliff brake (*Pellaea*), together with xerophytic mosses are common on the Illinois limestone cliffs. The tree stages are ushered in, as on other rocks, by conifers and by the same species that are found on siliceous rocks. The conifer stages are beautifully shown on the limestone cliffs near Sturgeon Bay, Wis., and here the species are those of the granite and sandstone of northern Michigan. In Illinois the conifers are those that occur also on the neighboring sandstone, *viz*. the white pine (*Pinus strobus*) and the red cedar (*Juniperus virginiana*). Following the conifers in Illinois on both limestone and sandstone are the yellow-barked oak [Scarlet Oak] (*Quercus coccinea tinctoria*) and the white oak (*Quercus alba*).

The first stage in the development of a river is the growth of a ravine; in this stage vertical cutting is commonly so rapid as to give a relatively deep and narrow topographic form. In such a place the conditions for plant life are of course quite different from those on a xerophytic bluff. From comparative studies made of sandstone, limestone and dolomite gorges in northern Illinois it appears that stages are essentially alike whatever be the character of the rock. In all cases there is a rich mesophytic flora, essentially alike as to species; in all cases liverworts of many species are abundant, also such plants as the fern, *Cystopteris* and the columbine (*Aquilegia*). The conditions and also the species are much the same in shale and sandstone ravines of northern Ohio and in shale and dolomite ravines of eastern Tennessee.

From the discussions which have preceded, it appears that siliceous and calcareous rocks are in the main alike in the species of equivalent stages. It must not be rashly concluded, however, that there are no differences. A careful investigation of this question was made in Ogle County, Ill., in the spring of 1901. While it was found that most species, and particularly the more characteristic species, grew equally well on either rock (including such forms as the cliff brake, *Pellaea*, usually called a limestone plant), nevertheless a few persistent limestone plants were noted. For example [the moss] *Sullivantia ohioenis* was found only in limestone ravines; some other species found sparingly on the sandstone were common on the limestone. A much more striking case of the same kind was found in the mountain districts of Montana in the summer of 1901. While the flora of granite, quartzite, basalt and dolomite were largely alike, a limestone area near Lake McDonald yielded most of the common forms of other rocks and also a large number of species that were found nowhere else. While these latter observations were somewhat too hasty to be conclusive, they indicate that chemical agencies may play a part in determining the distribution of rock floras.

In comparing the areas studied, it may be said, in the way of summary, that the various rock species are more alike than unlike during all stages of their history. It becomes obvious why many have hastily concluded that one rock type differs from another; it is because differential erosion has not been considered. In a given region a shale area may be clothed with a mesophytic forest while a dolomite outcrop is still xerophytic or a quartzite is scarcely more than a naked hill. The relations of the different types are splendidly shown in the Cumberland mountains of Tennessee. There the strata stand vertically, and it is easy to imagine the past and the future of the rocks and their vegetation. Ages ago the strata were exposed and perhaps all alike. [S]andstone, shale, dolomite, and limestone were essentially at a common level and on all alike there began to develop the first xerophytic stages. As time went on the shales, through easy mechanical disintegration, and the limestone, through easy chemical decay, eroded more rapidly than the more stable dolomites and sandstones. Thus the dolomite and sandstone areas became hills and remained xerophytic, while the limestone and shale areas became valleys and hence were clothed with mesophytic forests. Looking into the future it is easy to see that the valleys will become deeper, thereby making the hills relatively higher and more xerophytic, only until the valleys reach their final level. Then the sandstone and dolomite hills will wear away relatively as well as absolutely, and all areas alike will become mesophytic as all alike were xerophytic at the start.

Anthology: Ecology

THE CAUSES OF VEGETATIONAL CYCLES

Presidential Address delivered before the Association of American Geographers. December 29, 1910

THE DEMONSTRATION OF VEGETATIONAL CYCLES.—The work of the past decade has shown most clearly that there are cycles of vegetation which are comparable to cycles of erosion; in each there is a period of youth, which is characterized by vigor of development and by rapidity of change; in each there is a period of old age, which is characterized by slowness of transformation and by approach to stability, or at least to equilibrium. At the close of the vegetational cycle there is no such universal feature as the ultimate plain of the physiographer, since the final stage varies with the climate, and hence is called a climatic formation.[1] In the eastern United States, the final formation is a mesophytic deciduous forest;[2] farther to the north and in the Pacific states, it is a coniferous forest; in the great belt from Texas to Saskatchewan, the final formation is a prairie; and in the arid southwest, it is a desert. In every case, the ultimate plant formation is the most mesophytic which the climate is able to support in the region taken as a whole. In a prairie climate there may be trees, but they occur for the most part near lakes or streams, or in protected depressions, and in the planation of the region they give way to the prairie; quite the same may be said of trees in a desert climate.

It has been ascertained that the original plant formations in any habitat give way in a somewhat definite fashion to those that come after, a phenomenon that has been termed *succession*. Pioneer (*i.e.*, original) formations usually are hydrophytic or xerophytic, mostly xerophytic in arid climates, and more equally divided in moist climates. For example, the last retreat of the glacial ice left in our northern states a vast tract made up essentially of hills and hollows, the hollows, if deep enough,

---

[1] Plants associated under common conditions comprise collectively, a plant formation, or a plant association, the former term being the more comprehensive.

[2] Plant formations may be hydrophytic, xerophytic, or mesophytic, these terms implying, respectively, abundance of water, scantiness of water, and conditions that are intermediate as to moisture.

with lakes. The pioneer vegetation of the hills was xerophytic, and that of the hollows, hydrophytic. Finally, except on the higher hills and in the deeper hollows, these pioneer formations gave way step by step to the tundra, and, as the climate became ameliorated, this in turn gave way to coniferous forests, and then to deciduous forests as they exist today. So far have the higher hills and the deeper hollows lagged behind the less extreme habitats in their development that there are still to be found many places which continue to have pioneer formations, though, of course, they differ greatly from the original pioneer formations of the tundra.

While the general trend of vegetation is from diversity toward uniformity, it must not be supposed that complete similitude is ever reached even under like climatic conditions. There are species, for example, in the ultimate forest of New England which do not occur in Ohio, and species in Ohio which do not occur in Illinois; southward the difference is even more pronounced. And yet it cannot be denied that from the Maritime Provinces to Minnesota and south to the Coastal Plain the ultimate forest in its larger features is of a single type; the percentages and even the kinds of dominating trees may differ, but the aspect is essentially the same. Much more diverse from one another than are the pioneer or the ultimate formations are the formations of the intermediate stages. Our northern lakes, for example, differ much less from one another in the plant species they contain than do the swamps to which they give rise. The initial formations of a rock upland in Tennessee and in northern Michigan are much alike, both in aspect and in species; the ultimate formations in these two widely separated districts are even more alike, but the intermediate stages are very different, northern Michigan having nothing at all comparable to the oak stages in the vegetational development of eastern Tennessee, and the latter region being without the complex coniferous stages of northern Michigan. In this instance it is likely that some of the northern coniferous stages correspond to some of the southern oak stages; thus we may speak of *alternative* or *substitute* stages, when different plant formations occupy equivalent places in a successional series.

In a desert climate an upland may exhibit almost no succession, since the original xerophytic formation may remain with but little change; in comparison with a successional series in a mesophytic climate, one may speak here of the *elimination* of certain stages. In marked contrast to the lack of succession or to the slow succession on a desert upland is the rapid succession on uplands in humid climates; indeed, it is possible here for mesophytes to exist side by side with xerophytes in the pioneer stages—in such a case one may speak of *telescoped* successions. Even in a climate like that of the eastern United States, telescoping may take place, as in the successions of rich fallow land and in those which follow the cutting of a mesophytic forest. With this brief survey of recent progress in the field of physiographic ecology, we may pass to a similarly brief consideration of the historical development of vegetational dynamics, and then to a consideration of the main theme of the address.

THE DEVELOPMENT OF DYNAMIC PLANT GEOGRAPHY.— The systematic exploitation of developmental or dynamic plant geography presupposes the establishment of the principles of dynamic geology and of organic evolution; hence it could not have antedated Lyell, who brought general recognition of the former, or Darwin, who brought general recognition of the latter. Results frequently lag far behind their causes, and it is only now, a full half-century after the publication of Darwin's *Origin of Species,* and three-quarters of a century after the appearance of Lyell's *Principles,* that the dynamic method is coming to be regarded as the most fundamental thing in plant geography. As in other branches of science, there have been prophets far in advance of their time, though it is only within the last decade that the prophetic insight of these pioneers has had recognition. Lyell records the struggle of the developmental idea in geology, as opposed to the ruling theories of special creation or catastrophism, noting especially the keen philosophy of certain ancient Greeks and the renascence of these views in Italy through the influence of Leonardo da Vinci and of various contemporaries and followers.

So far as we know, the beginnings of dynamic plant geography are much more recent than are the beginnings of dynamic geology, nor is this strange, since it is easier to recognize the destruction of land by waves and the deposition of material by rivers than to observe the more silent transformation of one plant association into another. Doubtless the earliest observers of such transformations failed to record the things they saw. It is hardly to be doubted, for example, that long ago many a philosophic woodsman must have noted, when he cut down the trees of a forest, that there sprang up a new vegetation differing from the old, and that gradually these first trees of the newly developing forest were displaced by other trees, and there may have been some who were keen enough to see that, after a long time, there was a return to the primeval type of forest.

The earliest account which I have discovered that clearly deals with vegetational dynamics is in a short paper in the *Philosophical Transac-*

tions in 1685, in which William King[3] gives a good account of the origin of bog vegetation from floating mats; many times since, this has been reported as an original discovery. Perhaps the first to have a real glimmer of the doctrine of succession, as understood today, was the great French naturalist Buffon. Although better known for his splendid descriptions of animals, Buffon in his earlier life was much interested in forestry, and in 1742 he noted[4] that poplars precede oaks and beeches in the natural development of a forest. As a result of this observation, he gave the important advice to foresters that if they wished to cultivate beeches, they should plant them not in the open, but in the shade of those trees which they naturally succeed. Biberg[5] a student of the great Linnaeus, published his thesis in 1749, and in this he describes the gradual development of vegetation on bare rocks; here he observes accurately the pioneer activity of the lichens and mosses, and he notes as well the importance of *Sphagnum* [Peat Moss] in the development of bogs.

The seeds planted by Buffon and Biberg fell on sterile soil; in France it was observed that Buffon was trespassing on theological grounds, and he was obliged to recant any views which implied that the world was not made in the beginning once for all; in Sweden the influence of Linnaeus was wholly against anything dynamic; he never published anything dynamic himself, and when a student like Biberg set his face in that direction, the master frowned, and said that the student was departing from the true mission of the botanist. It is not strange, therefore, that there followed a sterile period of three-quarters of a century. Yet it was within this period that plant geography was first recognized as a definite branch of science, for this was the period of Humboldt. This also was the period of Joachim Schouw, who published the first general plant geography, and of the older DeCandolle, who gave the weight of his great name to several important treatises in the new subject. But none of these men, not even Humboldt, were permeated with the dynamic principle, so far at least as plant geography is concerned. They placed descriptive or static plant geography on a solid foundation, and gave it such momentum that for a full century it dominated the entire field of plant geography; indeed in certain places it dominates plant geography today.

---

[3] King, William, Phil. Trans. Roy. Soc. London 15: 948–960. 1685.

[4] Buffon, G.L.L., Hist. Acad. Roy. Sci. Paris 233–246. 1742.

[5] Biberg, I. J., Amoen. Acad. 2:1–52. 1749.

France, so often the birthplace of great ideas, gave the pendulum an impulse in the right direction. The sane influence of Buffon had not altogether been suppressed by the theologians, and finally there arose such men as Jussieu, who introduced a flexible natural system of plant classification, which finally displaced the rigid artificial system of Linnaeus, thus making possible the development of evolutionary theories; such men as Laplace, who conceived a theory of planetary evolution, thus making possible the development of evolutionary theories in other lines of science; and such men as Lamarck and Geoffroy Ste. Hilaire, who propounded evolutionary theories in biology. The birth of dynamical conceptions in France a century ago rejuvenated science throughout Europe, making possible the development of a Lyell and a Darwin. It also made possible the development of a dynamic trend in the new science of plant geography, though, as previously noted, the momentum given to descriptive geography was too great readily to be overcome.

Very properly the first work of the new period along dynamic lines was done in France; in 1825 Dureau de la Malle[6] published the first paper which gave the results of a careful study of plant succession involving the observations of a number of years. His work was done mainly in cut-over areas of forest, and no work done since greatly surpasses it in accuracy and thoroughness. The marvelous clear-sightedness of Dureau de la Malle is well shown in the title of his chief contribution, which (in English rendering) is "Memoir on alternation or on alternative succession in the reproduction of plant species living in association (*société*)—is it a general law of nature?" Dureau de la Malle (not Steenstrup, as frequently supposed) first used the term succession in the present sense; probably he was the first also to use the term society as an expression of plant grouping. The year 1845 is a noteworthy one because it was then that Edward Forbes gave a short paper[7] before the British Association, opening up an entirely new line of study, namely, the interpretation of past geographic features by the present. He was the first to understand the significance of endemism in relation to previous connections between islands and continents that now are isolated.

---

[6] Dureau de la Malle, A.J.C.A., Ann. Sci. Nat. I. 5:353–381. 1825.

[7] Forbes, Edward, Brit. Assoc. Rep. 1845: 67–68.

In 1841 a great advance was made by the Danish geologist Steenstrup,[8] who discovered the possibility of using the fossils of the immediate (*i.e.*, postglacial) past as a means of interpreting the climatic changes and the correlated vegetational changes of recent epochs. Vaupell, a student of Steenstrup, but more botanically inclined, applied his ideas in detail,[9,10] and in the years between 1851 and 1863 gave to the world his famous account of the postglacial development of Danish vegetation, showing that the birch was the chief early pioneer, and that later it was followed in turn by the pine and the oak, and finally by the beech, which dominates today. From 1856 to 1859 Reissek[11] worked out the dynamical development of the vegetation on the islands of the Danube. In 1876 Gremblich[12] seemed to realize the actuality of cycles of vegetation. In 1881 Hult, a Finnish botanist, made the first comprehensive study of succession[13] as it is now taking place in a given region, and he was the first to recognize that a comparatively large number of pioneer plant associations later give way to a comparatively small number of relatively permanent associations.

In 1888, Treub, whose recent premature decease we so keenly regret, began the study of the new vegetation of Krakatoa,[14] thus inaugurating one of the most fruitful lines of investigation in dynamic plant geography. In 1891 Warming, to whom more than to any other we owe the present large place occupied by formational studies in plant geography, published the first of his developmental studies of Danish dune vegetation.[15] This was followed by a similar treatment of the Rhone delta by Flahault and Combres,[16] and of the North German heath by Graebner,[17] and also by Warming's *Plantesamfund*,[18] the original Danish edi-

[8] Steenstrup, J.J.S., Dansk. Vid. Selsk. Afhandl. 9:17–120. 1842.

[9] Vaupell, C., Copenhagen. 1851.

[10] Vaupell, C. Ann. Sci. Nat. Bot. IV. 7:55–86. 1857.

[11] Reissek, S., Flora. 39: 622–624. 1856.

[12] Gremblich, J., Ber. Bot. Ver. In Landshut. 5:15–31. 1876.

[13] Hult, R., Meddel. Soc. Faun. Flor. Fenn. 8:1–156. 1881.

[14] Treub, M., Ann. Jard. Bot. Buitenzorg 7:213–223. 1888.

[15] Warming, E., Vid. Med. Naturh. For. Copenhagen 153–202. 1891.

[16] Flahault, C., et Combres, P., Bull. Soc. Bot. France 41:37–58. 1894.

[17] Graebner, P., Bot. Jahrb. 20:500–654. 1895.

[18] Warming, E., Copenhagen. 1895. (German edition, 1896).

tion of his well known *Plant geography,* in which there is much material of dynamic import, together with the formulation of a number of "laws of succession." In 1896 Meigen[19] made a systematic study of succession, somewhat along the lines previously followed by Hult, and he showed that there is a final tendency toward equilibrium. This brings us to the period in which dynamic plant geography was taken up actively in this country, and here our historical resumé may well give place to the main topic of this paper.

THE DELIMITATION OF SUCCESSIONAL FACTORS.—No systematic attempt has been made hitherto to group in an analytic manner the phenomena of succession from the standpoint of their causation. Warming [in *Plantesamfund*] made a great advance toward this end by gathering together the known records of vegetational change or succession; he noted that vegetational changes are particularly evident on new soil (as along sandy shores, and in marshes, on lava, on landslip soil and talus, and on burned and fallow land). He summarizes his studies by giving six laws appertaining to succession. Clements[20] attempted to distinguish between primary and secondary successions, the former being those on newly formed soils, and the latter those on denuded soils. This classification seems not to be of fundamental value, since it separates such closely related phenomena as those of erosion and deposition, and places together such unlike things as human agencies and the subsidence of land. Clements, like Warming, gives a summary of results in the form of laws.

While most observers very properly have paid chief attention to the actual facts of succession rather than to their underlying causes, a scrutiny of past results shows very clearly that the phenomena considered have differed greatly in kind. Obviously the phenomena of bog development, as observed by William King, had to do with a succession in which the activities of the plants themselves played the leading part; the humus accretions of the bog plants, such as the peat moss, *Sphagnum,* made possible the development of another vegetation on a higher soil level. In a comparable manner, the successions observed by Buffon, by Biberg, and by Dureau de la Malle had to do with plant activities; the forest trees of a given generation cast the shade necessary for the development of other trees which need shade rather than light for their

---

[19] Meigen, F., Bot. Jahrb. 21:212–257. 1896.

[20] Clements, F.E., Bot. Surv. Nebr. VII. Studies in the vegetation of the State. III. 1904.

development; Biberg's lichens accumulated a soil which made possible the development of higher vegetation on rock surfaces. Steenstrup, however, in his study of the fossils, introduced to the scientific world a new kind of succession phenomena, for in his elucidation of the post-glacial history of Denmark there were recorded changes of broader significance than those hitherto observed; it was clear that the transition from the tundra vegetation through the birch and pine vegetation to the oak and beech, as developed by him and by his student Vaupell, was a record of climatic change, inasmuch as the very same vegetational changes may be observed today in journeying from northern Scandinavia to Denmark. A third and equally diverse kind of succession phenomena was recorded by Reissek in his study of the islands in the Danube, for here the influence of physiographic change on vegetation was clearly recognized. Thus in succession we may distinguish the influence of physical and of biotic agencies. The physical agencies have two aspects, namely, chorographic or regional (chiefly climatic) and physiographic.

CHOROGRAPHIC SUCCESSIONS.—Chorographic or regional successions are so slow in their development that they can hardly be studied without the use of fossils. Hence the experimental method, which has proven so potent in unraveling many a biological tangle, is here of no avail. It is not strange, therefore, that these successions are and probably must remain the least understood of all. There are, perhaps, four great examples of extensive regional change, which may be accepted as demonstrated, namely: (1) the change from the Carboniferous to the Permian, which is made evident particularly through the replacement of the Carboniferous ferns, fern allies, and primitive gymnosperms by the *Glossopteris* flora and later by the modern gymnosperms; (2) the subordination of the gymnosperms to the angiosperms in the Cretaceous; (3) the elimination of tropical forms in boreal regions in the late Tertiary; and (4) the postglacial invasion of southern forms into boreal regions accompanying and following the retreat of the glacial ice. Generally it is held that the dominating factor in these vegetational successions is climatic change, and that this climatic change is chiefly one of temperature. Of this there can be no doubt in the case of the changes immediately before and after the Pleistocene ice invasion. The constant relation between glaciation and the development of the *Glossopteris* flora in the Permian makes it likely that the general vegetational changes of that epoch also were due primarily to temperature.

On the whole, however, there has been a general tendency to over-estimate the influence of temperature as an ecological factor. The trend of nearly all experiment has been to show that water is of vastly greater importance, and it well may be that the change from the atmospheric humidity which seems to have characterized the Carboniferous to the aridity which seems to have characterized the Permian had more to do than did the decreased Permian temperatures with the elimination of the Carboniferous flora and with its replacement by Mesozoic forms. The most puzzling of the great vegetative transformations of the past was the sudden change from the dominantly gymnspermous forests of the Jurassic to the domination of the world by angiosperms in the Cretaceous. We know that after the Permian there was a gradual climatic amelioration toward genial conditions similar to those which characterized the Carboniferous; this amelioration seems to have culminated in the Cretaceous, which, like the Carboniferous, was also in many parts of the world a period of extensive planation. Very probably the high temperatures and the great atmospheric humidity of the Cretaceous gave conditions that particularly favored the angiosperms, which as a group are much more mesophytic than are the gymnosperms.

To summarize on chorographic successions, it would seem that secular changes in climate, that is, changes which are too slow to be attested in a human lifetime, and which, perhaps, are too slow to be attested in a dozen or a hundred lifetimes, are the dominating factors. It is possible that these changes sometimes are more rapid than at other times, and there are those who would have us believe that the climate now is growing warmer, as witness the rapid recession of many of our North American glaciers; there are others who are quite as sure that the climate is growing colder, as witness the southward retreat of the "timber line" in Scandinavia. Still others feel equally confident that the recession of glaciers is due to increasing aridity; this explanation has the advantage also of accounting for retreating "timber lines." It is much more likely that all such changes are of short duration, as it were cycles within cycles, or feeble and short-lived oscillations of great climatic waves. It is to be pointed out that great earth movements, either of elevation or subsidence, that is, the far-reaching and long-enduring epeirogenic movements, as contrasted with the oscillations of coast lines, must be considered in accounting for regional successions; the elevation of the Permian and the planation of the Cretaceous must have played a stupendous part in instituting vegetational change.

PHYSIOGRAPHIC SUCCESSIONS.—In striking contrast to regional successions, which move so slowly that we are in doubt even as to their present trend, are those successions which are associated with the physiographic changes which result from the activities of such agents as gravity, running water, wind, ice, and vulcanism. In general these agencies occasion erosion and deposition, which necessarily must have a profound influence upon vegetation. I have considered elsewhere and in some detail[21,22,23] the influence of most of these agencies, and it will suffice in this place to summarize a few of the leading kinds of phenomena that are involved. As might be expected, the influence of rapid erosion generally is destructive to vegetation, or at least retrogressive (*i.e.*, tending to cause departure from the mesophytic), while the influence of deposition commonly is constructive or progressive (*i.e.*, tending to cause an approach toward the mesophytic). Progressive successions are well illustrated in the development of flood plains along rivers, and in the growth of sandy shores; retrogressive successions are associated with the eroding activities of streams and of receding shores. Slow erosion, such as characterizes advanced stages in physiographic cycles, is not destructive to vegetation and, after a time, erosion commonly becomes so slow as to permit the development of progressive successions.

Sometimes rapid erosion may not have a retrogressive influence and sometimes the effect of deposition is not progressive. For example, on a somewhat rapidly eroding clay cliff of Lake Michigan, there often occur certain xerophytic annuals, which develop during the comparatively stable summer period, and a few perennials, such as the sumac and *Equisetum* [Scouring Rush], which have underground organs that enable them to migrate landward as fast as the cliff recedes; here we have a remarkable instance of rapid topographic change without a corresponding plant succession, either progressive or retrogressive. A marked increase in erosive intensity would destroy all vegetation, and a marked decrease in erosive intensity might institute a progressive vegetational succession. Deposition unaccompanied by progressive changes may be illustrated by an instance from the Lake Michigan sand dunes. Frequently a growing dune is inhabited by xerophytic annuals and by a few shrubs or trees (as various willows and the cottonwood); such a place illustrates pronounced topographic change, but often the vegetation is static. A great increase in depositional intensity results in the destruction of all the plants, while a decrease in depositional intensity results in progressive succession. Retrogression or a static condition

---

[21] Cowles, H.C., Bot. Gazette 27:95–117, 167–202, 281–308, 361–391, 1899.

[22] _____, Bot. Gazette 31:73–108, 145–182. 1901.

[23] _____, Bull. Amer. Bur. Geogr. 2:163–176, 376–388. 1901.

of vegetation is to be seen also along rapid streams, where there is a considerable deposition of coarse material. A striking illustration of retrogression associated with deposition is afforded by lava flows.

BIOTIC SUCCESSIONS—*a. General Features.*—Of less interest, perhaps, to the physiographer than are the vegetational changes hitherto considered, but of far greater import to the plant geographer, are the vegetational changes that are due to plant and animal agencies. These are found to have an influence that is more diversified than is the case with the physiographic agencies; furthermore, their influence can be more exactly studied, since they are somewhat readily amenable to experimental control, but particularly because they operate with sufficient rapidity to be investigated with some exactness within the range of an ordinary lifetime. If, in their operation, chorographic agencies are matters of eons, and physiographic agencies matters of centuries, biotic agencies may be expressed in terms of decades.

It has been seen that changes of climate or of topography generally institute vegetational changes; indeed this would have been predicted to be the case, even without examination. But at first thought it seems somewhat striking that far-reaching vegetational changes take place without any obvious climatic change and without any marked activity on the part of the ordinary erosive factors. Indeed, it is probably true that the character of the present vegetative covering of the earth is due far more to the influence of these relatively silent and subtle factors than to the more obvious factors previously considered. So rapid is the action of the biotic agencies that not only the climate, but even the topography may be regarded as static over large areas for a considerable length of time. It has been said that many of our Pleistocene deposits exhibit almost the identical form which characterized them at the time of their deposition; in other words, the influence of thousands of years of weathering has been insufficient to cause them to lose their original appearance. These thousands of years would have sufficed for dozens and perhaps for hundreds of biotic vegetational cycles. For example, many a sand dune on the shores of Lake Michigan is clothed with the ultimate mesophytic forest of the eastern United States, and yet the sand dunes are products of the present epoch; furthermore, sand is regarded generally as a poor type of soil in which to observe rapid succession. If a clay upland were denuded of its forest and its humus, it is believed that only a few centuries would suffice for the mesophytic forest to return.

From the standpoint of dynamic plant geography, our land areas are divided into two well marked categories: on the one hand is the erosion topography that is characteristic of the eroding and depositing phases of present streams and shores, and on the other hand is the *pre-erosion* topography (as it may be termed) which is characteristic of those areas that have not as yet been invaded by erosive forces. In our northern states the areas characterized by the presence of a pre-erosion topography often greatly exceed in extent the areas which are characterized by an erosion topography. South of the glaciated region, however, the areas characterized by the presence of an erosion topography often greatly dominate. But the influence of biotic agencies is not confined to areas that are characterized by a pre-erosion topography. For example, in our eastern forested region the development of a ravine, which furnishes a characteristic illustration of rapid erosion, exhibits only here and there actual erosion or deposition; the ravine slopes as a whole are covered with a mesophytic vegetation, because at a given spot the interval between periods of active erosion often is sufficiently long to permit the development of an entire biotic cycle. Perhaps in no other way could there be brought out more strikingly the durational contrast between physiogrpahic and biotic cycles; a ravine is an index of extreme topographic youth, and yet in its development there is ample time for the complete development of many biotic cycles. Quite as in ravines, the cliffs of streams and shores often exhibit temporary exemption from erosion whereupon there is at once instituted a biotic cycle, which often has sufficient time for running its full course before erosion again becomes active.

b. *The Humus Complex*

a. Water.—It is now time to consider the varying aspects of the biotic agencies which institute succession. Of these the first to be mentioned, because of its unquestioned supremacy, is the accumulation of humus. There are a number of different ways in which the accumulation of humus affects the trend of succession. It can scarcely be doubted that the most important of these humus influences, and perhaps the most important of all influences, inheres in the change which the humus brings about in the water relation of the soil. Speaking generally, humus accumulation occasions an increase in soil moisture on uplands and a decrease in soil moisture in depressions; hence it is probable that the changed water relation due to humus accumulation is the dominating factor in determining the mesophytic trend, both in hydrophitic and in xerophytic habitats. Although bare sand supports a xerophytic flora, the accumulation of a thin humus layer is sufficient for forest development, and the Michigan dunes show that the most mesophytic of our forests can grow on a sand dune, if there is present a humus layer a few centimeters in thickness. On rock uplands, lichens commonly are the first humus accumulators; not only do they contribute humus by their own decay, but they give shelter and anchorage to plants of higher order, whose humus-accumulating capacity is greater. As long as the vegetation is open, the humus exposed to the sun and wind, accumulation is slow, because of oxidation. But when the vegetation cover is more fully developed, the humus is more and more protected and hence accumulates more rapidly.

The relation of swamp successions to humus accumulation is particularly close. For each level both below and above the water table, there is a characteristic plant formation. In the deeper ponds only submersed aquatics can develop, but after a time their humus debris accumulates to such an extent that plants with long stems or leaf stalks (such as the pondweeds and water lilies) are able to develop. They in turn build up the humus and prepare the way for their own elimination and for the development of such plants as the bulrush, which grows in shallow water. The latter again prepare the way by further humus accumulation for the first land plants, and they again for others. In all this well-known successional series, the dominating factor clearly is a decreasing water content due to the accumulation of humus.

b. Soil Organisms.—Another important influence associated with humus accumulation is the increase of soil organisms. These may play a part scarcely second to water, but as yet we know all too little of their activities to be certain of their precise place in the order of importance. We know, however, that nitrogen is one of the essential plant constituents, and that it is made available only by certain bacteria and fungi. Since these forms live on decaying organic matter, it seems likely that humus accumulation is likely to favor their increasing development and hence an increasing supply of available nitrogen. A single instance will suffice to show the possible importance of soil organisms in succession. The beech, which is a characteristic member of the culminating forest of the eastern United States, has roots which are enveloped by fungi; it is believed that these fungi represent the absorptive system of the tree, and it is likely also that they are able to make nitrogen available, since so many similar fungi are now known to possess this power. In any event, the beech is known to depend upon the fungus, being unable to flourish without it. Obviously, then, the beech can not appear in a successional series until its associated fungus finds conditions requisite for its development in the soil. It is likely too, that other soil organisms are detrimental to various green plants, thus becoming a factor in their elimination. There is opened up here a great field of investigation, and all that can be stated now with definiteness is that it is likely to be demonstrated that the accumulation of humus is of profound significance in the development of successive soil organisms, and probably on this account in the succession of the higher plants.

c. Toxicity.—Still another humus factor that seems likely to be of large significance, but whose exploitation is so recent that we cannot yet appraise it, is soil toxicity. It has been known for a long time that the roots of plants give off various excretions, but it only through the recent careful work of Livingston and his associates,[24] and later of Schreiner and Reed,[25,26] that we have come to know much concerning their nature and influence. In the case of wheat it has been ascertained that the roots give off certain substances which are deleterious and perhaps actually toxic, especially to wheat. Such results should not occasion surprise, since it is well-known that many bacteria excrete substances which retard or even prevent the further growth of their own kind.

One of the greatest puzzles to the student of plant dynamics has been afforded by the successional series in bogs, since in spite of the wet soil there are many plants that obviously are xerophytic. There is universal agreement that there is something in bog soils which is detrimental to plant growth, but there have been various theories as to its nature. Some years ago Livingston[27] discovered that bog waters have an effect on the growth of algae which is quite comparable to the effect of various toxic agents. More recently Dachnowski, following the lead suggested by Schreiner and Reed, has been making a careful study of bog toxins.[28,29] On account of the poor drainage of bogs, there is no other habitat where root excretions would be more likely to remain. Year by year these excreta would accumulate, thus making the bog more and more unfitted for the development of

---

[24] Livingston, B.E., Britton, J.C., and Reid, F.R., U.S. Dept. Agric., Bull. Bur. Soils 28. 1905.

[25] Schreiner, O., and Reed. H.S., U.S. Dept. Agric., Bull. Bur. Soils 40. 1907.

[26] _____, Bull. Torr. Bot. Club 34:279–303. 1907.

[27] Livingston, B.E., Bot. Gazette 39:348–355. 1905.

[28] Dachnowski, A., Bot. Gazette 46:130–143. 1908.

[29] _____, Bot. Gazette 47: 389–405. 1909.

ordinary hydrophytes; hence, for a time the dominating bog plants would be those which would be able to withstand the acids and other deleterious excreta given off by the roots or produced subsequently by changes in the accumulating humus. However when these bog xerophytes bring the humus level well above the water table, the deleterious plant products will be more and more oxidized, and ultimately there will be produced a soil of such character that ordinary mesophytes may flourish in it. While there is much in this theory which still requires confirmation, it certainly accounts for most bog phenomena and is not controverted by any known facts. It is likely also that some of the accumulating soil compounds may be of importance in neutralizing deleterious inorganic or organic soil constituents. In any event, the study of soil toxins and of their varied relations to plants is one of the great fields of investigation for the future.

d. Food.—Perhaps there are some who would have supposed that the chief significance of humus accumulation lies in the increased amount of plant food that thus is made available. Once it was believed that the well-known luxuriance of plants in humus is due to the large amount of plant food which it contains. Long ago this luxuriance was shown to be in the main due to other causes, but recent experiments have demonstrated that ordinary green plants are able to absorb certain foods (as glucose), and it may be that such plants actually utilize in this way some of the substances of the humus. It is likely that the increasing food supply in accumulating humus is an important factor in the succession of the soil organisms, but as yet this subject has never been investigated. It also offers a fascinating field for study. The depletion of mineral foodstuffs in the soil has been urged as a successional factor, but it is doubtful that this is of any consequence. The great abundance of the mineral constituents of plants in nearly all soils is in strong contract to the minute amounts which the plants contain. Furthermore, the plants in their decay return to the soil the mineral elements which they took from it.

e. Temperature and Aeration.—Finally humus accumulation alters the soil temperature and the air content of the soil. For the most part changes in air content and in temperature probably are insufficient to be of great influence in vegetative change. In bogs, however, there is evidence that each of these factors is of importance. Transeau has shown that in the growing season the temperature of the water and of the soil in bogs is below that of other soils, and of the superincumbent air. Such a condition certainly is detrimental to root activity. Similarly Transeau[30] has shown that the lack of aeration in bog soils is detrimental to root activity. Thus for these reasons (and probably also because of soil toxicity, as noted above) certain stages in bogs are characterized by the development of a xerophytic vegetation, since the unfavorable conditions for root absorption make existence in bogs difficult for any plants with aerial organs except such as have structures which reduce transpiration. That such bog plants are actual and not merely apparent xerophytes was demonstrated in brilliant fashion by Transeau [in the paper cited above], who produced plants with xerophytic structures from ordinary plants by growing them in bog conditions.

c. Shade

Next in importance to humus among the dynamic biotic agencies is shade. The foresters have known for generations that in the reforesting of a region the first trees to appear are those which require a large amount of sunlight for their development; conspicuous among such light-requiring pioneers are the poplars and birches. Rarely is a dense growth of these trees followed by trees of similar kind, since the increasing shade makes the development of seedlings of these species more and more difficult. Other trees, however, perhaps pines and oaks, are able to thrive in a degree of shade which aspens and birches might not be able to endure. Finally the pines and oaks in turn may be succeeded by such trees as the beech, the sugar maple, and the hemlock, since these trees are able to develop in a considerable amount of shade. The latter trees may continue indefinitely, unless climatic or topographic changes intervene, since, unlike most species of trees, their seedlings are able to develop in shade as dense as that which is cast by the parent trees. While the influence of increasing shade, as here set forth, is undoubted, the extent of its influence is not known; *pari passu* [at the same speed] with the increase of shade, and partly on account of it, there goes on the accumulation of humus. On uplands in our climate each of these factors tends to bring about the development of a mesophytic forest, but as yet it is impossible to determine which has the more potent influence. Increasing shade favors the mesophytic trend of upland successions in yet another way than through its direct influence and through its effect upon humus accumulation; the cutting off of light results in increased atmospheric humidity and hence in

---

[30] Transeau, E.N., Bot. Gazette 40:351–375, 418–448. 1905; 41:17–42. 1906.

decreased evaporation. Some recent observations by Fuller[31] show that the pioneer plant formations of the Indiana sand dunes are characterized by high evaporation, and that this evaporation progressively decreases until the minimum is reached in the mesophytic forest.

In contrast to ordinary uplands is the influence of light upon the development of vegetation in lakes. At the outset there are many lakes which are too deep to have a conspicuous vegetation of green plants on the bottom. Through the accumulation of inorganic detritus and of humus, the latter arising from the decay of green plants living in the upper waters and from the decay of other organisms at all levels, there gradually is made possible the development of a plant formation on the bottom, composed of plants which require only a minimum amount of light. In succeeding years the shallowing of the lake makes possible a greater and greater development of green herbage, unless the development of a rich floating vegetation again cuts off the light. It is obvious that the influence of light and shade on succession is not so explicitly related to life as is that of humus; humus can arise only from organisms, but shade may be cast by many other things than trees. The rapid development of a mesophytic forest in a canyon is due in large part to the increasing shade which is cast by the walls as the canyon deepens. However, the predominating influence of shade certainly is in connection with forest development, and hence it is not unfair to group it with biotic influences.

d. Plant Invasion

A further biotic influence is that of plant invasion. In the long periods of geologic history, plant migrations from one region to another must have played a tremendous part in the changing aspect of vegetation. There is reason to believe, however, that such changes, apart from those due to human influence, have been wrought almost as slowly as those due to climatic change. So imperceptibly do these migrations take place that we know of no profound change that has been wrought by this means in natural floras within historic time.

e. Man

The last of the biotic influences to be considered is that of man. Most of the factors hitherto considered, especially increasing shade and accumulating humus with its varied kinds of influence, cooperate to transform

---

[31] Fuller, G.D., Bot. Gazette 52:193–208. 1911.

originally hydrophytic and xerophytic plant formations into those that are more mesophytic; that is, they institute progressive successions. The influence of man, however, almost without exception, is retrogressive. Human culture reaches its highest expression in mesophytic climates or on mesophytic soils; the xerophytic soils of rocky crags and of sand barrens are unfavorable places for human exploitation and the desert is for man an unprofitable waste, except where he finds an oasis or makes a district mesophytic through irrigation. Similarly, the waters are of value chiefly as avenues of transportation and as a source of food, not as a habitation; and swampy tracts are considered valueless, unless made mesophytic by drainage. Man, therefore, in seeking a place of abode, in clearing land for agriculture, and in his search for timber, has destroyed chiefly mesophytic vegetation, in other words, the very vege-tation which, in most areas occupied by human culture, has been seen to be the culminating plant formation.

When a forest is destroyed by cutting, the succeeding vegetation commonly is more xerophytic than that which was destroyed, because of increased light and decreased humus. The influence of fires is still more retrogressive, because the vegetation of the forest floor, as well as the trees, is destroyed, and also because the humus is more largely oxidized. Both in such areas as these which gradually return to the forest, and in other areas which are prevented from making such re-turn, on account of their use for cultivation, or for habitation, or for grazing animals, there enter among the pioneers, a large number of cos-mopolitan weeds which follow in the train of man. Most of these weeds are of xerophytic tendencies, and hence are well fitted for these pioneer stages. In the revegetation of fallow land and in reforestation, these immigrants soon disappear, giving way before the returning native forms which inhabited the region before man entered with his destruc-tive axe and torch.

f. Plant Plasticity

Before concluding this section on biotic agencies, there should be noted some instances where change in the habitat meets with a reaction other than that of succession. Very frequently in the draining of a pond by humus accumulation, the same plants may be found in different stages, but characterized by a change of aspect. For example, the mermaid weed (*Proserpinaca*), the water hemlock [Tall Water Parsnip] (*Sium*), and the water smartweed (*Polygonum amphibium*) are fitted for exis-tence in a shallow pond and also in a swamp where the soil level is above the water table. In the former instance the plants possess so-called water leaves, which vary greatly in form and structure from the air leaves, which are seen in the following swamp stage. Such amphibious plants thus have the power through their great plasticity of existing in two distinct plant formations; many of their companions, however, in the two situations are quite unlike, indicating that the habitat range of the latter is narrower, on account of their smaller plasticity.

In the western forests, the Douglas spruce may be a xerophytic pioneer, and yet may remain through all the stages of forest development, including the culminating mesophytic forest; this remarkable tree may even dominate in each of the stages. The Douglas spruce differs from the amphibious plants in that it exhibits no such striking changes in leaf habit in the different conditions in which it lives; however, the change in the accompanying vegetation is much more profound than in the swamp, for at the outset the Douglas spruce may be accompanied by xerophytic pines and junipers, and at the close by the mesophytic hemlock and by a luxuriant carpet of mesophytic ferns and mosses. Thus it is clear that the life range of some plants is very broad and of others very narrow; obviously the latter are the best markers of habitat dynamics, for with a change of conditions they soon give way to other forms. Of especial interest to the physiologist is the situation in such plants as the Douglas spruce, whose leaves without change of form or structure seem equally fitted for light or shade, for dryness or humidity.

CONCLUSION.—It is not to be supposed that all the influences which are involved in plant succession have been outlined in the preceding pages. Indeed, some minor contributory factors have been purposely omitted, because of the brief time allotted upon such an occasion. However, it is to be hoped that the dominating factors, so far as known at present, are here mentioned. From a survey of the various agencies involved, it seems clear that the influences which bring about succession differ profoundly in their nature, and also in the rapidity of their action. Although they grade into one another as do all phenomena of nature, we may recognize chorographic agencies which institute vegetational cycles whose duration is so long that the stages in the succession are revealed only by a study of the record of the rocks. Within one such cycle there may be many cycles of erosion, each with its vegetative cycle. The trend of a physiographic cycle can be seen by a study of erosive processes as they are taking place today, but the duration of the cycle is so long that its stages can be understood only by a comparison of one district with another; by visiting the parts of a river from its source to its mouth, we can imagine what its history at a given point has been or is to be. Within a cycle of erosion there may be many vegetational cycles, and among these are some whose duration is so short that exact study year by year at a given point makes it possible to determine not only the trend of succession, but the exact way in which it comes about. We can see one formation replacing another before our eyes, and hence we may hope some day, if we exercise sufficient ingenuity and patience, to understand the underlying causes of the change. It is clear therefore that vegetational cycles are not of equal value. Each chorographic cycle has its vegetational cycle; each erosive cycle within the chorographic cycle in turn has its vegetational cycle; and biotic factors institute other cycles, quite independently of climatic or physiographic change. It is small wonder that within this complex of cycle within cycle, each moving independently of the others and at times in different directions, dynamic plant geography has accomplished so little in unraveling the mysteries of succession. It may be some small contribution to this end, if the preceding considerations assist in delimiting the problems.

THE ECONOMIC TREND OF BOTANY

Address of the vice-president and chairman of Section G, Botany, American Association for the Advancement of Science, Philadelphia, December, 1914.

It can scarcely be successfully denied that the most significant recent advances in American botany have been along economic lines. By many of our younger botanists the dominance of the practical point of view is taken for granted, but to some of our older investigators and teachers the changing attitude has brought something of a shock. And there are a few who are not yet conscious of the great economic tide which is engulfing us. For the sake of this last group it will be well to consider briefly a few historical facts. As yet within the memory of the older living botanists, American botany was scarcely more than the taxonomy of the vascular plants. In the eighties we began importing the laboratory method from Europe, particularly from Germany. It was the psychological moment, and naturalization took place with surprising swiftness. At first, the new movement found expression mainly in the direction of morphology and anatomy. By the early nineties, however, a pronounced physiological trend found large place, and in the late nineties ecologists began taking the laboratory method to the field.

No attempt will be made to picture here the rise of economic botany. It may be pointed out, merely, that in our older programs it had very little place. A somewhat notable exception to this is afforded by medical botany, which has long been paid attention to by botanists. Indeed, botany almost began with an attempt to find the cures for human ills. So it was natural enough that posts of botany in the olden time should be assigned so generally to physicians, and that so many physicians should cultivate botanical science. Even today, in many European universities botanists who know nothing of such things are often obliged to give lectures along these lines to medical students.

It is only a few years ago that our botanical programs were made up almost entirely of the reports of investigations in what we are accustomed to call pure science, as though applied were impure. But see what we have today! It is a conservative estimate to say that three fourths of our botanical investigation is now along economic lines, as compared with essentially none at all, when the oldest among us were beginning botanical research.

If one were to count the titles in the present program of the Botanical Society of America, he might be inclined to dispute this statement, but it must be remembered that the majority of the economic papers are now given in the various technical societies. Immediately previous to the formation of the American Phytopathological Society, approximately half of the titles offered in the combined programs of Section G and the Botanical Society were phytopathological. If we take account of the work done by the various divisions of the United States Department of Agriculture and by the many state agricultural colleges and experiment stations, by workers in bacteriology and plant breeding, and by investigators in the forest service, it will be realized that more rather than less than 75 per cent of our botanical investigation is economic.

Whatever may have been the scientific deficiency of much of this work in the past and of part of it today, it must be admitted that there is coming from these sources an increasing body of work of the highest value scientifically. This is well indicated by the *Journal of Agricultural Research*, which from the first number has taken rank with our best botanical journals.

It is scarcely to be supposed that economic botany is a passing fad, and that pure botany, as we call it, will once again come into a place of dominance. The shifting emphasis in botany is but a part of a great movement as broad as humanity itself. The three sections that have been most recently organized in the American Association for the Advancement of Science are practical rather than theoretical, and the last of these, agriculture, is one which is looming up everywhere as a competitor of botany. Chemistry and physics also are being swept with the same economic title.

No better index is to be seen of the trend of the time than in the curricula of schools and colleges. Once the central feature of our educational system was the disciplinary study of the classics. Latin and Greek, subjects which survived the barbarism of the middle ages and the changing viewpoints of subsequent centuries, have given way before our modern demand for culture that is practical; and it is doubtful if they can ever again take a leading place in educational systems. In many of our secondary schools botany has given way, and perhaps permanently, to agriculture, and in many others agriculture is introduced along with botany, or the demand is made that botany be made practical. Naturally the last institutions to feel the press of the new movement will be the private or endowed institutions, such as the University of Chicago, from which your speaker comes. But even we are feeling it. An increasing number of our students are demanding more practical courses or are going elsewhere through failure to find them with us, and what is more, an increasing number of schools are demanding teachers with more practical training than we have been supplying. Last summer one of our graduates, well trained in theoretical botany, was offered a position if she could teach agriculture. Fortunately we had imported a professor of agriculture for the summer, and the young lady took a hurried course, and secured the position. An increasing number of opportunities are offered to qualified graduates prepared to take up work in agricultural colleges and experiment stations, and a relatively decreasing number of places are available in theoretical botany.

If the situation above depicted is a general movement rather than a passing whim, it is evident that in many of our institutions botany to remain a living force must change its methods. It may, as did Latin and Greek, stand inflexibly for past ideals and decline, or it may adjust itself to present-day problems and live with increasing vitality. We must not be deceived by the fact that more of us than ever are engaged in the pursuit of theoretical botany. It is not a question of absolute, but of relative, numbers, and by that test theoretical botany is losing. For one, I mourn the passing of Greek and Latin. To me those languages have been immensely practical and I do not at all regret the seven years I employed in their study. Yet how much better off we all would be had the classics, as we took them, been related to our modern life! And they might have been so related, for there are many points of contact, but your teachers and mine held rigidly for classics for the classics' sake and for disciplinary values; and it is for this that they have fallen.

At Chicago, we still adhere to the ancient notion that the A.B. degree should stand for training in the classics, and the result, of course, is a great decline in A.B. graduates. Some convocations pass without a single student taking that degree. One day I asked one of our professors of Latin if the slump in Latin and Greek were general and permanent or merely local and temporary, and he replied with sadness: "I feel that it is world-wide and lasting; even Oxford feels it. Almost the only ray of hope for us is that the botanists still require the diagnoses of species to be in Latin."

It would be a world tragedy if theoretical botany should die, or even if it were to be less influential than it is at present. It is vastly more important than are Greek and Latin, and yet their decline is to be contemplated with profound regret. But botany is the foundation of agriculture, and agriculture is the most fundamental employment of the human race.

To be sure, we can farm without being botanists, but we cannot farm so well. Through the ages agricultural man has stumbled on many important facts and principles that the botanist has later on explained, thus making more scientific farming possible. Witness the enrichment of land by growing leguminous crops—a fact mentioned by Pliny, and explained by modern botany, and as a result utilized with vastly increased success by the present-day agriculturist. Witness, too, the history of our knowledge of the wheat rust, or the recently discovered hereditary symbiosis of bacteria and seed plants—phenomena seen by agriculturists as in a glass, but very, very darkly until the theoretical botanists explained them.

In spite of these instances and a hundred more, the practical man is coming increasingly to look with scorn upon the theoretical botanists. What matters it, say we? Alas, it matters much, unless we happen individually to be endowed. For botanical positions, like other things in life, are controlled by the law of supply and demand. In more than one institution that I know the tenure of position of the botanist depends upon his success in attracting students. The student, needing bread and butter, will not be attracted to lines in which he cannot earn it, and, as Mr. Dooley says, "There ye are." In several state universities the clash has already come, and in every case of which I am cognizant, the more practical botany of the agricultural department has won as against the more theoretical botany of the academic department. Even in our private institutions we commonly have practical trustees who sooner or later may see the trend of the time and act accordingly.

Notwithstanding the sorry picture just painted, I suspect that all of us believe at heart that the most fundamental aim of botany is the improvement of the human race. All of us desire as our supremest wish, that we may do something in our brief life to make man's lot better than before we came. Therefore, it remains only to make concrete our inmost ideals, in order to save the day for botany, as it was not saved for Greek and Latin.

A good many years ago I published a paper on the vegetation of the sand dunes of Lake Michigan, depicting the principles of plant succession, as there so strikingly illustrated. Shortly after, with an expression on my face betokening, "There now, isn't that something like?" I gave a copy to a man of the world, who said merely "Well, what of it?" Aghast, I said nothing and only, now, fifteen years afterwards, is the answer forthcoming. It is as follows:

Two years ago [i.e., in 1910], I was surprised to receive a message from the United States Department of Justice asking for my services as an ecological expert in some government cases in Arkansas. With many misgivings, and with the feeling that ecology, as I represent it, was now specifically on trial, I took up the work assigned to me. To my unalloyed gratification I discovered that matters which perplexed the Department of Justice were simple enough when examined by an ecologist rather than by an attorney. In 1847 the original survey was made by the United States of the bottomlands along the Mississippi river in eastern Arkansas, and the country was opened for settlement. A great deal of the area was surveyed as permanent lake, and is so shown even on the most recent detailed maps. At the present time these so-called lakes are occupied by heavy timber of great value. Furthermore, this "lake" land is very fertile, and much in demand for raising corn and cotton. However, as it is termed lake in the original survey, it cannot be homesteaded and farmed. A few years ago certain lumber interests, having used up the high-grade timber on the surveyed lands, looked with envy on the splendid timber growing in these so-called lakes. Consequently they conceived the idea of purchasing riparian rights from the owners of the adjoining surveyed land, and they proceeded to cut the timber. Shortly afterwards the United States Government instituted suit against these lumber interests, its contention being that the original survey was fraudulent, that lakes did not exist in 1847, and that riparian rights therefore did not inhere. In the meantime, pending settlement, provisional entries were made by "squatters." While test suits were made on only a few of these so-called lakes, there exist many tracts of similar nature, involving in the aggregate many thousands of acres and property values up into millions of dollars.

As an ecologist it was my duty to determine from present indications the nature of these so-called lakes in 1847. The work was ridiculously easy, since it was found that these "Lake beds" were covered with upland timber of great age. The attorneys for the lumber interests endeavored somewhat half-heartedly to show the inaccuracy of the method of determining the age of the trees by a count of the annual rings, but in the face of the hundreds of years of age shown by many of the ring counts, this contention had short shrift.

Somewhat greater efforts were put forth in support of their claim that trees can grow in lakes, much being made of the well-known fact that the bald cypress, *Taxodium distichum*, occurs in well-defined bodies of water. It was here that the ecological argument had the greatest force. Having visited the country of the lower Mississippi on two previous occasions and having made four trips to the territory in question during the course of my work for the government, I was in a position to know the main facts in the ecological succession on the Mississippi bottoms.

Employing the happy terminology of W.S. Cooper, there are two types of hydrarch succession in the area in question, that from the river and that from the lakes which generally are back of the levee or in old cut-offs due to a shifted course of the river. On the river front, as the alluvium is built up, there is frequently seen a sandbar vegetation of ephemeral annuals associated with low summer levels of the river. Back of this there appears the first ligneous vegetation, dominated usually by willows, such as *Salix interior* [Sandbar Willow] and *S. nigra* [Black Willow]. Further back there appear more or less definite stages of vegetation, each stage associated with a water table of a given depth, culminating in the great river bottom forests of *Quercus texana* [Texas Red Oak], *Q. lyrata* [Overcup Oak], *Acer rubrum* [Red Maple], *Liquidambar* [Sweetgum], *Celtis* [Hackberry], various hickories, *Populus deltoides monilifera* [Plains Cottonwood], *Ulmus* [Elm], *Platanus* [Sycamore], *Fraxinus americana* [White Ash], and the like. It is probable that this forest type is not the permanent climax of the region, but rather a very long-enduring temporary climax.

In the lakes, whether formed by the elevation of natural or artificial levees or through the shifting of the river channel, the course of vegetational development is somewhat different. At first there is a pond vegetation with *Nelumbo* [Lotus] and other pond aquatics. Following this one finds at times a flag grass prairie or again a willow belt, much like that of the river front. The most striking feature of these lake successions, however, is the stage dominated by the tupelo, bald cypress and water locust, which usually follows the willow or prairie stage. As shown by the great age of the trees (tupelos of 200 years, and cypress of 700 years having been observed), this stage may last for a long time.

It is particularly important to note that many tupelo and cypress trees were seen to have been killed by submergence during periods of high water, thus showing that these trees are properly trees of the land rather than of the water. If they occur in lakes, as they do, this fact would seem to indicate that the lakes are but temporary, or at least that there were only short periods of particularly high water during their early life. After these trees there comes a forest of red maple, sweet gum, pumpkin ash, planer, pecan, etc., and then again after a lapse of many more years there comes the characteristic forest of the so-called lakes, the temporary climax forest above noted, with its gigantic oaks, hackberries and other trees of the dry ground; therefore, when one cuts an overcup or Texan oak and finds it to have an age of 300 years, it is clear from these facts of ecological succession that it has been much more than 300 years since there was a lake, where the trees now are.

Through a study of trees that germinated on these lands in and about 1847 I was able to determine that at that time the conditions were essentially as at present, since in the so-called lake beds the same species of trees are developing now as in 1847. I testified that in the lands in suit the evidence of ecological succession shows beyond all question that even a thousand years ago these so-called lakes must have been land, and it is my firm belief that there have been no lakes in these sites for at least two thousand years.

The physiographic evidence corroborated the ecological evidence in striking fashion. It is a well-known fact that deposit is more rapid on the immediate banks of the Mississippi than farther back, much coarse material being deposited near the shore, whereas further back the material is finer and finer and constantly less in amount. It is this fact that accounts for the formation of the natural levees; thus in these so-called lakes which mostly lie some miles back of the riverfront, the alluvial accumulation is slight. It is mostly to the much slower accumulation of vegetable material that they owe their gradual elevation above the water table. Excavations in the river and in the so-called lakes brought out this difference most strikingly.

Furthermore, the spur roots which are sent out at the ground line are still uncovered by accumulated alluvium, even on the oldest trees. Had lakes existed in 1847 and been subsequently filled by detritus, it is clear that the spur roots of old trees would be deeply buried. In the so-called lake beds there are many logs of trees that fell in the earthquake of 100 years ago, and even these logs are still unburied, thus showing an absence of appreciable alluvial accumulation for at least a century.

Two questions may have occurred to you that are more of human than of ecological interest. What was the object of a fraudulent survey of such colossal magnitude, and how were the suits decided? As to the motive of the surveyors, it may be noted merely that in 1847, our government surveyors got a certain sum per mile for ordinary surveying, and considerably more for surveying lake shores because of the greater difficulties involved; it was an object to return lakes, even if the meander lines had to be traced while in camp. As to the decision of the suits, the district judge at Little Rock, in the first test suit, made a sweeping decision in favor of the government as against the lumber interests, though an appeal has been taken to the higher courts. It may be interesting to note that the judge based his decision largely on the ecological facts, in the face of testimony given by some of the oldest inhabitants that they had actually seen the lakes in question! However, other equally old and perhaps more respectable inhabitants testified that conditions in 1847 were essentially as they are today. It was brought out in court that it is safer to believe a tree than a man! Thus a line of investigation which we had supposed to be theoretical only has turned out to have large practical significance.

No claim is made, of course, that this is the first demonstration of the utility of ecology. A field of research of almost limitless possibilities is indicated by Shantz's splendid paper on the natural vegetation as crop indicators in the Plains. Just as untold sums of money have been wasted in the search for gold where the geological formation is such that the presence of gold is impossible, so countless amounts of time and money have been squandered in agricultural experiment on land whose natural vegetation, if studied, would have directed other uses. One of the best applications of ecology is afforded by the work of Coville, on the culture of the blueberry, of which we are to learn something more today. The utilization of acid lands by the growth of crops that thrive in the presence of certain organic acids is a large conception and will doubtless prove to be one of the great utilitarian discoveries of our day.

I will not trespass on your time by indicating further practical applications of my chosen field, ecology. Others will suggest themselves, as will similar applications in various lines of botany, particularly in physiology. If we are to keep botany alive and abreast of the time, we who are in academic botanical departments must give more attention than formerly to the economic aspects of our subject. We must offer more courses in the practical phases of botany. In our research we must not avoid practical problems, but look for them, and we must emphasize the practical possibilities of our theoretical problems. Our sister science, zoology, which perhaps is in a more serious plight than we, gives evidence at this meeting of an attempt to meet the situation by choosing for its symposium the significant topic, "The Value of Zoology to Humanity." Above all we must treat the economic relations of our subject, not as an annex, a thing apart, a "sop to Cerberus," but as the vital and essential thing, the very kernel of it all. By pursuing such a course we shall keep in close relationship with our practical modern life, and we shall justify ourselves to our fellows. We shall then have ample opportunity to continue our researches along theoretical lines. And one may never know how soon a purely academic study may come to be a factor of the first importance in the betterment of the human race.

THE SUCCESSION POINT OF VIEW IN FLORISTICS

Presented before the International Congress of Plant Sciences, Section of Ecology, Ithaca, New York, August 20, 1926.

I. Introduction

Warming recognizes a sharp contrast between the ecological and floristic points of view in plant geography. In the treatment of any given region, authors mainly have taken the ecological viewpoint or the floristic viewpoint, in the one case considering the area from the standpoint of its associations and successions, and in the other case from the standpoint of its floristic composition.

From the floristic point of view the flora of a region is considered as to its origin and immigration. From this angle the plants of any given region may be divided into four classes, first, those that are strictly proper to the region and distributed more or less equally in all directions from that region; second, plants that are proper to the region under consideration, but which are at or very near the edge of their range so that they are distributed unequally in different directions from the region under consideration; third, plants that are discontinuous or disjunct; and fourth, endemic plants. In most regions the first category noted above is much the largest as to number of species. It is also the least interesting because it is the thing that is expected. The remaining categories are all of a special interest to students of floristics, because they have a very definite bearing upon the past history of species, and upon the migration of species both past and present.

The present paper is a successional study from the floristic angle. The associations of a given region (the Chicago region) are presented in their dynamic relations or order of development, and comparisons are made of the floristic characters of the various associations. Since the Chicago region was covered by Pleistocene glaciers, the present flora is entirely post-glacial. Successive waves of vegetation have passed northward over the Chicago region, the first having been an Arctic or tundra wave, the second, a wave dominated by sub-Arctic types; then followed plants of cold temperate character, such as now occur about Lake Superior; then came the deciduous angiosperms and forest types that still dominate in the Chicago region; finally there came types that are even yet more characteristic of areas to the south of Chicago. Each of the vegetation waves of the past has left relics stranded in the Chicago flora of today, but these stranded relics are much more characteristic of certain associations or stages of succession than they are of others.

The waves of vegetation noted in the preceding paragraph must not be supposed to have passed strictly northward over the Chicago region. Some of the waves may have come from the southeast and passed toward the northwest. Other waves may have come from the southwest and passed to the northeast. In general the waves from the southeast represent the more humid elements of the flora and the waves from the southwest the more arid elements. Similarly, with changes in humidity and aridity, waves may have passed over the region from east to west or from west to east, as well as from south to north.

II. An Ecological Study of Floristics in the Chicago Region

A. The Beach-Dune Succession.

One of the most interesting successions floristically is that of the Dunes. The beach is especially characterized by maritime elements (*Ammophila americana* [Sea Rocket], *Lathyrus japonicus glaber* [Beach Pea], *Cakile edentula* [Marram Grass], *Euphorbia polygonifolia* [Seaside Spurge], etc.), whose presence along a fresh water lake 1000 miles inland is difficult to explain. The foredune and the pine dune that immediately succeeds it have a flora of distinctly northern aspect and are rich in relics of the vegetation waves that followed the ice retreat (*Salix syrticola* [Dune Willow], *Pinus banksiana* [Jack Pine], *Juniperus horizontalis* [Trailing Juniper], *Juniperus communis depressa* [Common Juniper], *Arctostaphylos uva-ursi* [Bearberry], *Populus balsamifera* [Balsam Poplar], etc.). The next succession stage dominated by oaks is largely characterized by plants of the present vegetation wave, however with some xerophytic western elements (*Opuntia* [Prickly Pear], *Castilleja sessiliflora* [Downy Yellow Painted Cup]). The climax forest that follows the oaks has plants that are mostly characteristic of the present wave, but more than any preceding stage, the climax forest is rich in recent invaders from the south (*Liriodendron* [Tulip Tree], *Cornus florida* [Flowering Dogwood], *Asimina* [Pawpaw], *Stylophorum* [Poppy], etc.). One of the noteworthy things in the pine or evergreen dune is the fact that not only are many northern species present, but that they also dominate over the other elements. The vegetation as a whole is much more northern than proper to the Chicago region.

B. The Pond-Bog-Forest Succession.

Another notable succession is that from the pond through the bog to the climax forest. The pond and the pond margin have a cosmopolitan or circumboreal (as *Calla* [Arum]) flora, but the sedge bog, the bog thicket, and the bog forest have a noteworthy congestion of relicts from the subarctic and later waves. (*Larix* [Tamarack], *Betula pumila* [Dwarf Birch], *Chamaedaphne* [Leatherleaf], *Andromeda* [Heath], *Salix* spp. [Willow], *Cornus canadensis* [Bunchberry], *Linnaea* [Twinflower], etc.). The climax in this succession has much the same composition as in the climax on the dunes. Both in the dune and bog successions the relicts characterize the earlier stages, while the new invaders especially characterize the climax forest. These relations probably may be referred to competition, which is greatest in the climax and less in the early stages. Though the relict plants in these successions are not particularly in harmony with the present climate, they can none the less continue by invading new areas from century to century. In the dunes this is made possible by the continued advance of the shore line into Lake Michigan, making constantly new places for the occupation of the northern relict plants as they are crowded out by the invasion of the oaks and climax forests on the older dunes to the south. In the bogs the continued existence of the northern relicts is made possible by the constant advance of the swamp flora into the ponds. In this instance, of course, there is a definite limit to the persistence of the northern relicts in the region for, after a time, all the ponds will be filled up and grown up to climax forest. The extinction, therefore, of the northern relicts in the bogs may be looked for before the extinction of the northern relicts in the dunes.

C. Other Successional Series.

Northern relicts occur also in at least three other successions in the Chicago region, the Rock Canyon Succession, the Lake Cliff Succession, and the Spring-Fed Clay Ravine Succession. In these successions also competition is less keen in the early stages than after the invasion of the oak forest or the climax forest of the region. Amongst the northern relicts found in Rock canyons are *Campanula rotundifolia* [Harebell],

Taxus [Yew], and *Galium boreale* [Northern Bedstraw]. A noteworthy relict of the Spring-Fed Clay Ravines is *Equisetum scirpoides* [Dwarf Scouring Rush]. A relict of the Lake Cliff is *Shephardia canadensis* [Buffalo Berry].

III. Southwestern Limits and Their Significance

One of the striking features of the Chicago region, as perhaps of other regions in the middle west of the United States, is the distribution of northern species at the southwest edge of their range. Their behavior there may be regarded as extremely significant of the present trend of migration either north or south or east or west, or a combination between two of these directions. The southwestern station of all of the following plants is probably in what may be called the Chicago region: *Thuja occidentalis* [Arbor Vitae], *Betula alleghaniensis* [Yellow Birch], *B. papyrifera* [Paper Birch], *Juniperus horizontalis*, and *Primula mistassinica* [Bird's Eye Primrose]; as with other northern relicts, these occur in pioneer edaphic situations. Four possibilities present themselves in the climatic changes of a region, not only in the recent past, but also probably at the present time. The region may be becoming drier and warmer, or drier and colder; or it may be becoming wetter and colder, or wetter and warmer. It is probable that the most usual changes are represented by drier and warmer or wetter and colder. Probably at the time of the southward invasion of the ice sheets, the climate in the Chicago region, as of regions generally, was becoming wetter as well as colder. Similarly, with the northward retreat of the ice, the climate probably became drier as well as warmer. Therefore, at the time of glacial advance, the climax forest must have retreated southward, and at the same time it may also have advanced westward because of increasing humidity. The combination of these two movements would mean a general dominant movement in a southwesterly direction. During the period of glacial retreat, there was not only a northern advance of the climax forest types, but also probably an eastern retreat of climax forest types, so that in general the resulting dominant movement was probably in a northeasterly direction. If, at any time, the Chicago region became drier and colder, there would have been a retreat of the climax forest in two directions, east and south, with the resultant movement dominantly southeast; and if there is a period that becomes wetter and warmer, it means an advance of the climax forest in a northerly and westerly direction, the resultant dominant direction being northwest. The above conclusions show, therefore, that at the southwestern edge of its range, the behavior of a species, whether it appears to be gaining or losing, indicates the trend of climatic change at the present; and the edaphic occurrence of these species may often yield important data also.

IV. The Disjuncts of the Chicago Region

Generally speaking, there are four categories of such disjuncts, those of eastern range; those of western range; those of southern range; and those of northern range. The disjuncts of northern range are much the more numerous and much the more readily explained. They have been referred to in preceding paragraphs and may be regarded as relicts that have been left behind in connection with a northward retreat of glacial ice and of the northern movement of the flora following this retreat. The disjuncts of the eastern range are mostly maritime species, either of the dunes or of the swamps. The most important maritime disjuncts of the dunes are *Ammophila*, *Cakile*, *Lathyrus japonicus glaber*, and *Euphorbia polygonifolia*. Among the maritime swamp disjuncts are *Triglochin* [Bog Arrow Grass], *Utricularia purpurea* [Purple Bladderwort], *Hibiscus palustris* [Swamp Rose Mallow], *Ranunculus cymbalaria* [Seaside Crowfoot], and *Juncus balticus littoralis* [Lake Shore Rush]. It is not easily possible to explain the maritime disjuncts, but certain authorities have suggested the possibility that in some period of post-glacial time the sea has been very much nearer the lake region than it is at present. It should also be noted that these species find congenial habitats on the sandy lake shores and might, therefore, migrate from lake to lake.

The disjuncts of western range are of very fascinating interest. They consist of two definite sorts of elements. *Actinea herbacea* [Lakeside Daisy] is a close relative of *A. acaulis* [Angelita Daisy], a typical xerophytic pioneer in the Rocky Mountain Region and occurs in one local habitat near Joliet, Illinois and also in northern Ohio. It may have migrated eastward in some dry post-glacial (xerothermic) period and been generally eliminated in a succeeding period of increased humidity. Equally striking is the appearance in the lake region of humid elements of the Rocky Mountain flora, although these do not occur to any extent in the immediate neighborhood of Chicago Among such plants are *Fatsia horrida* [Devil's Club], *Lonicera involucrata* [Bracted Honeysuckle], and *Vaccinium membranaceum* [Thickleaf Huckleberry]. These elements which occur in mesophytic habitats would seem to point to a humid period in post-glacial times, during which they may have existed between the lake regions and the mountains in areas where they now are absent. Perhaps the most striking of our disjuncts are those of southern range, notably *Populus heterophylla* [Downy Poplar], *Aesculus glabra* [Buckeye], and *Styrax americana* [Snowbell]. It is not easy to explain these southern disjuncts unless there has been, since the last ice epoch, a period that is warmer or wetter than the present. It is interesting to note that these southern relicts are found in the most favored spots of the regions where they grow, in this respect being quite in contrast to the northern relicts that inhabit pioneer situations that are unfavorable for the majority of plant species.

V. Endemics

The endemics may be briefly considered. Their significance is much like that of disjuncts. For example, *Sphaeralcea remota* [Wild Hollyhock], which is known to occur only on a small island in the Kankakee River, is closely related to certain western species of the genus. It may be explained as perhaps recently derived from some parent form that once connected the Chicago region with the west. Other endemics that occur in the Chicago region are *Sullivantia sullivantii* [Sullivant's Coolwort], *Synthryis bullii* [Bull's Coral Drops], and *Cirsium pitcheri* [Dune Thistle, Pitcher's Thistle]. These endemics are edaphic pioneers. In addition, there is the remarkable endemic known only from a small area within the city of Chicago, *Thismia americana* [Thismia], whose nearest known relative is in the East Indies. The occurrence of *Thismia* presents a situation of extraordinary difficulty.

In closing, the author wishes to make appeal for a general ecological study of floristic data in the hope of explaining many of the difficult facts of floristics by this means. It similarly would seem to offer a very interesting outlet for ecological investigation.

PERSISTENCE OF PRAIRIES

Presented before the Ecological Society of America at its meeting in Nashville,[Tennessee,] December 29, 1927.

From the days of the pioneers, the great treeless tracts of our middle western country have been subjects of wonder and discussion, not only to the man of science, but quite as much to the intelligent layman. Many theories have had their ardent partisans, but no previously offered theory or combination of theories seems adequate. Nor is it likely that anything here offered will solve the great enigma, though it is the author's hope that a forward step will be taken.

The most typical prairies occur in climates that are intermediate in their temperature and moisture relations. They are scarce in the humid east and in the arid west, in the heat of the tropics and in the frigid north. They are thus most characteristic of those parts of the temperate zones in which precipitation and evaporation are relatively moderate. True prairies also are commonly characterized quite as much by their rich dark soil as by their vegetation.

Some theories of the prairie have been based on climatic factors, such as rainfall or evaporation; other theories have been based on characters of soil, topography or drainage; still other theories have related prairies to conditions of the geologic past rather than to conditions now obtaining; and again other theories have emphasized the importance of fire or overgrazing. Much of the confusion incident to past discussion of the prairie has been due to a failure to discriminate between different types of prairies. Many authors have given the same explanation for the prairies of Illinois as for the short grass plains of Kansas; and some have made little or no distinction between the lowland prairies of Ohio and the upland prairies of Iowa.

The grasslands of very humid climates, such as the streamside meadows and coastal prairies of New England, are local in extent and are local in their causes. On the other hand, the grasslands of the plains are of great extent and are clearly due to insufficient water for tree growth. The local prairies of humid climates are ephemeral and have a forest destiny. The treeless condition of the plains is as permanent as the climate; trees tend to overspread the plains neither naturally nor from artificial plantings.

The midwestern prairies, so characteristic of the belt between the eastern forest and the western plains, are very different from the treeless tracts just mentioned, and it is here that our problem centers. In Illinois and Iowa we find natural grasslands and natural woodlands in close proximity It is here that the tension line between grassland and woodland is most in evidence and that the prairie problem is most acute. The rainfall theory here is of no avail, for rain falls on grass and trees alike. Evaporation may figure slightly, for the more exposed tracts are more likely to be grass-clad and the less exposed tracts the more likely to be tree clad. Drainage is of some importance also, for the better-drained areas along streams are more likely to have trees and the poorly drained areas away from streams are more likely to be grass-clad. Fire and grazing may be factors also, for where they are eliminated, trees frequently invade the adjoining prairies. Prairies are well-suited for tree growth, for when trees are planted artificially they not only thrive but spread spontaneously. Though each of these factors may have some validity, no one of them nor all combined is adequate to explain the prairie.

At this point, the author wishes to suggest another factor, hitherto largely neglected, that of soil evolution. The physiographers have established the concept of topographic evolution, and have shown that landscapes are born, come to maturity, and die. We plant ecologists have similarly proven that there exist vegetation cycles, in part corresponding to the cycles of physiography and in part independent of physiographic change; that there is a succession of vegetation from pioneer to climax forms. Glinka and other soil investigators of Russia have strongly emphasized the phenomena of soil evolution, as related to climate and vegetation. In America, Marbut has been instrumental in promulgating and expanding this point of view. To the author it would seem that we have here a factor of vital consequence in the solution of the prairie problem. Some would explain the prairie on the basis of factors operating in the past, others on the basis of factors operating in the present. The author feels that the explanation may rest on factors starting in the past but continuing to the present with cumulative force. When prairies and forests started it is likely that they started on similar glacial soil materials under similar climatic conditions. As centuries elapsed the substratum of the forest and the substratum of the prairie, originally alike, became increasingly unlike through the contrasting effects of forest vegetation and prairie vegetation upon the original soil materials. Eventually there has developed beneath the forest what we now term a forest soil, varying widely in different forest types, but differing conspicuously from prairie soil in color, the amount of leaching, and otherwise. Through the centuries prairies tend to persist on prairie soils and forests on forest soils, because each type of vegetation has produced a type of soil suited to itself. At the outset a very minute factor may have determined whether a grassland or a woodland originated on a given tract, but as centuries elapsed, the determining factors became accentuated, thus establishing more firmly the prairie on one site, the woodland on the other. Such is the suggestion offered with becoming modesty, as a possible factor in the solution of the prairie problem, a factor confessedly more pertinent to the explanation of the persistence of the prairie than to its origin.

From the preceding it would seem that the author is forced to the conclusion that the middle western prairies have a prairie destiny. However the problem has another angle. Many cases are known where forests appear to be invading prairies along their lines of tension. This is especially evident where fires, once prevalent, have been abated, or where areas, once grazed, have been fenced off from grazing animals. Some of these forest invasions may be in part on lands once wooded and hence on forest soil. This is but a portion of the answer. In an area near Chicago, certain soil studies were made this past summer in a place where forest seemed to be invading the prairie. Beneath the prairie vegetation there was disclosed a prairie soil of some antiquity. Beneath the larger trees of the woodland, back form the edge, a forest soil was disclosed, but near the prairie edge, a prairie soil was found beneath trees, thus apparently proving that at this place trees are now encroaching on the prairie and are invading prairie soil. We have many reasons for believing that since glacial times our climate has not become progressively drier and warmer, but that there have been fluctuations in temperature and moisture, and especially that past postglacial climates have been both wetter and drier than are the climates of today. The present distribution of our native plants can hardly be explained otherwise, for we have in the middle west isolated plants belonging to more humid climates and other isolated plants of more arid climates. The only adequate explanation for these is that they are relicts of times when the climate here was one time wetter and another time drier than the climate of today. In the drier postglacial past the tension line between prairie and forest was probably farther east than now, and in the wetter postglacial past this tension line was probably farther west than now. Thus the prairie-forest conflict probably has continued for many centuries, though the scene of action has shifted. Some periods have doubtless been periods of prevailing forest invasion and others of prairie invasion. A striking instance of probable climatic change as indicated in the soil profile is reported by Marbut from western Kansas and Nebraska, where the present plains type of soil is underlain by a black layer, apparently representing a soil formed under much moister climatic conditions than those now obtaining.

SUMMARY

It would seem that the existence of a prairie in a given place in our middle west may be due in part to factors operating at the present time and in part to the influence of cumulative soil factors operating through past centuries, that the evolution of a prairie soil through the influence of prairie vegetation favors the persistence of the prairie and that the evolution of a forest soil through the influence of forest vegetation favors the persistence of the forest. A climatic change may disturb the prairie-forest balance either way, favoring now the encroachment of the forest, now the encroachment of the prairie.

Anthology: Conservation

CONSERVATION OF OUR FORESTS.

Transactions of the Illinois Academy of Science
February 23 & 24, 1912

Many might think it strange that forest conservation should have a place of importance in the "Prairie State." And statistics might be cited to bear out the contention that for us the topic is one of small significance. Illinois is accustomed to occupy among our States a place near the top in almost any statistical table, whether it be a matter of bushels of corn, miles of railroad, number of people, gallons of whisky, or degree of intelligence. In amount of lumber production, however, there are more than thirty states ahead of us, and it is our lot to be classed with such humble company as Maryland, Connecticut, and New Mexico. Forest planting might for us appear to be a much more fertile symposium topic. And indeed this *is* a topic about which much might be said. Although our State has a vast amount of land that naturally was treeless, there is scarcely a foot of this prairie area which is unsuited for the growth of trees. As a rule, it has been much more profitable to devote our marvelously rich soil to other uses, but there is a reason for supposing that the time has arrived when we may well consider the desirability of tree planting to a much greater degree than has hitherto obtained. However attractive this subject might prove to be, it is not the one that has been assigned to me, and I must proceed forthwith to consider Forest Conservation.

Far from being one of the poorest states in which to exploit conservation theories concerning our forests, Illinois actually is one of the best, and for the obvious reason that it will not be necessary here to combat the undue cupidity of the lumber interests. In states like Washington or Louisiana, which are in the throes of extravagant timber exploitation, the sentiment of the ordinary intelligent citizens is against any large measure of forest conservation; as might be expected, the lumber interests in such states are vigorously opposed to any sort of conservation. Quite as unreasonable as the views of the average western lumberman, and very much harder for a rational conservationist to deal with, are the views of the idealistic conservationist, who lives for the most part well outside the regions of lumber exploitation, and chiefly in our cities. Many lumbermen are too much concerned in immediate gain to take thought for the future, and many conservationists are too impractical and too little familiar with forest conditions to be able to deal sanely with things as they are. One of the most pleasing signs of the times is the readiness of our most intelligent lumbermen to listen to plans of forest management which take the distant future into account; equally pleasing is the attempt made by the wiser conservationists to deal with the complex problem of forest conservation in the practical and conservative manner, which the name conservation ought to imply.

The establishment of forest reserves in our western states has met with vigorous opposition from many of the best citizens of the States concerned, and it is scarcely to be doubted that by the somewhat wholesale establishment of such reserves a good deal of injustice has been done to legitimate present interests. It must not be forgotten that it is quite as wrong to reserve everything for our descendants, leaving ourselves in want, as it is to appropriate everything for present needs. Nor may one rely too much upon statistical presentations which show that after a certain number of years (usually startlingly few) our supply of timber will be exhausted. It is not so many years ago that our ancestors were worrying themselves into premature graves, because of the rapidly diminishing supply of whale oil. We may well laugh at our forefathers who paid high prices for the poor light that whale oil gave, while we revel in the numerous cheap and satisfactory methods of lighting which are given us by coal, oil, gas, and electricity. And we may expect our descendants to laugh at us for many of the things which we worry about today. Who knows what inventions are to come that will enable us to do away with many of the economic uses of wood? Already the wooden house is being replaced, even outside the fire limits of our cities, by houses of brick, stone, or concrete; and one wonders just where, at the present rate of progress, the replacement of wood by concrete is going to stop. Steel is also replacing wood in the manufacture of railway cars, bridges, and in many other articles of construction. Possibly the somewhat exuberant zeal displayed by many of our lumbermen in forest destruction may be caused by the fear that the rapid replacement of wood by other substances is likely to leave them stranded with a lot of useless standing timber on their hands!

Whatever the merits of the discussion that is being carried on at long range between the lumbermen of the Far West and our city friends in the East, we well may congratulate ourselves that we in Illinois are not on the firing line. We can continue on in the even tenor of our way, and can indulge in a good deal of effective conservation without exciting a storm of controversy. This is not the only reason why Illinois is a peculiarly satisfactory state for the working out of conservation principles. Our forests are composed chiefly of the hard-woods, which as a class are much less subject to destructive fires than are the coniferous trees. Thus there is great likelihood that in Illinois long-continued experiments with timber tracts would not be suddenly terminated, as might be the case in a coniferous forest, no matter how carefully it might be guarded. Again, our Illinois forests are of unusual scientific interest because they abut upon the prairies. It is probable that, were artificial factors removed, the forest area would gradually encroach upon the area of prairie. No problem has been or is more fas-cinating than this forest-prairie problem, and we are only just begin-ning to understand some of the factors involved, when we are faced with the danger of the destruction of all our natural areas of vegeta-tion. This forest-prairie problem is not without its economic aspects, for it involves the natural forestation of treeless areas; if we can deter-mine how and why natural forests develop on prairie soil, we will have discovered a principle of forestry of the widest significance.

The advantages of forests commonly cited by conservationists are as real in Illinois as elsewhere. These advantages are self-evident and may be mentioned merely by name. Erosion is greatly retarded by an effec-tive forest cover; it would be possible to display views from various parts of Illinois, showing the destruction of rich layers of surface soil, owing to injudicious deforestation. Our prairies are often very windy, and wind incites excessive transpiration, which often is ruinous to crops; forests serve as effective windbreaks. Every farmer should have his wood-lot, and thus secure a large measure of independence; the wood-lot supplements the fuel supply and contributes much in mani-fold ways to the peace and prosperity of the farmer. The establishment of rational conservation and scientific forestry in Illinois will have an in-fluence beyond the borders of our State. It is probable that those States, which are now the chief seats of lumber exploitation will before many years realize the need of conservative forest management. Perhaps by then our State will have accomplished something of significance that may serve as a pattern for other commonwealths, which were endowed more plentifully with natural forests of commercial importance.

Illinois has started well and in the right direction by acquiring land for a State reserve at Starved Rock, between La Salle and Ottawa, along the Illinois River. Doubtless this area would not now be a State pre-serve but for the remarkable combination of historic interest and scenic beauty, with features of botanical and geological importance, that are centered there. Several representative forest types are there displayed, and now that their preservation is assured they may be expected to increase in interest and beauty from year to year. At least four forest types are there preserved: the river-bottom type, with elms, hackberry, mulberry, box elder, willow, ash, coffee tree, honey locust, and many more; the ravine type, with the hard maple, basswood, and ironwood; the rock-face type, with the white pine and arbor vitae; and the upland forest, with the red oak, white oak, black oak, and hickory.

Much has been said concerning the preservation of the white pine forest in Ogle County, by all odds the most important forest of this species in Illinois. There is no question as to the desirability of preserving this forest, as a monument to future generations of the type of forest which was originally the most important forest asset of our country. It is believed that only a slight effort will now be needed to secure the purchase and preservation of this splendid forest. After this has been accomplished, it would appear to be worth while to have set aside at least one example of each of the forest types of Illinois. Among these there should certainly be a river-bottom forest in southern Illinois, preserving some of the gigantic specimens of the primeval forest; a southern cypress swamp with its unique plant inhabitants; a yellow pine forest in southern Illinois; a beech forest; [and] a tamarack swamp in northern Illinois. These are to be taken only as important samples; a number of other important forest types should also be included

The forest reserves mentioned hitherto, probably should be State parks, but there remains to be mentioned a conservation scheme of yet wider significance. It has been proposed to establish county preserves; it is much to be hoped that this idea will be carried out. The expense involved should not be very great, and the return to the county would increase from year to year. In most counties such preserves might well be established in places of scenic interest, for such places usually have more less diversified topography, displaying several types of forest and many tree species. These preserves would furnish places for picnics, and for excursions in connection with the nature study work of the schools; not only would the tree life increase in interest and beauty from year to year, but the same would be true of the wild flowers beneath the trees, and of the birds, and in fact of all kinds of plant and animal life. Bits of forest here and there would gradually be restored to the primitive wildness and beauty of the forests of pioneer days.

Possibly conservation might go even farther than has been generally suggested; that is, there might be township preserves, at least in many instances. In this event our forest tracts would be numerous enough to be within easy reach of all our people. All of our boys and girls could come into contact with forest life in its many phases of beauty and interest, and all without any great expense and without any great sacrifice of arable land. With such development as this, we might hope some day to approach the standard of efficiency illustrated by Germany, where, in a thickly settled and long civilized country, the forests are made to serve many interests, economic, scenic, [and] educational. There the forest is an asset, as measured in financial terms, and it also ministers to German culture in various ways. What is possible in Germany is possible in Illinois, and more possible in Illinois than in most of our States, where forests are managed in terms of commercial exploitation rather than in terms of culture and human progress.

TESTIMONY OF
HENRY CHANDLER COWLES

Report on the Proposed Sand Dunes National Park, Indiana
By Stephen Mather, October 30, 1916

Mr. Secretary, ladies, and gentlemen . . . For 20 years, I have been studying the dunes more than anything else, more than everything else combined. In fact, that has been my chief reason for existence, perhaps, for those 20 years. During those 20 years, I have studied not only the dunes of Lake Michigan but nearly all the dunes of the world, having personally visited most of them and read about the others. And so this meeting here today seems to me almost the culmination of a lifetime of scientific effort, though I hope that my lifetime is not coming to an end just now, because I want to enjoy this great national park when it becomes such, together with all of the thousands and hundreds of thousands of people who are likely to go there when it is created into such a park. Three years ago I had the great privilege of conducting through our continent, or through our country, perhaps I had better say, a large number of the greatest scientists of Europe, the greatest botanists of Europe, men representing all the countries which are now at war with one another.

As there was so much to see in the brief time that we had to see it in, I asked these people who had come here to indicate what they wanted to see in the United States in two months. They mentioned things, of course, that it would have taken dozens of months to witness, even briefly; but there were three or four things that all of them mentioned as highly worth seeing, even in the briefest trip to the United States. One of those was the Grand Canyon of the Colorado; another was the Yosemite; another was Yellowstone Park; and the fourth was the Lake Michigan dunes. [Applause.] Those were the only four things that were mentioned by all of these European scientists; regardless of whatever else they wished to see. In other words, in Europe, among the scientific men, our Lake Michigan dunes are rated with the wonders of the West that already have been set aside, with the exception of the Grand Canyon, for national parks. Now, my studies for all these years have mostly been, as has been indicated, along the line of plant life, botany. Now, I am not going to read this manuscript to you of course; that would be a crime. But I am going merely to call your attention briefly to one or two of the things that have impressed me in those 20 years. The botanical features of the dunes may be considered under two heads: first, the dunes as a common meeting ground of trees and wild flowers from all directions; and second, the dunes as a pictur- esque battle ground between plant life and the elements. Botanically the Indiana dunes are a marvelous cosmopolitan preserve, a veritable floral melting pot.

There are few places on our continent where so many species of plants are found in so small compass as within the area suggested for conservation. This is in part because of the wide diversity of conditions prevailing there. Within a stone's throw of almost any spot one may find plants of the desert and plants of rich woodlands, plants of the pine woods, and plants of swamps, plants of oak woods and plants of the prairies. Species of the most diverse natural regions are piled here to- gether in such abundance as to make the region a natural botanical preserve, not only of the plants that are characteristic of northern In- diana, but also of the plants of remote outlying regions. Here one may find the prickly pear cactus of the southwestern desert hobnobbing with the bearberry of the arctic and alpine regions. The commonest pine of the dunes, the jack pine, is far out of its main range, reaching here its farthest south. One is almost startled at the number of plants of the far north, many of which, like the jack pine, are not found to the southward of our dunes. Among such plants of the Canadian for- est and tundra are the twin flower, the glandular willow, the poverty grass, and the northern rose. Northern plants are particularly charac- teristic of the dune swamps, and embrace such interesting species as the larch, bunchberry, dwarf birch, sage willow, numerous orchids, cranberry, leatherleaf, and many more. Many of these species are found nowhere for many miles outside of the dune region, so that the failure to conserve the dunes would result in the extinction of this wonderful flora for all time.

The picturing of the beauties of the dune wild flowers may perhaps belong to an artist rather than to a botanist, but I can not forbear not- ing that in the dunes, as nowhere else in our part of the world, is there a procession from April to October of beautiful flowers. Our wood-lands in spring and our swamps and prairies in summer are favorite haunts for flower lovers, but the dunes are beautiful the season through. In early spring one finds in the dunes the trailing arbutus (found nowhere else in our region), the sand cherry, the bearberry, and hepatica. In May there are splendid displays of the lupine, puccoon, phlox, trillium, and the magnificent bird's-foot violet. Somewhat later come many of the orchids, among which may be noted four species of ladies' slipper, the roses, columbine, twin flower, spiderwort, rock rose, and coreopsis. In midsummer there occur a bewildering number of attractive flowers, as the harebell, goat's rue, butterfly weed, flowering spurge, and the incomparable prickly pear cactus. In late summer one sees numerous kinds of golden rod and aster, and also sunflowers and yellow gerardias. Perhaps the culmination of this wonderful display comes in the autumn with the gentians, grass of parnassus, witch hazel, and various golden rods and asters. One should not neglect mentioning here the display of autumnal color, which nowhere else in this part of the country reaches the magnificence seen in the dunes. The sour gum, sassafras, sumac, oak, red maple, and many vines and shrubs contribute to the fascinating blaze of color.

The struggle for existence always interests, because our life is such a struggle. Nowhere perhaps in the entire world of plants does the struggle for life take on such dramatic and spectacular phases as in the dunes. A dune in the early days of its career is a moving landscape, a place that is never twice alike; it is a body of sand which under the influence of wind moves indifferently over swamp or town or forest. Perhaps nothing in all nature except a volcano with its lava flow is to be compared with such a moving dune as is to be seen at Dune Park, Tremont, or Furnessville, in the Indiana dunes. In my 20 years of study of the Indiana dunes I have many times watched the destruction of forests by sand burial. But the plants do not yield supinely. Many species, such as the oaks and pines, give up very quickly, but others, such as the cottonwood, various willows, wild grape, and dogwood, display an astonishing resistance, growing up and up as the sand advances over them, and often succeeding in keeping pace with the advance of the sand. The power to respond in such a way depends upon the possession of a capacity for the rapid extension of stems and roots; in such plants new roots develop freely from the buried stems. Even such a lowly plant as the common horsetail can extend its stems sufficiently fast to keep above a rapidly advancing dune. Some species can even start on a moving sand dune and flourish where all life conditions seem impossible. The average visitor to a moving dune would say that such a place is bare of life; not so a botanist, who finds small and scattering plants in almost every situation. To almost every condition, no matter how severe, some plants are found adapted.

Now, in closing, I believe that there is one particular why, as a student of the dunes for 20 years, and a student during that time of dunes in all parts of the world, I can make a special plea for the preservation of these particular dunes as a national park. There is only one Yellowstone Park in this or any other country, and it we have well conserved. There is only one such Crater Lake as we have set aside. There is only one such place as the Mesa Verde, which has been set aside, and there is only one such canyon as that of the Colorado, which is likely to be made a national park. It is well known that there are many dunes in the world, and many Americans, even, who know nothing of the marvelous dunes of Lake Michigan, have heard of the relatively insignificant dunes of Germany, France, and Belgium, or those of our own Cape Cod or Cape Henry. It is not so well known as it should be that the dunes of Lake Michigan are much the grandest in the entire world. Not necessarily the highest, though some of them reach up 400 feet and more above the lake, but more than any other anywhere, our dunes show magnificent and contrasting types of plant life, everything from the bare dunes to magnificent primeval forests. No other dunes than ours show such bewildering displays of dune movement and struggle for existence, such labyrinths of motion, form, and life. So just because its uniqueness preserved the Yellowstone—there are no such geysers elsewhere, so should their uniqueness preserve our dunes, for they are without parallel. I thank you. [Applause.]

Anthology: Contemporaries

Eugene Warming

OECOLOGY OF PLANTS;
AN INTRODUCTION TO THE
STUDY OF PLANT COMMUNITIES (1909)

Botanical Gazette August 1909

For a dozen years, English and American botanists have been more or less hopefully awaiting a translation of WARMING'S *Plantesamfund* [Copenhagen: 1895], which was promptly translated into German [1896] and thus made available to a larger audience. A peculiar accumulation of misfortunes of one kind or another prevented an English edition of this epoch-making work, but at last WARMING'S contributions are made available to all English and American botanists, and in the most happy way possible, through the preparation of an essentially new book. The author has excellent command of the English language, having frequently contributed articles in this tongue. The new volume was written in English by the author himself . . . [with assistance]. A preface written by the author calls attention to the more fundamental changes in the English work; these are so many and so important that an extended review is necessary.

The introduction contains considerable new matter concerning growth forms . . . together with a new and rather satisfactory classification of them. There are six categories of growth forms: heterotrophic, aquatic, muscoid, lichenoid, lianoid, and all other autonomous land forms. The final category is, of course, much the largest, and is subdivided into monocarpic and polycarpic forms. Monocarpic growth forms may be aestival annuals, hibernal annuals, or biennials to perennials. The polycarpic forms are much more numerous, and their subdivision is based largely on the idea of the character of their protection during the severest seasons, taking account of such things as the duration of the vegetative shoot, the length and direction of the internodes, the position of the renewal buds, the bud structure, size, leaf duration, and the adaptation of the nutritive shoot to transpiration. The sub-classes of polycarpic forms are renascent plants (subdivided into plants with multicipital rhizomes, mat geophytes, and traveling or rhizome geophytes), rosette plants (subdivided into ordinary rosettes and tree rosettes), creeping plants, and plants with erect long-lived shoots (subdivided into cushion plants, undershrubs, soft-stemmed plants, succulent-stemmed plants, and woody plants with long-lived lignified stems).

The first and second sections, dealing with ecological factors and their action and the communal life of organisms, are but little changed, except that they are brought up to date, as is true of every part of the book to a most remarkable degree. Sun and shade plants are called heliophytes and sciophytes respectively, and their leaves are denominated heliophylls and sciophylls. The third section brings together the parts referring to the adaptations of land and water plants, distributed under various heads in the Danish and German editions. Much more vital, however, involving new conceptions rather than rearrangement of material, is the new classification of plant formations. Here the author departs widely from his former fourfold classification of plants into hydrophytes, mesophytes, xerophytes, and halophytes. The new conception is that there is a fundamental twofold subdivision into land plants and water plants. The land plants are subdivided further into twelve primary groups, thus making with the hydrophytes thirteen main classes of plant formations, in place of the four classes of previous editions. For the new classification, the author states that Dr. VAHL is largely responsible, and especially for those following the psammophytes, as noted below.

In former editions it will be recalled that WARMING objected, and with good reason, to the word formation as an ecological unit, largely because of its varied use by different authors. But language is a peculiar thing, and ill-chosen words often stick. It has been so with formation, and the author now attempts to delimit the word, regarding a formation as "a community of species, all belonging to definite growth forms, which have become associated together by definite external characters of the habitat to which they are adapted." The chief classes of formations are microphyte, moss, herb, undershrub, shrub, and forest, and individual formations may be simple, compound, or mixed. An association is defined as "a community of definite floristic composition within a formation, a floristic species of a formation which is an ecological genus." The conception of a formation as an ecological genus and an association as an ecological species is now becoming generally accepted in principle, but this concrete statement by the father of modern ecology should make its acceptance universal.

The new classification of formations, with some of the leading subclasses under each, follows.

A. Soil wet; water available. (1) Hydrophytes; subdivided into plankton (further split up into haloplankton, limnoplankton, and saproplankton), cryoplankton (including the microphytes of ice and snow), hydrocharid formations or pleuston, the lithophilous benthos (in place of the nereids), the benthos of loose soil (including hot spring microphytes, sand algae, saprophytic microphytes, and the enhalid and limnaea formations, as in previous editions). (2) Helophytes or swamp plants; subdivided into reed swamps and bush swamps.

B. Soil physiologically dry. (3) Oxylophytes or plants of sour (i.e., acid) soil, characterized largely by xeromorphy; subdivided into low moors, grass heaths, high moors, moss and lichen heaths (or tundra), dwarf shrub heaths, and bushland or forest on acid soil. (4) Psychrophytes, or plants of cold soil, including chiefly the subglacial fell-fields. (5) Halophytes; subdivided into lithophilous, psammophilous, and pelophilous halophytes, salt swamps and deserts, and littoral swamp forests (mangrove swamps).

C. Soil physically dry and dominant in determining the vegetation. (6) Lithophytes; subdivided into the true lithophytes (chiefly lichens), chasmophytes, and shingle and rubble plants. (7) Psammophytes or sand plants. (8) Chersophytes or waste plants (i.e., ruderals); subdivided into waste herbage and bushland on dry soil.

D. Climate dry and dominant in determining the vegetation. (9) Eremophytes, or plants of steppes and deserts; subdivided into deserts, shrub steppes, and grass steppes (including prairies). (10) Psilophytes or savanna plants; subdivided into thorny savanna, true savanna, and savanna forest. (11) Sclerophyllous plants; subdivided into garique, maqui, and sclerophyllous forest.

E. Soil physically or physiologically dry. (12) Conifers.

F. Soil and climate favorable to mesophilous formations. (13) Mesophytes; subdivided into arctic and alpine mat grassland, meadow, pasture, mesophytic bushland, deciduous dicotylous forests, and evergreen dicotylous forests.

The classification here outlined does not strike the reviewer as an improvement over the one abandoned. For the most part the new groups of land formations are segregates from the old term xerophyte. It is true that the latter term had become unwieldy, but it is questionable whether the difficulties are solved. Among the advantages of the new scheme is the recognition of close relationship between heath and moor plants, which together form the category oxylophytes, and also the close ecological relationship between these plants and the plants of cold and salty soils, as emphasized by SCHIMPER. It is gainful too, to put the edaphic xerophytes (lithophytes, psammophytes, chersophytes) into one category and climatic xerophytes (eremophytes, psilophytes, sclerophylls) into another. Among the disadvantages of the new arrangement are many instances where unrelated things are placed together and related things are separated. The most conspicuous case of the former is seen in class 12, the conifers. While this group is a floristic unit, and even an ecological unit from the anatomical standpoint, it is far from being a geographic unit of any sort. It would seem better to put many conifers with the lithophytes and psammophytes, while others are certainly oxylophytes, and others still pronounced mesophytes, the most mesophytic forests of the United States being dominated by conifers. Again, classing the plants of steppes and deserts together as eremophytes does an injustice to the American prairie, much of which is essentially mesophytic. Repetitions in listing the plant formations of a region would be certain to occur, for example, as between lithophytes and psammophytes, oxylophytes and psychrophytes in northern regions, etc. It also seems unfortunate that so many Greek derivatives are employed. Nowadays we are getting more and more to abandon the classics and their lengthy derivatives for the vigorous and familiar terms of the vernacular, and it seems a pity to have to brush the dust once more from our Greek lexicons. The antiquated spelling of ecology (oecology) is unfortunate, and is made more striking by contrast with the frequently used economy, which has the same reason for appearing as oeconomy.

While words of adverse criticism seem necessary here and there, one may write volumes of praise. WARMING'S *Plantesamfund* will be for all time the great ecological classic, and the English volume now before us is the most important ecological work in any language. It is at the same time an old book and a new, a translation of the masterpiece of 1895 and a compendium of the ecological thought of 1909. WARMING has been contributing to ecology for more than forty years, and is the undisputed Nestor on the subject, but unlike many a Nestor, WARMING incarnates the ambitions and plasticity of youth. It will be pleasing to American ecologists to see the remarkable recognition accorded to their work in this new volume. The German edition of 1896 contained but one American title, though a half-dozen more might have been included. Now there are 600 titles in all, almost exactly twice the number published in 1896, and it is not unfair to say that half of the ecological work thus far accomplished is represented by the added titles of the last thirteen years. It will be flattering to Americans to note that 115 of the 300 new titles represent American contributions, a record that measures up well with the bare half-dozen that might have been named in the original 300. The new edition has ample footnote references, adding inestimably to the service of the work. The absence of illustrations will be a source of disappointment to many, but it accounts in large part for the extremely low price of the volume, a price that will insure a sale that has been accorded to no ecological work in the English language.

A.F.W. Schimper

PFLANZENGEOGRAPHIE AUF PHYSIOLOGISCHER GRUNDLAGE (1898) [PLANT GEOGRAPHY ON A PHYSIOLOGICAL BASIS]

Botanical Gazette March 1899

The impetus to a study of ecology as an integral part of botany, coordinated with morphology and physiology, dates back to Warming's *Ecological plant geography*, published only four years ago. The rapidity with which this new field of study is developing is shown by the large number of special treatises which have appeared since Warming's work. This latest work of Schimper is calculated to lead another great advance, and may be said probably to mark the beginning of a second epoch in the pursuit of ecological investigation.

Schimper, like Warming, is not a narrow specialist, but has made valuable additions to our knowledge in many fields of botanical research. His studies in morphology, cytology, physiology, taxonomy, and ecology have peculiarly fitted him to take up an immense work of this sort in a thoroughly scientific manner. The result of his labors is a volume of nearly 900 pages, a veritable compendium of ecological knowledge, systematized and brought up to date. In the preface the author says that the cue for ecological study was given by the study of plants in extreme conditions, since only there are the effects of environment strongly marked and easily understood. Hence investigations in the tropics and above all the studies of Haberlandt, Wiesner, and others at Buitenzorg [Botanical Garden in Buitenzorg, now Bogor, West Java], have given a great impetus to the study of ecology. Schimper appeals for a polar laboratory, so as to study the extreme but relatively simple effects of an arctic environment.

The general divisions of Schimper's *Plant geography* resemble those of Warming. First, the ecological factors are treated; water, heat, light, air, soil, [and] animals. Then there is a discussion of formations and associations in general. Over three fourths of the work is taken up with a detailed description of the formations of the various zones and regions, the tropical, temperate, and arctic zones, [and] the mountains and the waters.

There are several general features in the work which strike one at a glance, and which are highly commendable. There is a wealth of well-chosen illustrations of plant habits and plant formations, largely reproductions of photographs. These pictures are thoroughly representative, and illustrate the leading features of all regions thus far studied. A second highly commendable feature is the persistent correlation of ecological observations on plants in the field with physiological experiment carried on in the same region. Observation and experiment together check erroneous conclusions derived from one alone. Meteorological data and anatomical study also contribute their part to the interpretation of the facts of observation. In every case, Schimper has brought all possible data together in a more systematic and thorough manner than has been previously attempted. Hence, the probability that his conclusions are correct is very great. The bibliographies are remarkably complete and easy to consult because of their topical arrangement.

Another characteristic that will be pleasing to botanists everywhere is the absence of any undue predilection for Germany and German botanists. The work of botanists all over the world is given a proper share of attention. It is gratifying, too, to see the wealth of material furnished from tropical fields, and largely by the author himself. The use of the word ecology in place of biology is a pleasing departure and a deserved tribute to Warming.

Among the new points of view that are presented is Schimper's statement of the relation between plants and water. Hygrophytes are plants that further their transpiration, xerophytes are plants that check it, while the word tropophyte is introduced to include those plants which are hygrophytic at one season and xerophytic at another. According to this view, these terms are place on a physiological rather than a physical basis. The plant itself, rather than the soil in which it grows, is called hygrophytic or xerophytic.

Another striking difference from Warming is seen in considering various ecological agents equivalent with water as factors in classification. Thus the simplicity of Warming's classification is replaced by a much greater complexity. This is the common fate of all sciences, as is well illustrated by a comparison of the simple taxonomic system of Linnaeus with that of Engler. The great zones of the earth are determined primarily by the distribution of heat, while the great formations of these zones, such as forest, savanna, or desert, are determined chiefly by meteoric water. The local diversities in these great regions are said to be caused by differences in the soil. Thus we have two great types of formations: (1) climatic formations which characterize great regions and are caused by climatic factors, and (2) edaphic (from *edaphos* [the ancient Greek word for], soil) formations, which make up the local variations in any district and are due to a local dominance of edaphic over climatic influences. Schimper also lays much greater stress than does Warming upon the influence of light, heat, atmospheric density, and the chemical nature of the soil, in shaping the character of the vegetation.

It seems unfortunate to the reviewer that more attention was not paid to what may be called, speaking broadly, the geological relation. The short section on the transformation of edaphic to climatic formations is excellent and might well be much enlarged. In order to understand any formation it is necessary to know its history, and this history can be interpreted only by the most painstaking study of areas in which transitions from edaphic to climatic formations are now taking place. With this study there must be coupled a study of the physiographic history of the region. The study of the cumulative influence of past environments, the lagging of effects behind their causes, is still in its infancy. Perhaps it is because of our lack of knowledge along these lines that Schimper's great work deals so much more with static than with developmental ecology.

This new treatise is a distinct addition to our knowledge, both as a compendium of previously stated but scattered facts, and as a source of many new details and better points of view. Of course all ecologists must have it and must be familiar with its contents from cover to cover. This new volume is certain to stand always as one of the great botanical masterpieces.

Frederic E. Clements

THE PHYTOGEOGRAPHY OF NEBRASKA (1898) [BY ROSCOE POUND AND CLEMENTS]

Botanical Gazette May 1898

This is a distinct and noteworthy addition to the ecological plant geography of this country. It is a general survey, the first of a series of installments dealing with the floral covering of Nebraska from the phytogeographic standpoint. The authors follow very largely the methods of Drude, especially as outlined in his *Planzengeographie von Deutschland* [Plant Geography of Germany].

The introduction discusses the relation between phytogeography and biology, and gives an interesting history of the investigation of the Nebraska flora. The first chapter is introductory, dealing with the physiognomy and climatology of the state. The second chapter is entitled "Statistic and regional limitation," and after the enunciation of certain general principles there is to be found a characterization of the four regions into which the authors subdivide the state: the wooded bluff and meadow land, prairie, sand-hill and foothill regions. Then follow lists of species in which these regions agree and differ. The third chapter, the "Vegetation forms of the flora," is of great interest. The authors at this point depart somewhat from Drude's classification, but such departure seems almost inevitable in view of the great difference between the life conditions in Germany and Nebraska. The main subdivisions are into woody plants, half-shrubs, pleiocyclic herbs, hapaxanthous herbs, water plants, hysterophytes, [and] thallophytes. These groups are quite intimately subdivided, especially the pleiocyclic herbs and thallophytes. The next chapter has to do with the "Ecological and biological relations of the natural groups." The pteridophytes and spermatophytes are discussed in successive groups with regard to habitat, or as Warming would say, they are referred to their respective plant societies. The fifth and last chapter treats of the "Plant formations of the state." These are quite fully treated and are, of course, full of interest to plant geographers. Perhaps the most distinctive formations are those of the sand hills, with their bunch grasses, blow outs, and sand draws; and of the foothills, with their undershrubs, mats, and rosettes.

Inasmuch as this is the pioneer work of its kind in America, the task of its authors was peculiarly difficult. Questions of terminology in ecological plant geography are of no easy settlement because the field is so very new, and the transference of German classifications and technical terms to American soil involves great difficulty, just as the correlation of European and American geological strata caused confusion when the attempt was first made. The adverse criticisms suggested by a hasty perusal have to do largely with terminology, and hence are not of the most vital importance. There seems to be, for example, a strong tendency to use Greek derivatives in place of the simpler and more expressive English equivalents. The extension of the term "thallophyte" to include mosses and liverworts seems very objectionable, not only because the term has long been preempted by morphologists, but because there is a radical ecological distinction between the true thallus and the moss gametophyte. The rejection of Warming's term mesophyte is very questionable, since it involves the introduction of several new terms and destroys the unity of the classification; a subdivision of the mesophytes into forest, grass, and waste societies would serve the authors' purpose fully as well.

It may be too early as yet to predict whether the direction to future work in plant geography will be given by Warming or by Drude; and so whether we shall speak of ecology or phytogeography, of life forms or of vegetation forms, of plant societies or formations, is yet to be decided. Perhaps the solution will be by a division of labor, phytogeography including the larger problems of distribution and dealing with extensive formations, while ecology will have to do more with local and habitat relations, including anatomical as well as field investigation. In any event, the *Phytogeography of Nebraska* will be an indispensable work to all American students along either line.

THE DEVELOPMENT AND STRUCTURE
OF VEGETATION (1904)

Botanical Gazette October 1904

One of the most important recent contributions to the literature of ecology is a work on the development and structure of vegetation, from the hand of Dr. CLEMENTS. The object of this and a forthcoming volume is to present in a systematic and detailed manner the methods of ecological research that have been employed by the author for a number of years in the prairies and woodlands of Nebraska, and in the mountains of Colorado. The principles enunciated here were formulated as working hypotheses in 1898, and have since been submitted to rigorous field tests. The present paper deals in particular with the biological side of vegetation, while the forthcoming work is to be concerned more with the physical aspects.

The fundamental phenomena of vegetation are regarded as invasion and succession (dynamic), zonation and alternation (static), and association, the latter representing the stage to which vegetation has been brought. A section is devoted to each of these topics, and in each case there is given a historical survey of the phenomenon, followed by a keen analysis, and a bibliography. One may classify associations with relation to stratum, light, water, etc., but of these CLEMENTS strongly emphasizes the dominance of the water factor. He inclines not to accept SCHIMPER'S edaphic and climatic associations, holding that all but submerged associations are both climatic and edaphic. Invasion consists of the movement (migration) and establishment (ecesis) of species. In discussing this topic, a number of terms are introduced applying to the plant member that migrates, the character of the contrivance which facilitates migration, and the agent involved. Polygenesis (theory of polytopic origin) is carefully analyzed, and the author fully accepts it as a valid theory. Successions are divided into primary (on new soil), and secondary (on denuded soil). Some excellent terms are introduced, indicating the direction of movement in the succession, xerotropic, mesotropic, and hydrotropic, and their application is obvious.

The author gives laws of succession, which will be admitted at once in most cases, though it is likely that some may require modification. Zonation has been more fully considered by former authors than have the other topics treated here, but alternation is a phenomenon that has been discussed and developed only slightly except by Dr. CLEMENTS. Alternation is defined as the response of vegetation to the heterogeneity of the earth's surface, and is in sharp contrast to zonation as it is related to topographic asymmetry. A very interesting analysis is made of competition, which the author holds to be a physical factor in the last analysis.

This book is most difficult to review adequately, because of the great number of vital topics which are presented. The presentation is so logical and concise that a satisfactory review or summary would be little less than a verbatim reproduction of the work. The paper must be digested thoroughly from beginning to end by all who profess to be engaged in ecological research, and it should be studied by all botanists, especially those who think that ecology may not hope to deal with facts or have the logic or discipline of other lines of biology.

RESEARCH METHODS IN ECOLOGY (1905)

Botanical Gazette November 1905

We seldom receive a work whose central idea is essentially new, but Dr. CLEMENTS'S latest volume almost if not quite attains this distinction. The ecology of our day is to be divided into the true and the false, and most of it, unfortunately, is of the latter type. It is a subject which, on the surface, seems to lend itself well to the lovers of fads, and there are many "contributions" to ecology which consist of a hasty gathering together of notes made in leisure moments during summer holidays. The true ecology, the ecology that is to be, is developed only by the most arduous and long-continued work. The dilettante ecology is to pass away, and one of the foremost causes for this change will be this new book of CLEMENTS.

The opening chapter reveals the author's ideals as to the meaning and place of ecology, its historical development, its present status (largely deplorable, because so many tyros are making desperate attempts to enter the new and inviting field), and its relationships with other botanical lines of research. The second chapter, entitled the habitat, considers in detail the various ecological factors, and will be of extraordinary value to ecological research, because it recounts in full the ingenious and multiform methods that have been employed by the author in the study of the Nebraska and Colorado vegetation. Soil, water-content, atmospheric humidity, and light are regarded as direct factors, and hence more attention is paid to them than to indirect factors (such as temperature), or remote factors (such as altitude). The various instruments of precision, such as psychrometers, psychrographs, photometers, thermographs, and many others, are figured and their use explained in full. For the physical and physiological water-content of the soil, the author proposes respectively the terms holard and chresard. The word ecograph is employed as a general term embracing all instruments that are used for the determination of physical habitat factors. Much space is devoted, and properly, to the intelligent expression of results; we greatly regret that the metric system is not used exclusively in these tables.

"The plant" is the title of the third chapter, and an admirable survey is given of the more important adjustments and adaptations; the former word is used to denote functional response, the latter structural response. These most important distinctions are often disregarded, thus leading to deplorable confusion. Response to water is termed hydroharmose, to light photoharmose. In this, as in the preceding chapter, methods of measurement are described, but of course they are much less satisfactory. This is a difficulty that in part inheres in the more complex phenomena that are to be measured, but also in part in the fact that physiologists have failed to cultivate as they might this fertile and enticing field. One might wish for a softening of the teleological terminology, as in p. 129 and p. 143; whether there is or is not an ultimate teleology, it seems wiser to discard its vocabulary. It seems to the reviewer that expressions implying purpose are in part responsible for the disfavor in which ecology is sometimes held. The close of this chapter is devoted to a consideration of experimental evolution, and a full account is given of natural, habitat, and control cultures.

The final chapter considers plant formations, and their study is based on the quadrat method, much of which the author has previously published. Among the subjects here treated are cartography, photography, and formation herbaria. The discussion of the development and structure of vegetation is much like a separate treatise on the same subject already reviewed in these pages. Methods for the study of succession and competition are given. At the close is a helpful glossary.

One can scarcely praise this work too much; it is what is needed to prevent ecology from falling into a swift and merited disfavor. If read and pondered, it will prevent the thoughtless from entering the ecological field, and it will serve the higher end of directing the thoughtful as to the methods of procedure.

PLANT SUCCESSION: AN ANALYSIS OF THE DEVELOPMENT OF VEGETATION (1916)

Botanical Gazette December 1919

Clements has brought together in a satisfactory way and in sumptuous form the contributions of all previous workers dealing with the phenomena of succession in vegetation. The work of the various students of succession is conscientiously and sympathetically presented, and with great fullness. So admirably is this work done that it will henceforth be largely unnecessary to refer to original publications, prior to the appearance of this work, in order to get the substantial views of the various authors. The work is thus a compendium of our knowledge and theories bearing on the phenomena of succession. In the field covered by this work, CLEMENTS is himself a major contributor, and in no previous work has he contributed so much new material on the subject as this work includes. No more can be attempted here than to touch a few of the high spots.

As previously, CLEMENTS treats the formation as an organism, with structures and functions like an individual plant. As compared with previous studies by the same author, greater stress is placed on development and less on habitat. To the reviewer this seems a distinct step forward, although many workers, especially in Europe, will continue to emphasize habitat as the controlling factor in classification. The formation is defined as "the climax community of a natural area in which the essential climatic relations are similar or identical." Thus CLEMENTS' formation, as here presented, departs materially from the concept of the Brussels Congress, but agrees essentially with the "climax formation" of the reviewer, and with the still earlier "climatic formation" of SCHIMPER. SCHIMPER, however, probably failed to recognize that his "climatic formation" was really the topmost member of a series of his "edaphic formations." A number of new terms of classical origin are introduced in this volume, as is the wont of the author. Perhaps the most important of these is "sere," a term used to include the entire successional series leading up to the climax. This term is used, rather than its essential equivalent "series," because of its adaptability in combination, as in xerosere (a xerarch series), etc. CLEMENTS' treatment of the term "climax" is in general harmony with the often expressed interpretation of the reviewer; "the climatic formation is the real climax of the successional development." An apparent climax, short of the true regional climax, is termed a subclimax.

The chapter in which the views of the author and the reviewer clash most sharply is the one on direction of development. CLEMENTS states positively that "succession is inherently and inevitably progressive." The reviewer is as positive in his opinion as ever that succession may be retrogressive as well as progressive, although of course progression is much more abundant and important. What the reviewer would term retrogression is for the most part by CLEMENTS termed denudation, preparatory to the initiation of another successional series. This might pass, if all such denudations or retrogressions were sudden, resulting at once in the development of a habitat initial to a progressive series. In an area that is gradually sinking, there may be a gradual retrogression from a climax mesophytic forest to a hydrophytic association, with no denudation of any sort whatever. In a review of CLEMENTS' work by TANSLEY ["The Development of Vegetation." *Journal of Ecology*, 4: 198–204 (1916)], it is shown that it would be very difficult to apply to England the idea that succession is always progressive.

Chapters follow on the classification of "seres," the climax formations of North America, past climates and climaxes, and past succession. The chapters on past climates and vegetation will be of great value, because they bring together compactly results from widely scattered sources. The theories and the applications of the author's views to the past seem very tenuous. It is difficult enough to apply ecological principles to the vegetation of the present, and it is very much too soon to work out the characteristics and successions of past floras in any but the most superficial manner.

The work is a notable one, and must be on the working table of every ecologist and plant geographer. It is unfortunate, however, that the author has allowed his splendid classical training and love for Greek and Latin to carry him so far afield. The tendency nowadays is toward increasing emphasis on the vernacular, and it is to be feared that many of the author's best thoughts and most inspiring ideas will remain hidden among words.

THE INTERNATIONAL PHYTOGEOGRAHICAL EXCURSION IN THE BRITISH ISLES

IMPRESSIONS OF THE FOREIGN MEMBERS OF THE PARTY

The New Phytologist January 1912

It is too early to determine the most striking results of this excursion to the science of Phytogeography, but it is not too early to predict with certainty that its influence will be very important and far-reaching. It is easier to distinguish the benefits of the excursion to its participants than to the science in general. I have felt that the chief benefit to me has been the opportunity of living for a month in intimate relationship with my phytogeographic colleagues of other countries, of knowing them from many points of view, and thus of coming to feel that they are friends, as well as fellow scientists. This month of living and travelling together made us much better acquainted with each other's views and field interpretations, and also made it possible to read each other's writings much more understandingly than heretofore. Close companionship has made us more sympathetic with opposing viewpoints, and more ready to see at least some truth in views we thought were wholly wrong. Such results must come from every excursion of this sort, and if only we have enough of them to bring all the active phytogeographers of the world into sympathetic touch with others of their kind, we may hope soon to see a marked diminution in the misunderstanding of viewpoints, and in the amount of polemic literature. It is from such intimate acquaintanceship among the workers and, perhaps, only thus that we may hope for constructive advances in securing uniformity of terms and methods. For example, it is difficult for an American to understand from the literature the precise signification of such terms as heath or moor, but in the field last summer these and other terms of the European workers were so often illustrated by concrete examples that they became thoroughly familiar.

As an American, I was, of course, much interested in seeing intelligently new kinds of vegetation. To the European members of the party this joy was much less possible, although there seemed to be points of considerable variance, even with Continental Europe. I was amazed at the vast amount of wild country in densely populated England. The extensive areas of the Broads, the sand dunes and salt-marshes, the numerous heaths and moorlands, were more widespread and much more natural than I had expected them to be. While America may be more fortunate than Europe in the possession of great natural formations of plants, I was fully convinced that in the British Isles, at least, there is quite enough to occupy phytogeographic students actively for a long time to come. Many successional series were observed, whose progression or retrogression was quite as evident as in American formations, and to whose significance the British workers are fully alive.

I cannot close these rambling notes without expressing my admiration for the splendid organization of the British plant geographers. Doubtless it is largely this that has enabled them to accomplish so much in so short a time. My admiration for British social customs, as we saw them, is also very great. The hearty greetings that met us everywhere, the interest expressed in our work on the part even of those who could know little of it, the constant display of whole-souled British hospitality—all these things and many more have made August, 1911, a most memorable period in our lives.

A.G. Tansley

TYPES OF BRITISH VEGETATION (1911)

Botanical Gazette April 1912

In two respects, at least, the appearance of *Types of British Vegetation* marks an epoch in the development of plant geography. In the first place, the publication of the volume at this time is due to the organization of an International Phytogeographic Excursion in the British Isles during the summer of 1911. The volume was prepared in anticipation of this excursion; and advance copies were presented to the members of the party. The chief result of this excursion has been to internationalize for all time the subject of plant geography, and to divest it of the provincialism which has hitherto too greatly characterized it. Besides marking the initiation of internationalism in phytogeography, this volume marks another great advance, namely, the study of vegetation by an organization rather than by an individual. While edited by TANSLEY, the volume was gotten together by the "Central Committee for the survey and study of British vegetation," more popularly known as the "British vegetation committee." It is not so long ago that the study of vegetation played an insignificant part in British botany. Through the work of their vegetation committee, the British have not only caught up with their American and continental brethren, but, in organization at least, they have forged ahead.

The introduction deals with the units of vegetation, following the general lines previously marked out by MOSS. While all plant geographers seem to believe in the reality of the terms formation and association, and to believe that the formation should be used as the larger unit, including various smaller units or associations, it is evident from this book, as from the discussions of the 1911 excursion, that the British plant geographers differ radically from all others in the practical application of these terms. For example, calcareous soils are regarded as having a single formation, which includes such diverse things as limestone-pavement associations with almost bare rock surface, limestone grassland, limestone scrub, chalk heath, yew woods, ash woods, and beech woods. Similarly the sand-dune formation is composed of strand associations, morrain-grass and couch-grass associations, dune grassland, dune scrub with willows, and dune marshes. The reviewer has shown that on the sand dunes of Lake Michigan there is to be found nearly every kind of plant formation characteristic of the region, from the xerophytic vegetation of the moving dunes or the swamp vegetation of the dune depressions to a mesophytic climax forest of beech and maple. By the British concept all of these are to be considered as composing a single formation! It must be admitted that the British concept of formation is the most workable yet proposed, for it represents in essence the aggregate of plant associations which compose a successional series on a given habitat. It must be admitted also that those who oppose the British concept are not agreed among themselves, when it comes to actual field discriminations between associations and formations. However the British concept proposed by MOSS and adopted by the committee, represents a most radical departure from all past formational concepts, and seems to be out of harmony with the proposals internationally agreed upon in Brussels in 1910.

Whatever may be said concerning concepts and modes of classification, nothing but praise can be rendered for the detailed presentation of British vegetation. [This article concludes with a detailed review of British vegetation as described by the book's contributors.]

John Merle Coulter

OBITUARY

Botanical Gazette (March 1929)

JOHN MERLE COULTER, who founded the BOTANICAL GAZETTE, and who edited it for more than half a century, died December 23, 1928, at Yonkers, New York.

The Gazette in its infancy was a very unpretentious undertaking, consisting each month of a four-page leaflet, the first number of which was issued at Hanover, Indiana, in November, 1875. At first the new journal was known as the Botanical Bulletin, but from the second volume it has been known as the Botanical Gazette, the change of name being made out of regard for the previously existing bulletin of the Torrey Botanical Club.

For the first few years M.S. COULTER, now better known as STANLEY COULTER, was coeditor with his brother. In 1883 CHARLES R. BARNES, then at Purdue University, and J.C. ARTHUR, then at Charles City, Iowa, became joint editors with Professor COULTER. At that time the journal was much enlarged, and was organized into departments. For many years the Gazette was published by the editors, who bore all financial, as well as editorial responsibility for the journal. At first the subscription price was but $1.00 a year, and for several years there was no advertising matter, yet almost from the outset the journal paid its way. In the first twenty years of publication the home of the Gazette changed with the abode of one of the editors; at first it was issued from Hanover, Indiana, then from Crawfordsville, Indiana, and Bloomington, Indiana, the successive homes of Professor COULTER. From Bloomington it went to Madison, Wisconsin, at the time the residence of Professor BARNES.

In 1896 the Botanical Gazette was taken over by the University of Chicago Press, under whose auspices it has since been published. At the same time several prominent American botanists became associate editors, and the following year a group of foreign botanists was added to the list of associate editors. Commencing with 1900, Professor ARTHUR ceased to be a coeditor with COULTER and BARNES, and his name was added to the list of associate editors. Thenceforward the main editorial responsibility rested with Professor COULTER and Professor BARNES, with the assistance of the other members of the botany staff at the University of Chicago. Upon the death of Professor BARNES in 1910, Professor COULTER once more assumed the chief editorial responsibility, and he continued in this capacity until 1926, when the main responsibility passed to the writer of this sketch. Even after the chief editorial burden was set aside, Professor COULTER continued to maintain a lively interest in the journal, contributing many reviews and performing various other editorial functions.

The growth of the Botanical Gazette in size and in the number of fields covered in its articles is a measure of the growth of botany in America since 1875. At first the contributions were mostly short taxonomic or floristic notes, without illustrations. Gradually the major contributions lengthened, were more profound in character, and often were illustrated. Morphology was early added to taxonomy as a field of interest, and later contributions appeared in physiology, ecology, mycology, pathology, genetics, and the other fields of modern botany. If Professor COULTER had no other monument than the Botanical Gazette, his place in the botanical roll of honor would forever be assured.

JOHN MERLE COULTER was born in Ningpo, China, November 20, 1851, the son of missionary parents. Upon the death of his father in 1853, his mother returned to America with the children, taking up residence at Hanover, Indiana, her father's home. His boyhood days were spent in southern Indiana, mostly at Hanover. He attended Hanover College, from which he was graduated in 1870 with the degree of Bachelor of Arts. His first teaching position was at a Presbyterian Academy at Logansport, Indiana, where he remained from the autumn of 1870 through the spring of 1872, not as a teacher of botany, but as a teacher of Latin.

In 1872 an event occurred which had a profound influence on Professor COULTER'S subsequent career. He was given an opportunity to join the famous Hayden Survey of the Yellowstone, which occupied most of his attention for two years. His appointment was as assistant geologist, but while spending some weeks at Ogden, Utah, where the party was outfitting, he spent his time in collecting and studying the plants of the neighborhood. This came to the notice of Dr. HAYDEN, who needed a botanist, since the originally appointed botanist of the expedition had failed him. So the position was given to Mr. COULTER, who always regarded this incident as a veritable turning point in his life.

The degree of Master of Arts was conferred on the young botanist in 1873 by Hanover College, and from 1874 to 1879 he was Professor of Natural Sciences at that institution. It was during these years that he and his brother founded the Botanical Gazette. In 1879 he was called to the chair of Biology at Wabash College, where he remained until 1891. In 1882 he received the degree of Doctor of Philosophy at the University of Indiana, which called him to the botanical professorship and the presidency in 1891. In 1893 he went to the presidency of Lake Forest University. In 1896 he was called to the headship of the new Department of Botany at the University of Chicago, where he remained until his retirement in 1925. In the latter year he took up his residence at Yonkers, New York, the seat of the Boyce Thompson Institute for Plant Research, which he helped to organize, and on whose Board of Directors he was a member from the outset.

Professor COULTER was a charter member of the Botanical Society of America, and was twice its president. He was a long-time member of the American Association for the Advancement of Science and its president in 1919, a member of the National Academy of Sciences, and a member of many other scientific societies at home and abroad.

The early work of Professor COULTER was mostly in the field of taxonomy. This was natural enough, for in the seventies and eighties most American botany was in this field. When he went to Washington to work up his western collections, he chanced to meet ASA GRAY, who took a great interest in the young Indiana botanist; from that time forth until the death of GRAY in 1888, the friendship between the two was close and intimate. COULTER always attributed much of his success to the influence of GRAY. The Hayden expedition naturally enough suggested the early attention of Mr. COULTER to the flora of the Rocky Mountains, and one of his earliest works was a synopsis of the flora of Colorado, published in 1874 in collaboration with T.C. PORTER. Commencing with 1875, Professor COULTER contributed many articles to the Botanical Gazette, the first of which were mainly taxonomic. In 1885 there appeared his well known Manual of the Botany of the Rocky Mountain Region, and in 1909 was issued the Manual of Rocky Mountain Botany in collaboration with AVEN NELSON. His Botany of Western Texas appeared as a contribution of the United States National Herbarium in 1891–1894.

. . . [The article lists and describes other publications in taxonomy and morphology, his textbooks, and contributions to other fields.]

Great as were Professor COULTER'S contributions to taxonomy, morphology, and other fields, and as a botanical editor, it is probable that his greatest single influence was as a teacher. He was an inspiring lecturer, a splendid counselor, and a devoted friend. His kindly sympathy and help drew all his students closely to him, and made them devoted followers. He inspired many men and women to devote themselves to botanical research and botanical teaching. . . .

A scientific journal, such as the BOTANICAL GAZETTE, is hardly the place to speak more intimately and appreciatively of Professor COULTER'S life and influence, even though this is the journal that he founded and edited for so many years. It is perhaps enough to say that there has passed from us a man loved and admired, not only by his fellow botanists and former students, but also by many in other fields of science, and in every walk in life; that there has gone a great teacher, a gifted editor, an inspiring lecturer, and a facile writer; and that, as he himself said on the death of Professor BARNES, "a priceless asset has become a memory."

PLANT LIST

Abies balsamea	Balsam Fir
Acer dasycarpum	River Maple
Acer rubrum	Red Maple
Acer saccharinum	Silver Maple
Acer saccharium	Sugar Maple
Achillea millefolium	Yarrow
Acorus calamus	Sweet Flag
Actinea acaulis	Angelita Daisy
Actinea herbacea	Lakeside Daisy
Aesculus glabra	Buckeye
Agropyron dasystachyum	Western Wheat Grass
Agropyron smithii	
Agropyrum junceum	Sand Couch
Agrostis alba vulgaris Agrostis alba	Red Top
Aletris farinosa	Colic Root
Allium cernuum	Wild Onion
Alnus incana Alnus rugosa	Speckled Alder
Ambrosia	Ragweed
Ambrosia trifida	Giant Ragweed
Amelanchier canadensis	Juneberry, Serviceberry
Amelanchier arborea	
Ammophila brevigulata	Common Marram Grass
Amorpha canescens	Leadplant
Ampelopsis quinquefolia	Virginia Creeper
Parthenocissus quinquefolia	
Andromeda	Heath
Andropogon scoparius	Little Bluestem Grass
Anemone dichotoma	Forked Anemone
Anemone multifida	Pacific anemone
Anemone nemorosa	Blue Wood Anemone
Antennaria	Pussy Toes
Antennaria plantaginifolia	Plantain-Leafed Pussy Toes, Pussy Toes Everlasting
Aphyllon fasciculatum	Clustered Broomrape

Aquilegia canadensis — Wild Columbine
Arabis lyrata — Sand Cress
Arctostaphylos uva-ursi — Bearberry
Arenaria michauxii — Michaux's stitchwort
Arisaema dracontia — Green Dragon
Arisaema triphyllum — Jack-in-the-Pulpit
Artemisia canadensis — Beach Wormwood
    Artemisia caudata
Asclepias cornuti Asclepias syriaca — Common Milkweed
Asclepias incarnata — Swamp Milkweed
Asimina triloba — Pawpaw
Aspidium thelypteris — Marsh Fern
Asplenium — Fern
Aster laevis — Smooth Aster
Aster linariifolius — Flax-Leaved Aster

Baptisia — Wild Indigo
Basidiomycetes — Club Fungi
Batrachospermum — Alga
Betula alleghaniensis — Yellow Birch, Sweet Birch
Betula papyrifera — Paper Birch
Betula pumila — Dwarf Birch
Botrydium — Alga
Brasenia — Water Lily
Bryum — Moss genus

Cakile edentula — Sea Rocket
Cakile maritime — Sea Kale
Calamagrostis longifolia — Prairie Sand Reed
    Calamovilfa longifolia var. longifolia
Calla — Arum
Calopogon tuberosus — Grass Pink
Caltha palustris — Marsh Marigold
Campanula rotundifolia arctica — Harebell
Cardamine bulbosa — Bulbous Cress
Carex muhlenbergii — Sand Bracted Sedge
Carex pennsylvanica — Common Oak Sedge
Carex umbellata — Early Oak Sedge
Carya — Hickory
Carya alba — Shell-Bark Hickory
Carya porcina — Pig Nut
Carya tomentosa — Mockernut Hickory

Cassandra calyculata	Leatherleaf
Chamaedaphne calyculata	
Castanea	Chestnut
Castilleja coccinea	Indian Paintbrush
Castilleja sessiliflora	Downy Yellow Painted Cup
Caulophyllum thalictroides	Blue Cohosh
Ceanothus americanus	New Jersey Tea
Celastrus scandens	Climbing Bittersweet
Celtis occidentalis pumila	Common Hackberry
Cephalanthus occidentalis	Buttonbush
Ceratodon	Moss genus
Ceratodon purpureus	Fire Moss
Ceratophyllum	Hornwort
Cercis canadensis	Red Bud
Chamaedeaphne calyculata	Leatherleaf
Chara	Alga
Chelone glabra	Turtlehead
Cirsium pitcheri	Dune Thistle; Pitcher's Thistle
Cladonia rangiferina	Caribou moss; Reindeer lichen
Cladophora	Alga
Claytonia virginica	Spring Beauty
Clintonia borealis	Bluebead
Cnicus pitcheri Cirsium pitcheri	Pitchers thistle
Collinsia verna	Blue-Eyed Mary
Coptis trifolia	Goldthread
Corispermum hyssopifolium	Bugseed
Cornus baileyi	Red-Twigged Dogwood
Cornus canadensis	Bunchberry
Cornus circinata Cornus rugosa	Round-Leafed Dogwood
Cornus florida	Flowering Dogwood
Cornus stolonifera	Red Osier Dogwood
Corylus americana	Hazel
Crategus spp.	Hawthorn
Crategus coccinea	Scarlet Hawthorn
Crategus punctata	Dotted Hawthorn
Cryptotaenia	Honewort
Cuscuta gronovii	Dodder
Cyperus schweinitzii	Rough Sand Sedge
Cyperipedium spp.	Lady's Slipper Orchid
Dicentra spp.	Dutchman's Breeches
Diervilla trifida	Bush Honeysuckle

Dodecatheon	Shooting Star
Draba caroliniana Draba reptans	Common Whitlow Grass
Drosera rotundifolia	Round-Leafed Sundew
Dulichium spp.	Sedge
Elodea	Waterweed
Elodes campanulata	Marsh St. John's Wort
Elymus arenarius	Lyme Grass
Elymus canadensis	Canada Wild Rye
Epigaea repens	Trailing Arbutus
Epifagus virginiana	Beech Drop
Equisetum arvense	Horsetail
Equisetum hyemale	Tall Scouring Rush
Equisetum scirpoides	Dwarf Scouring Rush
Eriophorum	Cotton Grass
Eriophorum cyperinus	Wool Grass
Eryngium	Rattlesnake Master
Erythronium albidum	White Dog-Toothed Violet
Eupatorium spp.	Boneset
Euphorbia	Spurge
Euphorbia corollata	Flowering Spurge
Euphorbia polygonifolia	Seaside Spurge
Fagus ferruginea	Beech
Fatsia horrida	Devil's Club
Festuca tenella Vulpia octoflora	Slender Fescue Grass
Fragaria virginiana	Wild Strawberry
Fraxinus americana	White Ash
Galium aparine	Annual Bedstraw, Cleavers
Galium boreale	Northern Bedstraw
Gaultheria procumbens	Wintergreen
Gaylussacia resinosa	Black Huckleberry
Gentiana crinita	Fringed Gentian
Gerardia purpurea	Purple Gerardia
Geranium maculatum	Wild Geranium
Geranium robertianum	Herb Robert
Glechoma hederacea	Ground Ivy
Glossopteris	Seed Fern
Gymnocladus canadensis	Coffee Tree
Gymnocladus dioica	
Hamamelis virginiana	Witch Hazel

Helianthemum canadense	Common Rock Rose
Helianthus divaricatus	Woodland Sunflower
Hepatica triloba Hepatica americana	Round-Leafed Hepatica
Heracleum spp.	Parsnip
Heuchera richardsonii	Prairie Alum Root
Hibiscus palustris	Swamp Rose Mallow
Hudsonia tomentosa	False Heather
Hydrodictyon	Alga
Hydrophyllum virginianum	Virginia Waterleaf
Hypericum kalmianum	Kalm's St. Johns Wort
Hypoxis erecta	Star Grass
Ilex verticillata	Winterberry
Impatiens spp.	Jewelweed
Iris virginica	Blue Flag Iris
Isopyrum biternatum	False Rue Anemone
Juglans cinerea	Butternut
Juglans nigra	Walnut
Juncus balticus littoralis	Lake Shore Rush
Juniperus communis	Common Juniper
Juniperus horizontalis	Trailing Juniper
Juniperus sabina procumbens	Savin Juniper
Juniperus virginiana	Red Cedar
Koeleria cristata	June Grass
Krigia virginica	Dwarf Dandelion
Laportea canadensis	Wood Nettle
Larix americana (Larix laricina)	Tamarack
Lathyrus maritimus	Beach Pea
Lathryus japonicus glaber	
Lemnaceae	Duckweed
Lepachys	Coneflower
Lespedeza capitata	Round-Headed Bush Clover
Liatris spp.	Blazing Star
Linaria canadensis	Blue Toadflax
Linnaea borealis	Twin Flower
Liquidambar	Sweet Gum
Liriodendron tulipifera	Tulip
Lithospermum hirtum	Hairy Puccoon
Lithospermum croceum	

Lonicera involucrata	Bracted Honeysuckle
Ludwigia palustris	Marsh Purslane
Lupinus perennis	Wild Lupine
Lycopodium obscurum	Ground Pine
Lycopus spp.	Horehound
Melampyrum americanum	American Cow-Wheat
Melampyrum lineare	
Melilotus	Sweet Clover
Melilotus alba	White Sweet Clover
Mentha	Mint
Menyanthes trifoliata	Buckbean
Mertensia virginica	Virginia Bluebells
Mitella	Bishop's Cap
Mollugo verticillata	Carpet Weed
Monarda punctata	Horse Mint
Morus rubra	Mulberry
Myrica cerifera	Bayberry, Wax Myrtle
Myriophyllum	Water Milfoil
Naias	Naiad
Nasturtium palustre	Water Cress
Nelumbo	Lotus
Nepeta glechoma Glechoma hederacea	Ground Ivy
Nuphar advena	Yellow Pond Lily
Nympyhaea odorata Nymphaea tuberosa	White Water Lily
Nyssa sylvatica	Sour Gum
Oedogonium	Alga
Oenothera biennis	Common Evening Primrose
Oenothera rhombipetala	Western Sand Evening Primrose
Onoclea sensibilis	Sensitive Fern
Opuntia rafinesqii Opuntia humifusa	Eastern Prickly Pear
Osmorrhiza	Sweet Cicely
Osmunda	Flowering Fern
Osmunda cinnamonea	Cinnamon Fern
Osmunda claytonia	Interrupted Fern
Osmunda regalis	Royal Fern
Ostrya virginiana	Hop Hornbeam, Ironwood
Parnassia glauca	Grass of Parnassus
Parthenocnissus quinquefolia	Virginia Creeper
Ampelosis quinquefolia	

Pastinaca sativa	Wild Parsnip
Pellaea atropurpurea	Purple Cliff Brake
Penthorum sedoides	Ditch Stonecrop
Petalostemon (Petalostemum) spp.	Prairie Clover
Phlox divaricata	Blue Phlox
Phlox pilosa	Sand Prairie Phlox
Phragmites australis	Common Reed
Physocarpus opulifolius	Nine Bark
Pilea	Clearweed
Pinus banksiana	Scrub or Jack Pine
Pinus pungens	Table Mountain Pine
Pinus resinosa	Red Pine
Pinus rigida	Pitch Pine
Pinus strobus	White Pine
Plantago cordata	Heart-Leaved Plantain
Platanus occidentalis	Sycamore
Poa compressa	Canada Blue Grass, Wire Grass
Poa pratensis	Kentucky Blue Grass
Podophyllum peltatum	May Apple
Pogonia spp.	Orchid
Polemonium reptans	Jacob's Ladder
Polygala sanguinea	Field Milkwort
Polygonella articulata	Jointweed
Polygonum hartwrightii,	Water Knotweed,
Polygonum amphibium var.	Water Smartweed
stipulaceum	
Polygonum aviculare	Common Doorweed,
	Common Knotweed
Polygonum hydropiper	Water Pepper
Polygonum ramosissimum	Bushy Knotweed
Polygonum sagittatum	Arrow-Leaved Tearthumb
Polygonum tenue	Slender Knotweed
Polytrichum commune	Hair Cap Moss
Pontederia cordata	Pickerel Weed
Populus balsamifera	Balsam Poplar
Populus grandidentata	Large-Toothed Aspen
Populus heterophylla	Downy Poplar
Populus monilifera	Plains Cottonwood
Populus deltoides monilifera	
Populus tremuloides	Quaking Aspen
Potamogeton	Pondweed
Potentilla anserina	Silverweed

Potentilla argentea	Silvery Cinquefoil
Potentilla arguta	Prairie Cinquefoil
Potentilla fruticosa	Shrubby Cinquefoil
Potentilla palustris	Marsh Cinquefoil, Swamp Cinquefoil
Potentilla tridentata	Three-Toothed Cinquefoil
Prenanthes alba	White Lettuce
Primula mistassinica	Birds Eye Primrose
Prosperpinaca palustris	Mermaid Weed
Prunus pennsylvanica	Pin Cherry, Large Red Cherry
Prunus pumila	Sand Cherry
Prunus virginiana	Choke Cherry
Psamma arenaria	[European] Marram Grass
Ptelea trifoliata	Downy Wafer Ash, Hop Tree
Pteris aquilina	Common Brake
Pyrola spp.	Shinleaf
Pyrus arbutifolia	Red Chokeberry
Pyrus coronaria	Wild Crab
Quercus alba	White Oak
Quercus bicolor	Swamp White Oak
Quercus coccinea	Scarlet Oak
Quercus lyrata	Overcup Oak
Quercus macrocarpa	Bur Oak
Quercus nigra	Water Oak
Quercus primus	Chestnut Oak
Quercus rubra	Red Oak
Quercus stellata	Post Oak
Quercus texana	Texas Red Oak
Quercus velutina	Black Oak
Ranunculus cymbalaria	Seaside Crowfoot
Ranunculus longirostris	Whitewater Crowfoot (White Buttercup)
Ranunculus septrionalis	Common Buttercup
Rhus canadensis	Fragrant Sumac
Rhus copallina	Shining Sumac
Rhus glabra	Smooth Sumac
Rhus radicans	Poison Ivy
Rhus typhina	Staghorn Sumac
Rhus vernix, Rhus venenata, Toxicodendron vernix	Poison Sumac

Ribes cynosbati	Gooseberry
Ribes floridum	Wild Currant
Rosa blanda	Early Wild Rose
Rosa engelmanni Rosa acicularis	Bristly Rose
Rosa humilis Rosa carolina	Pasture Rose
Rubus hispidus	Swamp Dewberry
Rubus odoratus	Purple Flowering Raspberry
Rumex acetosella	Field Sorrel
Rumex verticillatus	Swamp Dock
Sabatia angularis	Rose Gentian
Sagittaria	Arrowhead
Sagittaria variabilis	Broadleaf Arrowhead
Salix adenophylla Salix syrticola	Dune Willow
Salix candida	Hoary Widow
Salix discolor	Pussy Willow
Salix glaucophylla Salix glaucophylloides	Blue-Leafed Willow
Salix humilis	Prairie Willow
Salix longifolia Salix interior	Sandbar Willow
Salix nigra	Black Willow
Salix syrticola	Dune Willow
Sanicula	Snakeroot
Sarracenia purpurea	Pitcher Plant
Sassafras officinale Sassafras albidum	Sassafras
Saxifraga pennsylvanica	Swamp Saxifrage
Scirpus lacustris	Bulrush
Scirpus pungens	Three-Square Bulrush; Chair Maker's Rush
Selaginella rupestris	Sand Club Moss
Shepherdia canadensis	Buffalo Berry
Silene stellata	Starry Campion
Silphium integrifolium	Rosin Weed
Silphium laciniatum	Compass Plant
Silphium terebinthinaceum	Prairie Dock
Sisyrinchium augustifolium	Stout Blue-Eyed Grass
Sium suave	Water Hemlock, Tall Water Parsnip
Smilacina stellata	Starry False Solomon's Seal
Smilax hispida	Bristly Green Brier
Smilax tamnoides var. hispida	
Solidago humilis gillmani	Dune Goldenrod
Solidago racemosa var. gillmani	

ANTHOLOGY: PLANT LIST

Solidago nemoralis	Old-Field Goldenrod
Solidago rigida	Stiff Goldenrod
Sparganium eurycarpum	Common Bur Reed
Sphagnum	Peat Moss
Sphalaraea remota	Wild Hollyhock
Spiraea salicifolia	Bridewort
Spiraea tomentosa	Steeple Bush
Spirodela	Duckweed
Spirogyra	Alga
Strophostyles	Wild Beans
Stylophorum	Poppy
Styrax americana	Snowbell
Sullivantia ohioensis	Moss
Sullivantia renifolia	Sullivant's Saxifrage
Sullivantia sullivantii	Sullivant's Coolwort
Symplocarpus foetidus	Skunk Cabbage
Synthyris bullii	Bull's Coral Drops
Talinum teretifolium	Appalachian Fameflower
Tanacetum huronense	Eastern Tansy
Taxodium distichum	Bald Cypress
Taxus	Yew
Tephrosia virginiana	Goat's Rue
Thalictrum purpurascens	Meadow Rue
Thismia americana	Thismia
Thuya occidentalis	Eastern White Cedar, Arbor Vitae
Tilia americana	Basswood
Tradescantia virginiana	Virginia Spiderwort
Triglochin maritima	Common Bog Arrow Grass
Trillium grandiflorum	Large-Flowered Trillium
Trillium recurvatum	Red Trillium
Tsuga canadensis	Hemlock
Typha latifolia	Common Cat Tail
Ulmus americana	American Elm
Ulmus fulva Ulmus rubra	Slippery Elm
Urtica gracilis	Stinging Nettle
Utricularia	Bladderwort
Vaccinium calaminaria	Cranberry
Vaccinium canadense	Canada Blueberry
Vaccinium myrtilloides	

Vaccinium corymbosum	Highbush Blueberry
Vaccinium macrocarpon	Large Cranberry
Vaccinium membranaceum	Thickleaf Huckleberry
Vaccinium pennsylvanicum	Early Low Blueberry,
Vaccinium augustifolium	Dwarf Blueberry
Vaccinium vaccilans Vaccinium palladium	Late Low Blueberry
Vallisneria	Tape Grass
Vaucheria	Alga
Verbascum thaspus	Common Mullein
Viburnum acerifolium	Maple-Leafed Arrowwood
Viola cucullata	Hooded Violet
Viola incognita	Hairy White Violet
Viola lanceolata	Lance-Leafed Violet
Viola lutea	Mountain Pansy
Viola pedata	Birdsfoot Violet
Viola pubescens	Yellow Violet
Viola sagittata	Arrow-Leafed Violet
Vitis spp.	Grape
Vitis cordifolia Vitis vulpina	Frost grape
Vulpia octoflora	Six Weeks Fescue
Woodwardia virginica	Virginia Chain Fern
Woolfia	Water Meal
Xyris torta	Yellow-Eyed Grass
Zizania aquatica	Wild Rice
Zygadenus (or Zigademus) elegans	White Camass
Zigademus glaucous	

PART THREE:
REFERENCE

REFERENCE

Books, Pamphlets, and Contributions to Books

NOTE ON OFFPRINTS: Following academic custom, Cowles circulated off-prints of his articles, which were bound in paper covers. The Geographic Society of Chicago published offprints of two major Cowles articles. Libraries gave some of these publications more durable covers and catalogued them as books. Since offprints are simply periodical publications in another form, they are ignored here and described under Contributions to Periodicals.

1902

Picturesque Savanna Chicago: Chicago, Milwaukee & St. Paul Railway (Series No. 31) n.d., but probably 1902.

This 15-page promotional booklet—a true curiosity—was possibly part of a series about sites served by the Chicago, Milwaukee & St. Paul Railway (the route is now called the Milwaukee Road). Sue Mobley of the Milwaukee Road Archives at the Milwaukee Public Library dates the pamphlet 1902. She says that the last page uses the same wording as a 1901 Chicago, Milwaukee & St. Paul Railway ad that claimed "6600 miles of thoroughly Equipped Road." Also pointing to a 1902 date is the identification of two career railroad employees, J.H. Hiland and F.A. Miller, with titles they held from 1901 to 1903. Cowles is identified in the booklet as "instructor," a title he held from 1902 to early 1907. Only two copies of *Picturesque Savanna* are known to the author—one at the Chicago Historical Society Library and one in the C.C. Adams Collection of reprints at the University of Western Michigan Library in Kalamazoo. Cowles presumably wrote *Picturesque Savanna* to augment his salary. It describes the geographical, botanical, and scenic interest of the Savanna, Illinois vicinity.

1908

"Physiography and its Effects on Plants and Animals: The Response of Plants to Soil and Climate" in *Physiography for High Schools* by Rollin D. Salisbury, part of American Science Series, Briefer Course (NY: Henry Holt and Company, 1908), 462–73.

Salisbury was Professor of Geographic Geology and head of the Department of Geography at the University of Chicago. According to the Preface, *Physiography for High Schools* is aimed at "first or second-year high school pupils." In his 12-page chapter, Cowles writes that differences in the life and structure of plants and the outdoor environment serve to explain differences in plant distribution. He reviews key influences on plant distribution: water, temperature, light, air, and soil.

1911

A Textbook of Botany for Colleges and Universities by John Merle Coulter, Charles Reid Barnes, and Henry Chandler Cowles *Volume II: Ecology* (NY, Cincinnati, Chicago: American Book Company, 1911). Cowles wrote the second half of this two-volume text. Coulter, who headed the Department of Botany at the University of Chicago from 1894 to 1926, and Barnes, who was Professor of Plant Physiology at the University of Chicago from 1898 to 1910, wrote Volume I (*Morphology and Physiology*), which was published in 1910. This two-volume work, which became known as the "Chicago Textbook," was quite successful. Among the Botany Department records at the University of Chicago Library, Department of Special Collections is an advertising flyer with praise from academics from all over the United States. In court testimony of 1921, Cowles stated that he judged that his text was used "rather widely [in U.S. colleges] by the royalties I get every year on it."

In 1930, Charles A. Shull, Professor of Plant Physiology, University of Chicago, revised and updated Volume I, dividing it into Volume I: *Morphology* and Volume II: *Physiology*. In 1931, George D. Fuller, Associate Professor of Plant Ecology, revised and enlarged the ecology text, which became Volume III in the series (NY: American Book Company, 1931). Fuller may well have started the revision after Cowles began to show symptoms of Parkinson's disease, suggesting that he did all the work himself.

Cowles' ecology text focuses almost exclusively on physiological adaptation and devotes just 14 pages to plant association and adaptation. In a review of this book *Botanical Gazette* 51, No. 1 [January 1911] 67–68, W.F. Ganong stated that the authors' effort to eliminate teleological language brought a result that was "not always happy." He thought it better "in most cases, to retain the familiar and expressive, even though teleological and animistic, terminology, giving frequent warning to the student as to its scientifically erroneous character."

1915

A Spring Flora For High Schools by Henry Chandler Cowles and John Gaylord Coulter (NY, Cincinnati: American Book Company, 1915).

John Gaylord Coulter, son of John Merle Coulter, head of the Botany Department at the University of Chicago, taught biology at the University High School in Normal, Illinois. Cowles and Coulter wrote this flora "to provide, especially for young people in high schools, a ready means for the identification of the more common and wide spread spring flowering plants." The dark olive book cover reads "A SPRING FLORA/ FOR HIGH SCHOOLS/ Cowles and

Coulter" and the backstrip reads "COWLES AND COULTER'S SPRING FLORA."

The 144-page text consists of a key, a descriptive flora illustrated with line drawings, English and metric scale, glossary, and index. According to the authors, the flora describes "380 familiar plants which flower before July in the North Central and Eastern states" and omits grasses, sedges, rushes, and most willows and hawthorns because these present "taxonomic difficulties."

As of July 1937, the American Book Company had 1,099 copies of this book on hand and 494 unbound sets of sheets. There were 490 copies sold in 1934, 937 copies in 1935, 180 copies sold in 1936, and 427 copies sold between January 1 and July 1, 1937. On July 13, 1937, the Editorial Committee of the American Book Company decided that this book might have "a good sale in colleges if the title did not definitely limit it to high schools." By September 16, the publisher had issued a version in a light gray binding with a floral design entitled "COWLES AND COULTER'S/ A SPRING FLORA" on the front cover and backstrip. The title page was reset and a preface that did not mention high schools replaced the 1915 introduction. Otherwise the text was unchanged.

1916

"Remarks," In *Report on the Proposed Sand Dunes National Park Indiana* by Stephen T. Mather. Washington, Government Printing Office, 1916, 93–96.

Stephen Tyng Mather was a successful businessman who became interested in the national parks, toured them, and found them in deplorable condition. He complained to the Secretary of the Interior, who was an old college friend, and was appointed first Head of the National Park Service in 1916. Cowles' remarks are a speech presented Oct. 30, 1916, in Chicago at a hearing on the proposed sand dunes national park. Cowles "very heartily" seconds the move toward establishment of a national park in the Midwest. "For 20 years," he says, "I have been studying the dunes more than anything else . . . In fact, that has been my chief reason for existence, perhaps, for these 20 years." He wants the dunes preserved for their size, the beauty and interest of their plant life, and their international importance. [The text of his speech is published in this volume.]

1918

"Part III: Botany," In *Starved Rock State Park and Its Environs* by Carl Ortwin Sauer, Gilbert H. Cady and Henry Chandler Cowles with an introduction by Rollin D. Salisbury, *Bulletin of the Geographic Society of Chicago No. 6* (Chicago: University of Chicago Press, October 1918), 129–41. Sauer was Professor of Geography at the University of Michigan and Cady worked for the Illinois State Geological Survey.

According to Salisbury's introduction, this bulletin "has been prepared for the benefit of those who, in their visits to Starved Rock State Park, are interested in knowing more about the region than can be gathered by personal observation in the few hours, or the few days, commonly spent in the park." It has three parts: geography (Sauer), geology (Cady), and botany (Cowles). Cowles' account of park botany is comprehensive and detailed, with Latin names for the plants. His portion of this book is noticed in *Botanical Abstracts*, 3, No. 6 (June 1920), 283–84.

1921

Quotations in *Preserves of Natural Conditions* by The Ecological Society of America, Committee on the Preservation of Natural Conditions (Reprinted for the Committee in 1921 with the Aid of the National Research Council), pp. 13, 14.

This 32-page pamphlet is a guide to securing the preservation of natural areas, which was inspired by the Committee on Ecological Survey of the Illinois State Academy of Science. The text covers reasons for preserving natural areas; different constituencies and how they use preserves; preserve management; securing acreage for preserves; impediments such as agriculture and drainage; and descriptions of natural areas. There are signed quotations from ecologists under each subject heading. Cowles is quoted on page 13 about the Governor of Illinois' wish to have preserves averaging 1,000 acres and on page 14 about how sheep destroy young trees in preserves.

"The State Park Possibilities of Southern Illinois" (pp. 97–108) and "State Park Possibilities Along the Mississippi River" (pp. 109–112). In *Proposed Park Areas in the State of Illinois: A Report With Recommendations* (Chicago: The Friends of Our Native Landscape, n.d. [1921].

Bound in dark green paper covers and illustrated with fifty-four photographs and twelve maps, this 120-page booklet surveys prospective park sites throughout Illinois. Cowles served on the State Park Committee of the Friends of Our Native Landscape and on the committee that prepared this publication with chapters by several people with knowledge of Illinois natural areas. Cowles contributed two chapters himself. In "The State Park Possibilities of Southern Illinois," he characterizes the region geographically and reviews prospective park sites in Jackson, Williamson, Saline, Gallatin, Union, Pope, Hardin, Alexander, Pulaski, and Massac Counties. In "State Park Possibilities Along the Mississippi River," he does the same, reviewing prospective park sites in Randolph, St. Clair, Madison, Jersey, Calhoun, Pike, Adams, and Hanover Counties

1925

The Book of Plants by Bertha Morris Parker and Henry Chandler Cowles, (Boston, MA; Houghton Mifflin Company, 1925, (part of The Houghton Mifflin Science Readers for Elementary Schools series) [Also published by Cambridge: The Riverside Press, Cambridge, 1925], 252 pp.

This book was issued with varying title page designs. Cowles is junior author of this book. Bertha Morris Parker, M.S., the senior author, was an elementary school teacher in the natural sciences at the University Elementary School, part of the laboratory schools of the University of Chicago. Cowles probably met Parker through the University of Chicago Laboratory school that his daughter Harriet attended.

According to the introduction, *The Book of Plants* "is designed to serve as informational silent-reading material for children of the sixth, seventh, and eighth grades." It is one of a series of elementary school books that introduces children to science. Cowles "used and tested" the material in the book at the University Elementary School of the University of Chicago. *The Book of Plants* teaches plant science with examples from daily life, such as mold growing on bread and material (i.e., "plants that eat insects") that will interest young people.

In a letter to Stephen A. Forbes of the Illinois Natural History Survey (March 10, 1928), Cowles states that "the writing was entirely Miss Parker's. My contact with the book was merely in the way of reading the material and giving any necessary criticism, which I might say was very little." This may well be true, but the book is written in two styles, which suggests that Cowles wrote—or heavily edited—parts of it.

1926

"Illinois," In *Naturalist's Guide to the Americas*, Prepared by the Committee on the Preservation of Natural Conditions of The Ecological Society of America [assembled and edited by the Chairman Victor E. Shelford, University of Illinois and Illinois State Natural History Survey] (Baltimore: The Williams & Wilkins Company, 1926). Cowles makes short signed contributions to the chapter on Illinois natural areas and regions: "North Shore Ravines" (p. 473); "The Shore of Lake Michigan" (with W.C. Allee, p. 475); "Inland Lakes, Swamps, and Bogs" (p. 475); "Cedar Swamp of Kane County" (p. 475); and "Morton Arboretum" (p. 477).

Planning for this "list of all preserved and preservable areas of North America in which natural conditions persist" started in 1917, but it took almost a decade to bring the book into print. Cowles was a key member of the Committee on the Preservation of Natural Conditions of the Ecological Society of America when it began, but he almost disappears from this book. His signed contributions are enumerated above. He is not listed among the associates and special editors, but is acknowledged in a footnote on page 59 as one of several committee members whose suggestions that were incorporated into a map of biotic areas of northern North America. On page 724, he is listed as Illinois state representative for botany.

"Interactions between Plants and Their Environment," In *The Nature of the World and of Man*, edited by Horatio Hackett Newman (Chicago: University of Chicago Press, 1926: 2nd ed., 1927), Chap 9.

Newman was a Professor of Zoology at the University of Chicago who directed a survey course that was offered annually for top-ranking first year students. Cowles' chapter in this book comprises his lecture in the course, which was taught by sixteen16 faculty members whose chapters make up the book.

Cowles divides his presentation into "The Nature of the Plant Environment" (light, temperature, water, carbon dioxide, chemical and mechanical factors of the soil, other plants, and animals) and "The Reactions of Plants to their Environment" (photosynthesis, water relations).

1927

"Foreword." In *An Annotated Flora of the Chicago Area* by H.S. Pepoon, B.S., M.D. (Chicago: Chicago Academy of Sciences, 1927).

Herman S. Pepoon, was head instructor in botany and agriculture at Lake View High School in Chicago. He and Cowles were both very active with the Chicago Academy of Sciences (CAS). Cowles, as President of the CAS, welcomes this new flora, which replaces and amplifies the long out-of-print flora by Higley and Raddin (1891) that Cowles used at the Indiana Dunes for his studies there.

1928

"Ecology and Human Affairs," In *Lectures on Plant Pathology and Physiology in Relation to Man* (Philadelphia, London: W.B. Saunders Co., 1928), 33–41.

Cowles delivered this lecture five times between January 31 and February 4, 1927 to audiences in Iowa City, Des Moines, and Ames, Iowa; and Rochester and Minneapolis, Minnesota. The lectures were part of a Mayo Foundation sponsored series on plant pathology and physiology. Emphasizing the critical importance of plants to human life, Cowles states that "plant agriculture may be defined as practical plant ecology" and that "the modern science of forestry is also a division of applied ecology." He talks about the role of insects in plant reproduction, plant life and climate, plant succession, the dangers of overgrazing, and the role of ecologists in settling land disputes.

1929

"The Content and Scope of Physiographic Ecology," "Vegetative Cycles," and "Plant Associations of the Chicago Region," In *Readings in Physiographic Ecology*, arranged and edited by George D. Fuller (University of Chicago, 1929). The title page states that the book was "Mimeographed and Printed by Edwards Brothers," a book and journal manufacturer in Ann Arbor, Michigan. (Edwards Brothers says that it no longer has any records from this time.)

Fuller, who served in the Department of Botany from 1907 to 1935 and functioned as Cowles' assistant, edited this book. There is a single copy among his papers at the University of Chicago Library, Department of Special Collections and there are also copies on the library shelves. The book is typewritten, mimeographed, and perfect bound in stiff dark brown paper wrappers with a black cloth tape backstrip, which suggests that it was probably printed in a small edition and sold or given to students. Fuller's preface (dated March 1929) states that "In the absence of any adequate text-book dealing with the subject of plant communities it has seemed advisable to arrange a collection of extracts from the writings of American and British ecologists on certain phases of the subject. In this collection, a leading place is given to 'The Physiographic Ecology of Chicago and Vicinity' by Professor Henry C. Cowles, published first in the Botanical Gazette 31:73–182 1901. This paper has been revised in its terminology, chiefly by substituting for 'plant societies' the more current terms of 'plant communities' or 'plant associations.' The specific names of plants have been changed, when necessary, to those of Gray's New Manual of Botany and certain other minor changes have been effected." Cowles' contributions consist of two excerpts from "The Physiographic Ecology of Chicago and Vicinity" (1901) and an extract from "The Causes of Vegetative Cycles" (1911). The book also reprints work by George E. Nichols, A.G. Tansley, Tansley and T.F. Chipp, and George D. Fuller.

1977

American Plant Ecology 1897–1917 (NY: Arno Press, 1977). This book photoreplicates early ecological texts including three Cowles contributions to the *Botanical Gazette:* "The Ecological Relations of the Vegetation of the Sand Dunes of Lake Michigan" (1899); "The Physiographic Ecology of Chicago and Vicinity: A Study of the Origin, Development, and Classification of Plant Societies" (1901); and "The Causes of Vegetative Cycles" (1911).

Ecological Succession, edited by Frank B. Golley (Stroudsburg, PA: Dowden, Hutchinson & Ross, 1977) (Benchmark Papers in Ecology 5) *Part II: The Pattern* begins with excerpts from "The Physiographic Ecology of Chicago and Vicinity: A Study of the Origin, Development, and Classification of Plant Societies" *Botanical Gazette* 31 (3) (1901), 170–177.

1991

Foundations of Ecology: Classic Papers With Commentaries Edited by Leslie A. Real and James H. Brown (Chicago: University of Chicago Press, 1991) (published in association with the Ecological Society of America).

Part 1, Paper 2 consists of excerpts from "The Ecological Relations of the Vegetation on the Sand Dunes of Lake Michigan" (1899) which originally appeared in *Botanical Gazette*.

MISCELLANEA

1897

Lectures on Ecology The [Milwaukee] College Endowment Association Science Section 1897.

Six-page pamphlet outlines six lectures on ecology: (I) Light and Vegetation; (II) Heat and Vegetation; (III) Air and Vegetation; (IV and V) Water and Vegetation; and (VI) Soil and Vegetation. A copy of this pamphlet among the papers of Paul D. Voth at the University of Chicago is inscribed "Compliments of Henry C. Cowles."

The Milwaukee College Endowment Association was founded in 1890 to support Milwaukee College, a woman's college in Milwaukee, Wisconsin, with fund raising and sponsorship of lectures that supplemented the college curriculum. By 1897, the Association had over 500 members, three divisions of literary study, and two divisions in science: astronomy and ecology. The pamphlet among Voth's papers suggests that Cowles delivered six ecology lectures during 1897.

The Wisconsin Historical Society owns a pamphlet that lists twelve12 ecology lectures by Cowles: October 13 and 27, November 10 and 24, December 8, 1897; and January 19, February 2 and 16, March 2, 16, and 30, and April 13, 1898. Cowles was a doctoral candidate at the University of Chicago in 1897 and 1898. The Milwaukee lectures presumably helped to support him.

1898

"An Ecological Study of the Sand Dune Flora of Northern Indiana." Dissertation, University of Chicago, 1898.

Cowles's dissertation for his Ph.D. in botany and geology. The original thesis is not in the University of Chicago Library and is presumed lost. The last scholar to see it was apparently Sarah Gibbard Cook, who states in *Henry Chandler Cowles (1869–1939) and Cowles Bog, Indiana* (1980; rev. 1999) that the "original dissertation is not identical with the published form [in *Botanical Gazette.*]," but provides no further details. The thesis was published as "The Ecological Relations of the Vegetation on the Sand Dunes of Lake Michigan" in *Botanical Gazette*, 27, Nos. 2, 3, 4, 5 (February, March, April, May 1899), 95–117, 167–202, 281–308, 361–91.

1907

"Plants in their Environment: Syllabus of a Course of Six Lecture-Studies" By Henry Chandler Cowles, Ph.D., Instructor in Ecology (Chicago: University of Chicago Press, 1907).

Fifteen-page pamphlet from the Extension Division of the University of Chicago provides a list of recommended readings and an outline of six lectures: I "How Plants Respond to their Environment;" II "The Plant Life of the Water;" III "The Plant Life of the Desert;" IV "The Plant Life of the Seashore;" V "The Plant Life of the Mountains;" and VI "The Forest." Each lecture outline includes Topics for Library, Laboratory, and Field Study. This pamphlet is preserved among the Charles Olmsted papers at the University of Chicago Library, Department of Special Collections.

1908

"A Proposed Ecological Survey in Illinois"

Abstract of paper delivered at the Fifth Annual Meeting of the Association of American Geographers, Baltimore, Maryland, January 1 and January 2, 1909. Published in *Preliminary Program with Abstracts*, a 12-page pamphlet issued by the Association of American Geographers in 1908. Cowles writes that there have been few ecological surveys and states that the Illinois survey is organized by the new State Academy. The "ultimate aim" of the survey is "a most detailed series of maps and a series of monographs that will exclude no groups of plants and animals if workers can be found to study them."

1910

"Succession BC 580–AD 1896"
Typewritten lecture outline of the "History of Botany" course given in autumn of 1910 by members of the University of Chicago Botany Department. Cowles recounts the history of plant succession theory beginning with early belief in sudden creation and concluding with the work of Warming and others in the 1890s. (Preserved at the University of Chicago Library Department of Special Collections.)

1912

An International Phytogeographic Excursion in America in 1913: Preliminary Announcement
Dated November 30, 1912 and signed by Cowles and Frederic Clements, the 4-page *Preliminary Announcement* invites the recipient to participate in the excursion and states that it will begin in Chicago "about August 1" and end in New York "about October 5." The preliminary itinerary includes Chicago and environs; Lincoln, Nebraska; Akron, Colorado; the Rocky Mountains, Colorado; Salt Lake City, Utah; Seattle, Washington and environs; San Francisco, California, and environs; Mecca, California; and Tucson, Arizona, and environs. (The University of Chicago Library Department of Special Collections has copies of this and other Phytogeographic Excursion texts.)

1913

The International Phytogeographic Excursion (IPE) in America, 1913
Excursion Program First Section, New York, [New York] to Lincoln, [Nebraska]
Sixteen-page itinerary (dated July 24, 1913), excursion notes, and list of personnel for the first section of the excursion with Cowles listed as author on the final page. Covers the period from Sunday, July 27 (New York, New York) through Saturday, August 9 (Lincoln, Nebraska). The pamphlet tells participants what they can expect to see, includes suggested readings, and promises informational handouts.

Excursion Program Second Section, Lincoln, Nebraska to Salt Lake City, Utah
Sixteen-page itinerary (dated July 31, 1913) and signed by Frederic E. Clements. Cowles' contribution to this portion of the itinerary probably consists of setting dates in partnership with Clements.

Excursion Program Third Section, Salt Lake City [Utah] to San Francisco [California]
Sixteen-page itinerary (dated August 21, 1913), field notes, bibliography, and list of personnel for the third section of the excursion, with Cowles listed as author on the final page. Covers the period from Sunday, August 24 (Salt Lake City, Utah) through Sunday, September 7 (San Francisco, California). On page 5 is a condensed calendar for the trip from San Francisco back to New York (September 7 through October 5), which takes the group through northern and southern California, Arizona, New Mexico, Texas, and Louisiana.

Excursion Program Fourth Section, San Francisco [California] to Carmel [California]
Fifteen-page itinerary (dated September 1, 1913) covering the excursion from September 7 through September 14, signed on the final page by W.L. Jepson, University of California. Cowles' contribution to this portion of the itinerary probably consists of setting dates in partnership with Jepson.

1915

A Proposed Ecological Society
A Circular (8.5 x 11 in) that describes a meeting in Philadelphia, Pennsylvania, on December 30, 1914, in which "about twenty men interested in ecology met informally" to consider forming an ecological society. Announces a follow-up meeting to take place between December 28 and December 30, 1915. Signed by Cowles and dated September 20, 1915. The 1915 meeting created the Ecological Society of America. (Copy at the University of Chicago Library Department of Special Collections.)

A Proposed Ecological Society Second Notice
Circular similar to the above announces meeting for Tuesday, December 28 in Columbus, Ohio "to consider the advisability of forming an American Ecological Society. Signed by Cowles and dated December 20, 1915. (Copy at the University of Chicago Library Department of Special Collections.)

1919

Botany 36 Summer 1919 First Term Garrett Bay, Wisconsin
Course description for this outdoor field class, which ran from June 30 to July 26, 1919. Cowles gives detailed instructions to students, warning that a "spirit of complaint will not be tolerated and the undersigned reserves the right to dismiss summarily from the class any who complain, any who fail to harmonize with the other members of the party, and any who for any reason are deemed unqualified to pursue the work." Cowles probably wrote very similar announcements for all of his Botany 36 expeditions. (Copy at the University of Chicago Library Department of Special Collections, also among the papers of Paul B. Sears, Yale University Library.)

Contributions to Periodicals

1896

"Reviews." *Journal of Geology*, 4, No. 1 (January–February 1896), 125–26. Reviews Les Glaciers Pliocènes et Quarternaires de l'Auvergne [Pliocene and Quaternary Glaciers of the Auvergne Region] by Marcellin Boule. Cowles writes that Boule spent several years making a detailed geologic map of the Auvergne region and praises the author for providing much new information in unprecedented detail.

"Dr. Emil Knoblauch" *Botanical Gazette*, 22, No. 12 (December 1896), 506. Describes a paper by Knoblauch on ecological anatomy (i.e., drought adaptation) among woody plants of the South African evergreen bush-region.

1897

"The Ecological Relations" *Botanical Gazette*, 23, No. 6 (June 1897), 478–79. Describes studies by Rimbach and Areschoug of the ecological adaptations of plant root systems.

"Current Literature." *Botanical Gazette*, 24, No. 1 (July 1897), 68–70. Describes studies by Erikson on sand flora, Ryan and Hagen on mosses, Grevillius on plant societies on different rock types, Sernander and Kjellmark on succession in a peat moor, Wittrock on epiphytes, and Rabot on the altitude limits of northern Scandinavian forests.

"Current Literature." *Botanical Gazette*, 24, No. 2 (August 1897), 134–35. Describes a study by Johow of plant geography in the volcanic Juan Fernandez island group west of Chile; Dusen's account of a Swedish botanical expedition to Tierra del Fuego; and Sievers on the physical geography of Venezuela.

"Current Literature." *Botanical Gazette*, 24, No. 4 (October 1897), 298–99. Describes an address given by Dr. Robert Bell of the Canadian Geographical Survey before the Royal Scottish Geographical Society at Edinburgh in March of 1897. In it, Bell describes the geographical distribution of forest trees in Canada and claims that *Pinus banksiana* is the only truly Canadian tree, entering the U.S. only along the south shore of Lake Superior. Cowles asserts that *Pinus banksiana* is "very common about Lake Michigan, extending as far south as northern Indiana."

"Current Literature; Notes for Students." *Botanical Gazette*, 24, No. 6 (December 1897), 445–46. Describes a study by Stahl on the cause of nyctitropic and related movements. A second entry describes Kohl's studies of the photosynthetic energy of light of different colors.

1898

"Current Literature." *Botanical Gazette*, 25, No. 1 (January 1898), 69–70.

Reviews a study by Wiesner on the mechanical influence of rain on plants that asserts that rain does little damage alone, but can be destructive in combination with wind.

"Current Literature; Notes for Students." *Botanical Gazette*, 25, No. 3 (March 1898), 214–15.

Reviews a paper by W.L. Bray on the geographical distribution of the Frankeniaceae, a small family of extremely halo-xerophytic plants found in salt steppes worldwide. Bray's study correlates Frankenia taxonomy with the facts of ecology and plant geography.

"Current Literature." *Botanical Gazette*, 25, No. 5 (May 1898), 370–72. [Republished in this volume.]

Reviews *The Phytogeography of Nebraska* by Roscoe Pound and Frederic E. Clements, calling it "the pioneer work of its kind in America" and a "distinct and noteworthy addition to the ecological and plant geography of this country." Stating that ecology is still so new that scholars are struggling to establish acceptable terminology, Cowles complains that the authors "use Greek derivatives in place of the simpler and more expressive English equivalents." After cautioning that it is too early to predict "the direction to future work in plant geography," Cowles speculates that the field may divide into "phytogeography including the larger problems of distribution and dealing with extensive formations, while ecology will have to do more with local and habitat relations, including anatomical as well as field investigation."

"Reviews." *The Journal of Geology*, 6, No. 4 (May–June 1898), 436–38.

Reviews *Fossil Plants For Students Of Botany And Geology (Vol. I)* by A.C. Seward. Cowles writes that *Fossil Plants*, which is aimed at both botanists and geologists, "pleads for the recognition of paleobotany as a science of and for itself, with its own peculiar problems," such as determining the historical succession of plants in geological time. Cowles praises the author for his caution in making statements, his ability to cull important facts from masses of detail, and his readable style. Cowles' review of this book (with minor textual changes), also appears in *Botanical Gazette*, 26, No. 1 (July 1898), 59–61.

"Current Literature." *Botanical Gazette*, 26, No. 5 (November 1898), 356–58; 361–62.

Reviews *Grundzüge der Pflanzenverbreitung in den Karpathen* [Plant Distribution in the Carpathian Mountains] by Ferdinand Pax in Engler and Drude's series, *Die Vegetation der Erde* [Vegetation of the Earth]. This study, which describes the flora of the Carpathian mountains in the eastern part of Hungary, covers Carpathian physical geography, plant formations, and relations between Carpathian flora and those of neighboring districts. In his review of the second edition of *Pflanzenleben, zweite, gänzlich neubearbeitete Auflage* by Anton Kerner von Marilaun, which was translated into English as *The Natural History of Plants*, Cowles lists improvements in the new edition—new illustrations, omission of 100 pages on plant classification that never fitted, and a new chapter on "the relation between man and plants—economic botany in the broader sense."

1899

"The Ecological Relations of the Vegetation on the Sand Dunes of Lake Michigan." *Botanical Gazette*, 27, Nos. 2, 3, 4, 5 (February, March, April, May 1899), 95–117, 167–202, 281–308, 361–91. (The University of Chicago Press offprinted these four articles in 1899, retaining the *Botanical Gazette*'s format and adding a paper cover.)

This is Cowles' dissertation, revised and published in four parts, under the head "Contributions from the Hull Botanical Laboratory." In this pioneering text, Cowles explains how light, heat, wind, soil, and water determine plant distribution on dunes and demonstrates how dunes vegetation modifies topography to create conditions for a succession of plant communities. Other scientists had observed plant succession before, but Cowles was the first to describe the phenomenon in detail. "The Ecological Relations" is republished in this volume and summarized in Chapter Two.

"Current Literature; Reviews of Books; Notes for Students." *Botanical Gazette*, 27, No. 3 (March 1899), 214–16; 229.

Reviews *Pflanzengeographie auf physiologischer Grundlage* [Physiological Plant Geography] by A.F.W. Schimper. Cowles writes that ecology is developing rapidly and that Schimper's book is "calculated to lead another great advance, and may be said probably to mark the beginning of a second epoch in the pursuit of ecological investigation." Cowles acknowledges that the book assembles and organizes current knowledge in ecology, departing from Eugen Warming in several areas. Though he wishes that the author had paid more attention to "the geological relation," Cowles concludes that this work will be "one of the great botanical masterpieces." In "Notes for Students," Cowles describes a study by Rimbach on rhizome growth and a forthcoming paper by Overton on experimentation in the physiology of autumn coloration. The Schimper review is republished in this volume.

"Current Literature; Notes for Students." *Botanical Gazette*, 27, No. 6 (June 1899), 491–92.

Describes recently published experiments on leaf color by Overton, who connects formation of red cell sap in leaves with a rich sugar content.

"Current Literature; Book Reviews." *Botanical Gazette*, 28, No. 4 (October 1899), 277–78.

Reviews *On Buds And Stipules* by John Lubbock, which, according to Cowles, contains nothing new, but presents the results of Lubbock's past studies in a popular style.

"Current Literature; Notes for Students." *Botanical Gazette*, 28, No 6 (December 1899), 435–38.

Describes experiments on tuberous plants by Vöchtling that establish their adaptability.

1900

"Current Literature; Book Reviews." *Botanical Gazette*, 29, No. 4 (April 1900), 283–85.

Reviews *Minnesota Plant Life* by Conway MacMillan. Cowles finds this non-technical book attractive, but challenges some of the author's "extremely fanciful" ideas.

"Studies in Ecology." *Science*, N.S. (New Series) 12, No. 297 (September 7, 1900), 371.

Cowles, who was in charge of botanical work done at Cold Spring Harbor Biological Laboratory, Cold Spring, Long Island, during the summer of 1900 writes that the succession of plant communities along the xerophytic shores of Long Island "strikingly resembles that along the Great Lakes."

"Current Literature; Book Reviews." *Botanical Gazette*, 30, No. 5 (November 1900), 354–55.

Reviews *La nature tropicale* [Tropical Nature] by J. Constantin, the French botanical philosopher. Cowles finds "little that is new" in this account of the plant world of the tropics, but states that the book contains "one of the best summaries we have of many topics, such as lianas and parasites."

"Plant Geography of North America." *Science*, N.S. 12, No. 306, (November 9, 1900), 708–9.

Cowles contributes "The Physiographic Ecology of Northern Michigan" to this three-part article, stating that his Michigan field studies suggest that Warming's classification of plant formations is incomplete. Water, for example, is ecologically critical, but the difference between the flora of drained and undrained swamps is probably caused by drainage, not by water. He adds that a classification of plant formations "must be dynamic," presenting the flora of a district "from the standpoint of its past and future, thus dealing with genetic relationships." This material is incorporated into Cowles' dissertation, "The Ecological Relations of the Vegetation on the Sand Dunes of Lake Michigan."

"Current Literature; Book Reviews; Notes for Students." *Botanical Gazette*, 30, No. 6 (December 1900), 416–17; 428–29.

Reviews *Éléments de Paléobotanique* [Elements of Paleobotany] by R. Zeiller. Cowles writes that Zeiller can be "used with impunity by general readers and elementary students." The author is cautious with facts and concludes with two important chapters—a "wonderfully graphic" description of "the succession of floras and climates" and the final chapter, which challenges evolutionary theory. [Cowles publishes this same review in *Journal of Geology*, 8, No. 8 (November–December 1900), 779–80.] In "Notes for Students," Cowles describes studies by Bray on the relations between North American and South American flora; Ule on the influence of animals on plants in the tropics; Long on the ecological distribution of fungi near Austin, Texas; and Shibata on the calyx hydathodes.

1901

"Current Literature; Notes for Students." *Botanical Gazette*, 31, No. 2 (February 1901), 133; 136–37.
  Describes studies by Miyake on starch production in Japanese evergreens. In "Notes for Students," writes about Scottish botanist Robert Smith, who was preparing an ecological survey of Scotland when he died before his time.

"The Relation between Base-Leveling and Plant Distribution." *Science*, N.S. 13, No. 323, March 8, 1901, 372–73.
  Summary of a paper read at the Second Meeting of Naturalists (part of the American Association for the Advancement of Science) in Chicago, Illinois, on December 27 or 28, 1900. Cowles says that topography largely determines local plant distribution, but that it constantly changes, influencing the plants. Ecological study of plants and plant societies must therefore be dynamic.

"Current Literature; Notes for Students." *Botanical Gazette*, 31, No. 3 (March 1901), 208–11.
  Describes studies by Eberhart on the influence of dry and humid air on plant structures; Nestler on the glandular hairs of *Primula obconica*; Rodrigue on the anatomy of variegated leaves; Nillson on the dynamics of some Swedish plant communities, especially of cliffs and moors; several scientists on latex; and Brenner on succulent plants.

"The Physiographic Ecology of Chicago and Vicinity: A Study of the Origin, Development, and Classification of Plant Societies" (Contributions from the Hull Botanical Laboratory, 24). *Botanical Gazette*, 31, Nos. 2, 3 (February, March 1901), 73–108, 145–82.
  This two-part article states that plant geography is determined not only by the availability of moisture, as Warming suggested, but also soil and physiography. Expanding upon his work in "The Ecological Relations," Cowles names and describes different plant communities in relation to topography and provides examples from Chicago and its suburbs.
  The Geographic Society of Chicago reprinted this text as "The Plant Societies of Chicago and Vicinity" in the *Bulletin of the Geographic Society of Chicago*, No. 2, in 1901. "Plant Societies" seems to be aimed at a less professional readership. In both versions, the second half of the introduction and entire body of the paper are identical. Cowles shortens the first half of the introduction in "Plant Societies," omitting some literature review. "Plant

Societies" omits the "Summary and Conclusion" of "The Physiographic Ecology" an adds an appendix "The Principal Localities about Chicago for the Study of Plant Societies" with directions to key sites and ways to reach them on public transportation. "Plant Societies" is republished in this volume and summarized in Chapter Two.

On April 18, 1912, the University of Chicago Press published an edition of 1,023 offprints of "Plant Societies of the Chicago Region" for sale at 50 cents per copy. All royalties for the offprint went to the Geographic Society. By January 2, 1924, G.J. Laing, Editor at the University of Chicago Press informed Anna Conwell, Assistant Secretary of the Geographic Society that the Press had three copies on hand and was prepared to let it go out of print. On October 24, Cowles protested that he wanted a reprint of "Plant Societies," because he used it in the classroom. The Press discovered that "Plant Societies" would have to be reset and new cuts made, but the Geographic Society was willing to pay for this. Cowles set to work on the text, but soon protested that the original illustrations were scattered among several people and unobtainable. He promised several times to deliver copy, but he had not done so by spring of 1930 and the last entry in the University of Chicago Press records is his obituary.

In order to have copies of "Plant Societies" for classroom use, Cowles apparently had a typescript made of the text from *Botanical Gazette* and an unknown number of copies printed by Edwards Brothers, Inc., academic book manufacturers of Ann Arbor, Michigan, and bound in stiff brown wrappers. The reprints, which were presumably made in 1924 or later, were apparently given to students or sold to them at cost. Though the reprinted text refers to photographs that appeared in *Botanical Gazette*, there are none in the copy among the Charles Olmsted papers at the University of Chicago Library, Department of Special Collections.

"The Influence of Underlying Rocks on the Character of the Vegetation." *Bulletin of the American Bureau of Geography*, 2 (June, December 1901), 163–76, 376–88.

This two-part article was offprinted (Winona, MN: Jones & Kroager Printers, 1901) under the same title, bound in paper, and labeled "Contributions from the Hull Botanical Laboratory, The University of Chicago, 34." [Republished in this volume.]

Noting that different soils support different plants, Cowles reviews possible explanations—chemical characteristics of the soil, its structure, water and humus content, the relationship between soil and the rock beneath it, and the struggle for existence (i.e., plants grow where life is easiest but are also able to grow elsewhere). He concludes that most vegetation is tending toward a mesophytic forest climax and that different plants and soils are at different stages of succession. Based on observations he made over four years at Lake Superior near Marquette, Michigan; the Allegheny Mountains of East Tennessee; northern Illinois and eastern Iowa; and Connecticut, Cowles states that rock types are more alike than different in their effects. Harry N. Whitford reviews this article in the *Botanical Gazette*, 33, No. 4 (April 1902), 316.

"Current Literature; Notes for Students." *Botanical Gazette*, 31, No. 4 (April 1901), 278; 282–83.

Describes studies by Lewin on raphide crystals and Miyoshi on the influences of substances in the soil on plant colors. Describes work by Ward on the Triassic and Jurassic flora of the U.S.; Knowlton on the flora of the Montana formation; White on the stratigraphic succession of the fossil floras of the Pottsville formation in the Carboniferous of Pennsylvania; Seward on the Wealden flora of the Bernissart in Belgium; Eury on the Carboniferous forests of France; and Penahallow on the flora of the Canadian Pleistocene.

"Current Literature; Notes for Students." *Botanical Gazette*, 31, No. 5 (May 1901), 361–62.

Describes studies by Wheeler on the ecology of vegetation in southeastern Minnesota; Wilcox on a rhizomorphic root-rot that damages fruit trees; efforts to secure a uniform nomenclature in plant geography; von Schrenk on diseases of New England conifers; and Davis on marl formation.

"Current Literature; Notes for Students." *Botanical Gazette*, 32, No. 5 (November 1901), 376–77.

Describes studies by Flahault on nomenclature in phytogeography and Hesselman on mycorrhiza of arctic plants.

"Current Literature; Notes for Students." *Botanical Gazette*, 32, No. 6 (December 1901), 429–31.

Describes studies by Jost on synthesis of proteids; Friedel on synthesis of carbohydrates; and Tammes on the distribution of carotin.

1902

"Current Literature; Book Reviews; Notes for Students." *Botanical Gazette*, 33, No. 1 (January 1902), 70; 73–84.

Reviews *Flowers and Ferns in their Haunts* by Mabel Osgood Wright; *Our Ferns in their Haunts* by Willard N. Clute; and *With the Wild Flowers* by Maud Going. All volumes are aimed at the general public. Cowles praises Wright and Clute, but states that Going does not stick to scientific facts and carries impersonation of plants "to an extreme and even hurtful degree." In "Notes for Students (pp. 73–84)," Cowles describes studies by Czapek on the transformation of starch to sugar; Tucker and Tollens on the autumnal migration of carbohydrates, proteids, phosphoric acid, and potash from dying leaves to perennial stems of plants; Beneke on decomposition of NaCl by *Cakile* and *Salicornia*; Pethybridge on nutrition of wheat; Bernard on precocious tuberculization in plants and a study suggesting that tubers of the potato are essentially galls and due to fungus infection; Tansley and Chick on the conducting tissue system of bryophytes; studies on the structural differences of the white and green parts of leaves; Thomas on subterranean leaves (scales); organographic studies by Teodoresco; and several recent papers on the physiological ecology of chlorophyll and carbohydrate synthesis.

"Current Literature; Book Reviews; Minor Notices." *Botanical Gazette*, 33, No. 1 (January 1902), 71.

Reviews *Lessons in Physical Geography*, a textbook by Charles R. Dryer, stating that it has "a fuller account than is usual" of plant geography. Cowles welcomes "more cogent ecological facts presented in place of the time-worn statements in the older physical geographies.

"A.F.W. Schimper; Current Literature; Notes for Students." *Botanical Gazette*, 33, No. 2, (February 1902), 160–61; 164–65.

Obituary of the German botanist, author of *Pflanzengeographie* [Plant Geography] (1899), which Cowles says that he used "almost daily." In "Notes for Students," Cowles describes a study by Blackman and Matthaei on the responses of certain leaves to traumatic stimulation.

"Current Literature; Book Reviews; Notes for Students." *Botanical Gazette*, 33, No. 3 (March 1902), 236–38; 240.

Reviews *Die Mutationstheorie: Versuche und Beobachtungen über die Entstehung von Arten im Pflanzenreich* [The Theory of Mutation: Experiments and Observations on the Genesis of Species in the Vegetable Kingdom] by Hugo de Vries, which is the first of a projected two-part set on the theory of mutation. Experiments with *Oenothera* led de Vries to reject natural selection in favor of mutation. Cowles concludes that the field is still in flux and that this book will "lead to a flood of experimental investigation." In "Notes for Students," Cowles describes a study by Giovannozzi on the mechanism and functions of hygroscopic movements in plants.

"Current Literature; Book Reviews; Notes for Students." *Botanical Gazette*, 33, No. 4 (April 1902), 311–12; 314–15.

Reviews three volumes of Engler and Drude's *Vegetation der Erde* [Vegetation of the Earth] series. Studies in different parts of the world suggest that adaptations to climate and topography are very similar. In "Notes for Students," Cowles describes studies by Friedel and Harroy on gas exchanges, which are associated with photosynthesis in living plants.

"Current Literature; Book Reviews; Notes for Students" *Botanical Gazette*, 34, No. 4 (October 1902), 309–10; 316–17.

Reviews *Die Vegetationsverhältnisse der illyrischen Länder begreifend Südkroatien, die Quarnero-Inseln, Dalmatien, Bosnien und die Hercegovina, Montenegro, Nordalbanien, den Sandzak Novipazar und Serbien* [Plant Distribution in the Illyric Provinces: Southern Croatia, the Quarnero Islands, Dalmatia, Bosnia and Herzegovina, Montenegro, the Sandzak Novipazar, and Serbia] by Beck von Mannagetta and Dr. Günther Ritter, which is the fourth volume of Engler and Drude's *Vegetation der Erde* series. The area surveyed includes the areas then called Serbia, Montenegro, part of European Turkey, and the southern part of the Austro-Hungarian Empire. Cowles concludes that this study is "of peculiar importance since it is the only available work which sums up for general use the broad facts of plant distribution in southeastern Europe." In "Notes for Students," Cowles describes Dr. Adolph Engler's written plan for a "vast botanical garden [in Berlin], which shall display the characteristic plant formations of the world."

"Current Literature; Recent Contributions to American Phytogeography: the Eastern United States." *Botanical Gazette*, 34, No. 5 (November, 1902), 383–87.

Describes thirty recent studies. [In the February, 1903 edition Cowles reviews literature on the central U.S.]

"Current Literature; Recent Studies Upon Regeneration." *Botanical Gazette*, 34, No. 6 (December 1902), 464–66.

Describes a volume on regeneration edited by Morgan and studies on regeneration by Goebel, Palisa, Winkler, Noll, and Hübner.

1903

"Current Literature; Recent Contributions to American Phytogeography: The Central United States." *Botanical Gazette*, 35, No. 2 (February 1903), 147–49.

Describes studies by Mackenzie and Bush on flora of Jackson County, Missouri; Westgate on the vegetation on an island in Kansas; Shimek on forest trees in Iowa; Bessey on timber areas in Nebraska; Hall on tree planting experiments in Nebraska; Thornber on prairie grass formation near Nebraska City; Hedgcock on the relationship between water content of the soil and certain plants, principally mesophytes; Wheeler on vegetation of southeastern Minnesota; Lange on revegetation in Minnesota; and Holzinger on moss distribution in Minnesota. [Cowles covered 30 studies of the eastern U.S. in November, 1902.]

"Contrasts and Resemblances Between the Sand Dune Floras of Cape Cod and Lake Michigan." *Science*, N.S. 17, No. 424 (Feb. 13, 1903), 262.

Abstract of paper presented Dec. 30 or 31, 1902, in Washington, DC, to the Society for Plant Morphology and Physiology, meeting in conjunction with the American Association for the Advancement of Science and the American Society of Naturalists. Cowles states that the resemblances between Cape Cod and Lake Michigan sand dune floras are "more far-reaching than the contrasts, showing that halophytic and tidal factors are relatively unimportant in determining sand dune or even sand-beach floras on Cape Cod." He concludes that the "contrasts which exist are probably due, in the main, to differences in moisture and wind relations."

"The Contribution of Linnaeus and his Students to Phytogeography." *Science*, N.S. 17, No. 429 (March 20, 1903), 463–64.

Abstract of paper delivered at the American Association for the Advancement of Science meeting on December 30 and 31, 1902. Cowles writes that the history of phytogeography should begin with Linnaeus and not Humboldt, since Linnaeus and his students produced "a vast amount of material, which should be more fully recognized."

"Current Literature; Book Reviews; Minor Notices." *Botanical Gazette*, 35, No. 4 (April 1903), 293–96.

Cowles reviews *Die Heide Norddeutschlands und die sich anschliessenden Formationen in biologischer Betrachtung* [The Heath of Northern Germany and its Subsequent Formations from a Biological Perspective] by P. Graebner, which is the fifth volume of Engler and Drude's *Vegetation der Erde* series. In this account of the heaths of northern Germany, Graebner states that heaths show no tendency to return to forests when left alone, possibly because the soils are inimical to tree growth. Cowles also reviews *Vegetationsbilder* [Plant Pictures] by G. Karsten and H. Schenck, a series of illustrations of the world's vegetation; and *Ueber Aehnlichkeiten im Pflanzenreich* [On Similarities in the Vegetable Kingdom] by F. Hildenbrand, which shows similarities among different plants and between plants and animals.

"Current Literature; Book Reviews; Minor Notices; Notes for Students." *Botanical Gazette*, 36, No. 5 (November 1903), 392–97.

Reviews *Botany of the Faeroes* (two volumes; several authors); *Biologie der Pflanzen* [Plant Biology] (2nd edition) by Julius Wiesner, an update of a pioneering work on ecology; *Der Hercynische Florenbezirk* [The Hercynic Flora Sector] by Oscar Drude (sixth volume of Engler and Drude's *Vegetation der Erde* series), in which the author reviews the plants of Saxony in "marvelous detail"; and *Vegetationsbilder* [Plant Pictures] by G. Karsten and H. Schenck, three new volumes of illustrations of plants in a continuing series. In "Notes for Students," Cowles describes studies by Adams on postglacial origin and migration of life in the northeastern U.S.; McKenney on plant distribution in Orange county California; Blankinship on plant formations of eastern Massachusetts; and Smith on the distribution of British plants.

"Current Literature; Notes for Students." *Botanical Gazette*, 36, No. 6 (December 1903), 471–73; 477–78.

Describes studies by Charpentier on the green alga *Cystococcus humicola*; Artari on the relation of chlorophyll to light in some algae; Kindermann on the resistance of guard cells; Buck on the stomata and aeration tissues of Swiss plants; and Heinricher on green half-parasites.

1904

"Current Literature; Notes for Students." *Botanical Gazette*, 37, No. 1. (January 1904), 69–74.

Describes studies by Renault on vegetative activity in the Carboniferous age; Molliard on *Ascobolus sp.*; Bernard on tuberization; and Bonnier on the anatomy of experimental plants.

"Current Literature; Notes for Students." *Botanical Gazette*, 37, No. 3 (March 1904), 226–30.

Describes studies by Bouilhac and Giustiniani on soil-nutritive mixtures of bacteria with algae; Bernard on orchid germination; and Zeiller and Fliche on fossil Sequoia discovered in France.

"Current Literature; Book Reviews; Notes for Students." *Botanical Gazette*, 37, No. 4 (April 1904), 307–09; 312–15; 317.

Reviews *Desert Botanical Laboratory of the Carnegie Institution* by F.V. Coville and D.T. MacDougal. Cowles expects "great things, particularly in physiology and ecology" from this laboratory, which was established after reviewing many prospective sites. He also reviews *Geschichte und Herkunft der schweizerischen Alpenflora* [Origin and History of Swiss Alpine Vegetation] by Marie Jerosch, an account of Swiss Alpine vegetation; *Die Alluvionen des unteren Lena-Thales* [The Alluvia of the Lower Lena Valley] by A.K. Cajander, about the ecology of Russia's Lena Valley; and *Ecological Study of Big Spring Prairie, Wyandot County, Ohio* by T.A. Bonser, about a former lake bed which became a prairie. In "Notes for Students," Cowles describes three new volumes of Karsten and Schenck's *Vegetationsbilder* [Plant Pictures].

"Current Literature; Book Reviews." *Botanical Gazette*, 37, No. 5 (May 1904), 392–93.

Reviews *Plant Geography upon a Physiological Basis* by A.F.W. Schimper (translated from the German). Cowles writes that botanists have been using the German original for years, but that the translation will bring the work to a wider public. "There can no longer be any reason for omitting ecological work from the higher botanical curricula," he concludes.

"Trees and their Life Problems." *Birds and Nature Magazine*, 16, No. 1 (June 1904), 41–44.

Popular treatment of trees, their anatomy, growth and life cycle. Cowles concludes that more forestry studies are needed.

"The Work of the Year 1903 in Ecology." *Science*, N.S. 19, No. 493 (June 10, 1904), 879–85.

Full text of a paper read on December 29, 1903, at St. Louis, to the American Association for the Advancement of Science, Section G (Botany). Cowles surveys major ecological writings and studies of 1903, emphasizing theories of adaptation and evolution. It is "more than impossible," he states, to survey current work in ecology because the field is "in chaos." Ecologists don't even agree on basic terminology.

"Current Literature; Book Reviews." *Botanical Gazette*, 38, No. 2 (August 1904), 146–48.

Reviews *Physiologische Pflanzenanatomie* [Physiological Plant Anatomy] (3rd edition) by G. Haberlandt. Cowles enthusiastically welcomes the new edition, noting that much in the book has been rewritten to acknowledge major advances made by the author and others.

"Current Literature; Book Reviews; Minor Notices; Notes for Students." *Botanical Gazette*, 38, No. 4 (October 1904), 303–10.

Reviews *The Development and Structure of Vegetation* by F.E. Clements, which is the first of two books in which Clements presents his ecological research methods. This volume deals with "the biological side of vegetation," Cowles writes, while the next will focus on the physical aspects. Cowles finds Clements' presentation "so logical" that "a satisfactory review or summary would be little less than a verbatim reproduction of the work." [The Clements review is reprinted in this volume.] Also reviewed are *Phyllobiologie nebst Uebersicht der biologischen Blattypen von einundsechzig Siphonogamenfamilien* [Phylobiology and Survey of Biological Leaf Types in Sixty-One Siphonogam Families] by A. Hansgirg, a book on leaf ecology; and the outline of a lecture course, *Relation Of Plants To Environment (Or Plant Ecology)* by G.F. Atkinson. In "Notes for Students," Cowles describes studies by Olsson-Seffer on bog study methods; Maiden on a botanical study of New South Wales; Bray on xerophytic plant anatomy in Texas; Westgate on reclamation of Cape Cod sand dunes; Britton on sand plains near New Haven, Connecticut; Parkin and Pearson on the patanas of Ceylon; and several short papers by MacDougal.

"Current Literature; Book Reviews." *Botanical Gazette*, 38, No. 5 (November 1904), 385–86.

Reviews *Die Theorie der direkten Anpassung und ihre Bedeutung für das Anpassungs- und Deszendenzproblem* [The Theory of Direct Adaptation and its Significance for the Adaptation and Evolution Problem] by Carl Detto. This book reinvestigates the theory of direct adaptation to environment "in the light of the most modern botanical knowledge," Cowles writes. He finds the book useful, but thinks that Detto spends too much time refuting long-abandoned theories.

"Current Literature; Book Reviews." *Botanical Gazette*, 38, No. 6 (December 1904), 464–65.

Reviews *Botanische Forschungen des Alexanderzuges* [Botanical Research of the Expeditions of Alexander the Great] by Hugo Bretzl, an account of Theophrastus, the ancient Greek who wrote a treatise on plants that was based in part on reports brought back from India by companions of Alexander the Great.

1905

"A Remarkable Colony of Northern Plants along the Apalachicola River, Florida, and Its Significance" and "Importance of the Physiographic Standpoint in Plant Geography." *Report of the Eighth International Geographic Congress.* Washington, DC: Government Printing Office, 1905, 599–600.

Abstracts of papers presented Sept. 8, 9, or 10, 1904, in Washington, DC, to the Eighth International Geographic Congress. In the first paper, Cowles states his belief that *Torreya taxifolia*, which he found along the Apalachicola River, is a "northern mesophytic plant left stranded" after the glaciers retreated. In "Gametophytes and Embryo of *Torreya taxifolia*" (*Botanical Gazette*, 39, No. 3 [March 1905], 161–62), John M. Coulter and W.J.G. Land quote several paragraphs of Cowles' notes on *Torreya taxifolia* and his conclusion that *Torreya* is a "northern plant of the most pronounced mesophytic tendencies." In the second paper, which was "read by title" (i.e., the title of the paper was read, acknowledging that the work had been done, but the text was not read for lack of time), Cowles states that the physiographic approach to plant geography helps make sense of plant associations.

"Current Literature; Notes for Students." *Botanical Gazette*, 39, No. 1 (January 1905), 68–70; 72–73.
Reviews studies by Andrae and Giltay on insects and flower colors; and Laurent on the carbon nutrition of green plants.

"Current Literature; Notes for Students." *Botanical Gazette*, 39, No. 2 (February 1905), 155–58.
Reviews studies by Cockayne on New Zealand flora and Alboff on the flora of Fuegia (southern tip of Latin America).

"Current Literature; Notes for Students." *Botanical Gazette*, 39, No. 3 (March 1905), 226; 233–37.
Reviews studies by Hesselman on Swedish meadows; Ganong on adaptation; Tansley on ecological terminology and the limitations of the field; Cooley on tamarack ecology; Olsson-Seffer on the reputation of Linnaeus; Newcombe on natural history surveys; Karsten and Schenck's *Vegetationsbilder* [Plant Pictures] series; Harper on the flora of Georgia; Woodruffe-Peacock on the study of rock-soil floras; and Tansley on ecological surveying.

"Current Literature; Book Reviews." *Botanical Gazette*, 40, No. 2 (August 1905), 148–49.
Reviews *Species and Varieties: Their Origin by Mutation* by Hugo de Vries, calling it "the greatest contribution since Darwin" to evolutionary theory. Cowles writes that de Vries has systematized the discoveries of Darwin and "given us an experimental basis for the belief in evolution." He adds that this is not just a simple translation, but an updating and adaptation of work that was originally only available in German.

"Current Literature; Book Reviews." *Botanical Gazette*, 40, No. 4 (October 1905), 314–15.
Reviews *Mutants and Hybrids of the Oenotheras* by D.T. MacDougal et al.; *Ecological Study of Brush Lake* by J.H. Schaffner et al.; and *A Biological Reconnaissance of the Base of the Alaska Peninsula* by W. H. Osgood.

"Current Literature; Book Reviews; Notes for Students." *Botanical Gazette*, 40, No. 5 (November 1905), 381–82; 392–98. [Republished in this volume.]

Reviews *Research Methods in Ecology* by F.E. Clements. Cowles writes that this book, with its precise descriptions of Clements' methods, will continue professionalizing the field of ecology. He lists new ecological terminology that Clements proposes, expresses some reservations, but concludes that "one can scarcely praise this work too much." In "Notes for Students," Cowles describes studies by Harper on the flora of Georgia; a guidebook to the Royal Botanical Garden in Berlin; Smith's botanical survey of Scotland; Clements on formation and succession herbaria (which "illustrate the dynamics of plant formations, and are the most desirable of ecological herbaria, but the most difficult to prepare"); Darbishire on Mamillaria; Tansley and Fritsch on the shore vegetation of Ceylon; Collins on a Rhode Island bog; Spaulding on the giant cactus; Blankenship on botanical work in Montana; Leavitt on monstrosities in Drosera, Gentiana, and Saxifraga; Olsson-Seffer on plans for a permanent ecological laboratory in Greenland; Remer on plants that need light to germinate; Cockayne on *Discaria toumatou*, a New Zealand xerophytic shrub; Harshberger on the term "zone" in plant geography; Swellengrebel on dunes of the Netherlands; and Lloyd on the Desert Botanical Laboratory.

"Current Literature; Minor Notices; Notes for Students." *Botanical Gazette*, 40, No. 6 (December 1905), 464; 471–76.

Reviews *Vegetation of the Bahama Islands* by W.C. Coker. In "Notes for Students," Cowles describes studies by Wiesner on leaf fall; Adamovic on the plant geography of Serbia; Hesselman on plant distribution on slopes in Sweden; Oliver and Tansley on large-scale vegetation survey methods; Detto on floral color and insects; Adams on postglacial migration; and Bessey on forest encroachment on Nebraska prairies.

1906

"Current Literature; Notes for Students." *Botanical Gazette*, 41, No. 1 (January 1906), 77–79.

Describes studies by Jumelle on tuberization and Warming and Wesenberg-Lund on shore formations in Denmark.

1907

"Current Literature; Book Reviews; Minor Notices; Notes for Students." *Botanical Gazette*, 43, No. 2 (February 1907), 139–41; 149–50.

Reviews *Plants and Their Ways in South Africa* by Bertha Stoneman, an elementary textbook for South African schools that incorporates an ecological point of view. In "Minor Notices," Cowles reviews *Species and Varieties: Their Origin by Mutation* by Hugo de Vries, a revised edition of this book, translated into English from the original German. In "Notes for Students," Cowles describes studies by Ewart on correlation and leaf size; Herriott on leaf structure;

and Bureau of Forestry bulletins on forest belts in Kansas and Nebraska and white pine in New England.

"Current Literature; Notes for Students." *Botanical Gazette*, 44, No. 5 (November 1907), 392–94.
    Describes studies by Raunkiaer on resting buds as indices of ecological types and Edith S. Clements on leaf structure and physical factors.

"Current Literature; Book Reviews; Minor Notices; Notes for Students." *Botanical Gazette*, 44, No. 6 (December 1907), 456–60.
    Reviews *An Investigation of Evolution In Chrysomelid Beetles Of the Genus Leptinotarsa* by W.L. Tower. Even though this book is about potato beetles, Cowles considers it important because of its contributions to the theory of evolution, which can be applied to botany. In "Minor Notices," Cowles reviews *Distribution and Adaptation of the Vegetation of Texas* by W.L. Bray and *An Ecological Survey in Northern Michigan* by Charles C. Adams. In "Notes for Students," Cowles describes studies by Cockayne on New Zealand botany and Fries on Argentina's alpine flora.

1908

"The Desirability of an Ecological Survey of Illinois Based on Plant Association." *Transactions of the Illinois State Academy of Science*, 1 (1908), 61.
    Abstract of a paper delivered in Decatur on February 22, 1908. Cowles wants Illinois "systematically surveyed by botanists and zoologists" with maps made showing the "distribution of the associations." Work in the Chicago area already begun; (On page 71, Cowles is listed as a participant in a "Symposium on the Atmosphere," but he apparently does not speak.)

"Current Literature; Book Reviews; Notes for Students." *Botanical Gazette*, 45, No. 1 (January 1908), 55–56; 71.
    Reviews *Dansk Plantevaekst* [Danish Vegetation] by Eugen Warming, the first volume in a projected series that will treat the vegetation of Denmark from an ecological standpoint. Regretting that the book is only published in Danish, Cowles writes that "the thoroughness of this work makes us long for the other members of the series." In "Notes for Students," Cowles describes studies by Reed and Smoot on seed dispersal in *Polygonum* and Grisch on Swiss vegetation.

"Current Literature; Notes for Students." *Botanical Gazette*, 45, No. 2 (February 1908), 138–39; 143.
    Describes studies by Fernald on soil chemistry and plant distribution; Cockayne on New Zealand ecology; and Shantz on plankton in lakes near Pike's Peak, Colorado.

"The American Association for the Advancement of Science Section G—Botany." *Science*, N.S. 27, No. 684 (February 7, 1908), 205–15.

Cowles as secretary *pro tem* of the section, submits abstracts of twenty-three technical papers.

"Current Literature; Notes for Students." *Botanical Gazette*, 45, No. 3 (March 1908), 204–5; 211; 213–15.

Describes studies by Harper on coastal plain vegetation; Whitford on Philippine vegetation (a first test of physiographic ecology principles in the tropics); Fraysse on the ecological relations of parasitic seed-plants; Pearson on desert vegetation in South Africa; Heinze on nitrogen fixation by algae; and Friedel on chlorophyll that has lost its synthetic power.

"Current Literature; Notes for Students." *Botanical Gazette*, 45, No. 4 (April 1908), 279–80.

Describes a study by Witte on extensive treeless plains whose underlying rock is a Silurian limestone.

"An Ecological Aspect of the Conception of Species." Part of "Aspects of the Species Question." *American Naturalist*, 42, No. 496 (April 1908), 265–71.

Account of a symposium presented Jan. 1, 1908, in Chicago, to the Botanical Society of America. Participants were Bessey and Britton (taxonomy), Arthur and MacDougal (physiology), and Clements and Cowles (ecology). Cowles says that taxonomy should be scientific, rigorous, and standard worldwide. Discussion follows.

1909

"Current Literature; Book Reviews; Notes for Students." *Botanical Gazette*, 47, No. 1 (January 1909), 73–75; 81–82.

Reviews *Grundzüge der Pflanzenverbreitung in Chile* [Plant Distribution in Chile] by Karl Reiche, which is the seventh volume in Engler and Drude's *Vegetation der Erde* series. Cowles calls this book "a masterpiece" because the author has been working on Chilean vegetation for fourteen years. Chile contains many different climatic zones, making it particularly rewarding to botanists and ecologists. Cowles also reviews *Die Pendulationstheorie* [Pendulation Theory] by Heinrich Simroth, which he finds strained and unconvincing. In "Notes for Students," Cowles describes a study by Nieuwenhuis von Uexküll-Güldenbandt on extra-floral nectaries.

"Current Literature; Minor Notices; Notes for Students." *Botanical Gazette*, 47, No. 2 (February 1909), 159; 170.

Reviews *Naar Californië II* [Toward California II] by Hugo de Vries, a popular account of travel in the U.S. by a Dutch botanist. In "Notes for Students," Cowles describes a study by Leavitt, which suggests that theories of evolution must harmonize with the facts of plant and animal distribution.

"Current Literature; Notes for Students." *Botanical Gazette*, 47, No. 3 (March 1909), 252.
Describes studies by von Schrenk on Rhododendron branch cankers and Hus on virescence in *Oxalis stricta*.

"The American Association for the Advancement of Science Section G—Botany." *Science* N.S. 29, No. 753 (June 4, 1909), 903–16.
Cowles, as secretary *pro tem* of the section, submits abstracts of 40 technical papers.

"Present Problems in Plant Ecology: The Trend of Ecological Philosophy." *American Naturalist*, 43, No. 510 (June 1909), 356–68. [Offprints exist.]
Presented December 30, 1908, in Baltimore, to the Botanical Society of America. Cowles begins by asserting the "close interdependence of physiology and ecology." Plants live—and evolve—outdoors, which means that lab work cannot solve "our most important problems," he adds. Cowles adamantly opposes the use of teleological language in ecology. Discussion follows.

"Current Literature; Book Reviews." *Botanical Gazette*, 48, No. 2 (August 1909), 149–52. [Republished in this volume]
Reviews *Oecology of Plants* by Eugen Warming et al. Cowles says that this is not just a translation, but "an essentially new book," with much new information that did not appear in the Danish original or the German translations that followed. After quibbling with some of Warming's changes, Cowles concludes that "while words of adverse criticism may seem necessary here and there, one may write volumes of praise." He notes that the book contains 600 references, of which 115 are American in origin.

"Current Literature; Book Reviews." *Botanical Gazette*, 48, No. 4 (October 1909), 307–8.
Reviews *Botanical Features of North American Deserts* by D.T. MacDougal. Cowles writes that "this treatise will be the *sine qua non* for all ecological workers" because it collects what is known of the North American desert and adds discoveries made at the Carnegie Institution's Desert Botanical Laboratory in Tucson, Arizona.

"Botany at the British Association; Ecological Papers." *Nature*, 81 No. 2087 (October 28, 1909), 537.
Describes "The Fundamental Causes of Succession among Plant Associations," a paper that Cowles delivered in 1910. [It is listed under that year.]

"Current Literature; Minor Notices." *Botanical Gazette*, 48, No. 6 (December 1909), 465–66.
Corrects an error in his August review of Warming's *Oecology of Plants*.

1910

"The Fundamental Causes of Succession among Plant Associations," In *Report of the Seventy-Ninth Meeting of the British Association for the Advancement of Science*. (London: John Murray, 1910), 668–70. [Also published in *Nature*, 81 No. 2097 (October 28, 1909), 537.]

Paper presented August 27, 1909, in Winnipeg, Manitoba, to the British Association for the Advancement of Science. Cowles lists factors that contribute to succession, including accumulation of humus, increasing or decreasing shade, plant invasions, and changes in topography and climate. He adds that further observation and experimentation are needed because it is not presently possible to reach firm conclusions.

"Current Literature; Book Reviews." *Botanical Gazette*, 49, No. 4 (April 1910), 305–7.

Reviews *Essai de géographie botanique des districts littoraux et alluviaux de la Belgique* [Plant Geography of Littoral and Alluvial Belgium] by J. Massart. Calling this work a "comprehensive monograph," Cowles writes that "perhaps no other similar work has been so detailed." The author spent fifteen years studying the ecology and ecological history of a small area of Belgium, which includes dunes.

"Charles Reid Barnes." *Science*, N.S. 31, No. 797 (April 8, 1910), 532–33.

Obituary summarizes Barnes' life and his contributions to botany as a taxonomist and the co-founder (with John Merle Coulter) of *Botanical Gazette*.

"Current Literature; Book Reviews; Notes for Students." *Botanical Gazette*, 49, No. 5 (May 1910), 382–84; 389–90.

Reviews *Distribution and Movements of Desert Plants* by Volney M. Spaulding, an account of succession in the desert, and *Vorlesungen über Descendenztheorien mit besonderer Berücksichtigung der botanischen Seite der Frage, gehalten an der Reichuniversität zu Leiden* [Lectures on Theories of Evolution, with Special Consideration of the Botanical Side of the Question, given at Reich University, Leiden] by J.P. Lotsy, a study of evolution. In "Notes for Students," Cowles describes studies of animal ecology by Shelford, Ruthven, and Hankinson.

"Current Literature; Book Reviews; Notes for Students." *Botanical Gazette*, 49, No. 6 (June 1910), 463–65; 467–68; 476.

Reviews *Native Trees of Kentucky, a Handbook* by Sarah Webb Maury and *Gedenkboek Franz Junghuhn 1809–1909*, a memorial volume for Junghuhn, who was a pioneer scientific explorer of Java. In "Notes for Students," Cowles describes studies by Ostenfeld on the land vegetation of the Faeröe Islands and the ecology of *Zostera marina*, as seen in Denmark.

"Current Literature; Minor Notices." *Botanical Gazette*, 50, No. 4 (October 1910), 312.

Reviews *Die Geographie der Farne* [The Geography of Ferns] by H. Christ, which he calls "a mine of information" that "will be of the highest value to all botanists."

"Current Literature; Notes for Students." *Botanical Gazette*, 50, No. 5 (November 1910), 394–95.
Describes study by Groom on the ecology of conifers.

"Current Literature; Book Reviews." *Botanical Gazette*, 50, No. 6 (December 1910), 468–70.
Reviews *Die Pflanzenwelt Afrikas inbesondere seiner tropischen Gebiete* [Africa's Plant World, with Special Consideration of its Tropical Districts], the ninth volume in Engler and Drude's Vegetation der Erde series. Cowles notes that this is one of four volumes that will deal with African flora and phytogeography.

1911

"Discussion." *Transactions of the Illinois Academy of Science*, 4, No. 11 (1911), 132.
Cowles comments on "Reproduction by Layering in the Balsam Fir and Other Conifers," a presentation by William S. Cooper. He says that Cooper's findings suggest that ecologists should look with greater care at the ground level and beneath.

"Current Literature; Book Reviews." *Botanical Gazette*, 51, No. 1 (January 1911), 65–67.
Reviews *Researches on Fungi: An Account of the Production, Liberation, and Dispersion of the Spores of Hymenomycetes Treated Botanically and Physically* by A.H. Reginald Buller. Cowles writes that the book contains "much that is new to botanists," expresses astonishment at the number of spores that fungi produce, and says that the book's "most important contributions" concern the fall of the spores.

"Current Literature; Notes for Students." *Botanical Gazette*, 51, No. 2 (February 1911), 147–50.
Cowles writes that "recent work on graft hybrids, which has resulted in such astonishing discoveries as to their exact nature, seems to call for a collective review." He describes studies by Winkler, Strasburger, Baur, MacFarlane, and Buder.

"Report to the American Association for the Advancement of Science and Affiliated Societies Meeting of December 28–30, 1910 Section G—Botany." *Science*, N.S 33, No. 842 (February 17, 1911), 259–64.
Cowles as secretary *pro tem* of the section, submits abstracts of nine technical papers.

"The Causes of Vegetative Cycles." *Botanical Gazette*, 51, No. 3 (March 1911), 161–83.

Paper presented Dec. 29, 1910, at Pittsburgh, to the Association of American Geographers in Cowles' capacity as retiring president. Summing up 15 years of research into plant succession, Cowles states that vegetational cycles are immensely complex phenomena that may play out over eons or just a few years—and that longer cycles may comprise several shorter cycles. He concludes that he can only describe problems that science has failed to solve. Cowles' text is republished in this volume and summarized in Chapter Two.

"The Causes of Vegetative Cycles" was also published in 1912, in the *Annals of the Association of American Geographers* (see below). The article exists as an offprint, bound in tan wrappers and entitled "The Causes of Vegetative Cycles: Contributions from the Hull Botanical Laboratory 143 (March 1911)."

"Current Literature; Notes for Students." *Botanical Gazette*, 51, No. 4 (April 1911), 312–13; 319–20.

Describes studies by Whitford on Philippine forests and York on American mistletoe.

"Current Literature; Minor Notices." *Botanical Gazette*, 51, No. 5 (May 1911), 395.

Reviews *The Conservation of Natural Resources in the United States* by Charles Van Hise, a volume of lectures on forests, mineral resources, and soils. Cowles welcomes this expert treatment of the subject by a well-known scientist.

"Current Literature; Book Reviews." *Botanical Gazette*, 52, No. 5 (November 1911), 402–4.

Reviews volumes on Africa, the Balkan countries, and the Peruvian Andes in Engler and Drude's Vegetation der Erde series.

1912

"The Causes of Vegetative Cycles," In *Annals of the Association of American Geographers*. Albany, NY, 1912, Vol. 1, pp. 3–20, 107. Reprinted from *Botanical Gazette*, 51, No. 3 (March 1911), 161–83. [Offprints exist. Republished in this volume.] Page 107 of the *Annals* abstracts

Cowles's description of the 1911 phytogeographic excursion ("An International Phytogeographic Excursion").

"Conservation of our Forests." *Transactions of the Illinois Academy of Science*, 5 (1912), 48–53. [Republished in this volume.]

A paper presented at the "Symposium on Conservation" on Feb. 23 or 24, 1912, in Bloomington, to the 5th Meeting of the Illinois Academy of Science.

Cowles seeks a middle ground between idealistic, but impractical-minded conservationists who want to prevent all timber harvest and lumbermen who want immediate gain. Illinois can experiment toward a solid forest policy, he says, because it does not have large lumber resources and powerful interests seeking to harvest them. He applauds the acquisition of Starved Rock State Park and favors establishment of more state and local forest preserves.

"A Fifteen-Year Study of Advancing Sand Dunes," In *Report of the Eighty-First Meeting of the British Association for the Advancement of Science* (London: John Murray, 1912), 565.

Abstract of paper presented Aug. 31, 1911, in Portsmouth, England, to the British Association for the Advancement of Science, Section K (Botany). Cowles has studied advancing high dunes by Lake Michigan at Dune Park, Furnessville, and Glen Haven and at Cape Cod, Massachusetts. He notes that swamp plants like dogwood and willow survive burial by a dune, as do the American elm and American basswood, which simply grow taller as the sand covers them. This paper is abstracted in *The New Phytologist*, 12 (March 1913), 78 and in *Journal of Ecology*, 1 No. 1 (March 1913), 78.

"The International Phytogeographical Excursion in the British Isles IV: Impressions of the Foreign Members of the Party." *The New Phytologist*, 11, No. 1 (January 1912), 25–26. [Republished in this volume.]

Cowles states that the chief benefit to him "has been the opportunity of living for a month in intimate relationship with my phytogeographic colleagues of other countries." Cowles now can read his colleagues' writings with greater understanding and has more sympathy for their views, even when he disagrees with them. (A multi-author article about the International Phytogeographical Excursion with no contribution from Cowles was published in *The New Phytologist* in 1911. In 1913, A.G. Tansley reprinted Cowles' reflections and the other articles in a hard-covered edition, adding a preface. [For more details see "Miscellanea" in this volume.]

"Current Literature; Book Reviews." *Botanical Gazette*, 53, No. 2 (February 1912), 181–82.

Reviews volume on North America in Engler and Drude's *Vegetation der Erde* series. Cowles finds it unfortunate that only one volume in the series is devoted to North America. He finds errors of commission and omission throughout this book, but admits that the task of compiling it was "stupendous."

"Notes and Comment." *The Plant World*, 15, No. 2 (Feb 1912), 46–48.

A description of the itinerary and participants in the August, 1911 International Phytogeographical Excursion in the British Isles. This alternative account of the trip with considerable detail of day-to-day activities is summarized in Chapter Two of the narrative.

"Current Literature; Book Reviews; Notes for Students." *Botanical Gazette*, 53, No. 3 (March 1912), 254–56; 270; 276.

Reviews *The Subantarctic Islands of New Zealand* by Charles Chilton et al., and *Esquisse de la géographie botanique de la Belgique* [Phytogeography of Belgium] by J. Massart. Cowles emphasizes the phytogeographic and ecological aspects of these books in his reviews. In "Notes for Students," Cowles describes studies by Zeidler on the causes of thorn development and Bouget on calcareous and siliceous vegetation.

"Current Literature; Book Reviews." *Botanical Gazette*, 53, No. 4 (April 1912), 348–51.
Reviews *Types of British Vegetation* by A.G. Tansley et al. Cowles writes that this book was prepared to coincide with the 1911 International Phytogeographic Excursion in the British Isles. Advance copies were presented to all participants. The book, he writes, represents a step toward internationalizing "for all time" the study of plant geography.

1913

"A Fifteen-Year Study of Advancing Sand Dunes." *Journal of Ecology*, 1, No. 1 (March 1913), 78 and *The New Phytologist*, 12 (March 1913).
Abstracted in both publications, but first abstracted in *Report of the Eighty-First Meeting of the British Association for the Advancement of Science* (1912). See above for details.

"Current Literature; Book Reviews." *Botanical Gazette*, 55, No. 4 (April 1913), 327–28.
Reviews *Biologische und morphologische Untersuchungen über Wasser- und Sumpfgewächse: III Die Uferflora* [Biological and Morphological Explorations of Aquatic and Marsh Plants: III Shore Vegetation] by Hugo Glück. Cowles writes that this book, which limits itself to central and southern Europe, "may be regarded as encyclopedic in nature." He concludes that it belongs "in every botanical reference library."

"Current Literature; Notes for Students." *Botanical Gazette*, 55, No. 5 (May 1913), 407–8.
Describes a study by Boshart on the cause of leaf asymmetry.

"Special Articles: The American Association for the Advancement of Science Section G—Botany; Botanists of the Central States." *Science*, N.S. 38, No. 966 (July 4, 1913), 32.
Reports from the American Association for the Advancement of Science meeting on December 31, 1912, signed by Cowles in his capacity as Secretary of the two groups. The Section G report lists papers delivered and the Central States report describes a discussion of the desirability of again holding scientific sessions.

"Current Literature; Minor Notices." *Botanical Gazette*, 56, No. 6 (December 1913), 515–16.
Reviews *Experiments in Blueberry Culture* by F.V. Coville, whose book says that it may be possible to raise blueberries and huckleberries commercially in peat soils.

1914

"The International Phytogeographical Excursion." *Transactions of the Illinois Academy of Science*, 7 (1914), 29–30.

Describes the itinerary and participation for the 1913 Phytogeographical Excursion in the United States, from July 26 to October 5, 1913.

"Current Literature; Notes for Students." *Botanical Gazette*, 57, No. 3 (March 1914), 255–56.

Describes study by Halket on absorption of water by the aerial parts of salt-marsh plants.

"Current Literature; Notes for Students." *Botanical Gazette*, 57, No. 4 (April 1914), 336–41.

Describes studies by Rayner on the ecology of *Calluna vulgaris*, the common European heather; Forbes on plant invasion of Hawaiian lava flows; Collins on drought-resistant Hopi maize; Thomas on the vegetation of Gothland; and Harper on the vegetation of the Hempstead plains.

"Current Literature; Minor Notices." *Botanical Gazette*, 57, No. 5 (May 1914), 437–38.

Reviews the first volume of *The Journal of Ecology*, edited for the British Ecological Society. Recommends the *Journal* as "absolutely necessary for the working ecologist."

"Special Articles: Botanists of the Central States." *Science*, N.S. 40, No. 1029 (September 18, 1914), 406–7.

In his capacity as Secretary, Cowles writes that in accordance with a vote, the American Association for the Advancement of Science will reorganize the Botanists of the Central States, which will hold a meeting on October 15–17, 1914, at the Missouri Botanical Garden.

"Current Literature; Book Reviews; Notes for Students." *Botanical Gazette*, 58, No. 5 (November 1914), 449–51.

Reviews *Die Vegetation des Untersees (Bodensee), eine floristisch-kritische Studie* [The Vegetation of the Untersee (Lake Constance), A Floristic-Critical Study] by Eugen Baumann, a study of the vegetation of the Untersee, which is an arm of Lake Constance on the border of Germany and Switzerland. In "Notes for Students," Cowles describes a study by Yapp on the ecology of marsh plants, specifically *Spiraea ulmaria*.

"Scientific Books." *Science*, N.S. 40, No. 1039 (November 27, 1914), 788–89.

Reviews "A Study of the Vegetation of the Sandhills of Nebraska" by Raymond Pool as published in *Minnesota Botanical Studies*, III, No. 4 (1914), 189–312. Cowles finds many correspondences between the behavior of dunes and sandhills and the vegetation that grows on them.

"Current Literature; Minor Notices; Notes for Students." *Botanical Gazette*, 58, No. 6 (December 1914), 530–36.

Reviews *The Botany of Iceland* by Rosenvinge et al., *Pflanzengeographische Wandlungen der deutschen Landschaft* [Phytogeographic Mutations of the German Countryside] by Hans Hausrath, and *Nos arbres* [Our Trees] by J. Massart. In "Notes for Students," Cowles describes studies by Pool on the vegetation of the Nebraska sandhills (shortened version of the review in *Science* for November 27, 1914); MacDougal and Spalding on the water-balance of desert succulents; and Moss et al. on the woodlands of England.

1915

"Current Literature; Minor Notices; Notes for Students." *Botanical Gazette*, 59, No. 1 (January 1915), 61–63; 66–80.

Describes studies by von Faber on the symbiotic relations of five species of Rubiaceae and Miehe on hereditary symbiosis. In "Notes for Students," Cowles describes studies by Fuchs on the mycorrhiza of forest trees; Bews on the vegetation of Natal (South Africa); Hallier on the origin and relationships of Indonesian flora; Escherich and Miehe on ant-loving plants; Shreve on desert vegetation; Coker on the plant life of Hartsville, South Carolina; Cockayne on evolution in New Zealand; Cannon on root characteristics, ground water, and plant distribution; Bates and Pierce on sand hill forestation; Zellner on the chemistry of symbiosis; Bachmann on lichens; Aaronsohn on Palestinian phytogeography; Treboux on antagonistic symbiosis in lichens; Cannon on the vegetation of California; Docters van Leeuwen on branching of *Rhizophora* roots; and Allard on bees and cotton blossoms.

"Current Literature; Minor Notices." *Botanical Gazette*, 59, No. 2 (February 1915), 158–67.

Reviews *Submerged Forests* by Clement Reid and *Plant Life and Evolution* by D.H. Campbell. In "Notes for Students," Cowles describes studies by Nichols on the vegetation of Connecticut; Wilson on plant distribution in England; Delf on transpiration in succulent plants; Praeger on the vegetation of Clare Island, Ireland; and Henslow on the origin of monocotyledons by self-adaptation.

"The Economic Trend of Botany." *Science*, N.S. 41, No. 1050 (Feb. 12, 1915), 223–29. [Republished in this volume.]

Paper delivered to the American Association for the Advancement of Science meeting in Philadelphia in late December, 1914. Cowles says that economic botany (i.e., agriculture and forestry) is replacing pure taxonomy, in the same way that the Greek and Roman classics are losing favor in education. He describes his work as an expert witness and says that botanists must have a more practical orientation.

"Current Literature; Notes for Students." *Botanical Gazette*, 59, No. 3 (March 1915), 259–64.

Describes studies by Harshberger on south Florida; Brenchley on weeds; Free on soil physics and soil movement; Harper on defoliation of *Larix* in England; Dachnowski on the ancient vegetation of Ohio; and Campbell on the vegetation of Guiana and Trinidad.

"University and Educational News: A Proposed Ecological Society." *Science,* N.S. 42, No. 1084 (October 8, 1915), 496. The same text appears in *Torreya,* 15, No. 11 (November 1915), 245.

Cowles writes that a group formed the American Ecological Society at the Philadelphia meeting of the American Association for the Advancement of Science (December 30, 1914). He invites interested people to attend a formal organizational session at the next A.A.A.S. meeting in Columbus, Ohio, late in December of 1915. Cowles is founding Secretary-Treasurer of the new organization.

1916

"Current Literature; Notes for Students." *Botanical Gazette,* 61, No. 1 (January 1916), 83–84.

Describes studies by Allard on the mosaic disease of tobacco and Adamson on the leaf anatomy of Veronica.

"Current Literature; Minor Notices." *Botanical Gazette,* 61, No. 2 (February 1916), 170.

Reviews *Das Phytoplankton des Süsswassers mit Besonderer Berücksichtigung des Vierwaldstättersees* [On Freshwater Phytoplankton, with Special Consideration of the Lake of Lucerne] by Hans Bachman, stating that it will be "of great value to all students of the phytoplankton" and particularly useful for identification.

1918

"Retrogressive and Progressive Successions in Arkansas Sunk Lands." *Journal of Ecology,* 6, No. 1 (April 1918), 95–96.

Abstract of paper presented between Dec. 28, 1917, and Jan. 1, 1918, in Pittsburgh, to the Ecological Society of America. Cowles describes two types of sunk lands and their vegetation: flood plain succession, starting with sandbars, leading to willows, continuing with sycamore, cottonwood, and other flood plain pioneers, and reaching a temporary climax with bottom land oaks, hickories, and hackberry. The second type occurs in cut-offs when rivers change course. Cypress swamps begin the succession, which continues as described above. Cowles also discusses the sudden retrogression in vegetation caused by extensive sinking of the earth's crust connected with the New Madrid earthquake of 1811. He also publishes this abstract in *Botanical Abstracts,* 1, No. 5 (January 1919), 191–92. A full-length version of this paper was apparently never published.

"Current Literature; Book Reviews." *Botanical Gazette*, 65, No. 6 (June 1918), 564.

Reviews *The Botany of Crop Plants* by W.W. Robbins. Cowles writes that the book was produced primarily as a text for "botanical courses in agricultural colleges," but that it provides so much up-to-date information that every teacher of botany should use it as a ready reference work.

"Ecology." *Botanical Abstracts*, 1, No. 1 (September 1918), 2–3.

Cowles, as editor for ecology and plant geography, abstracts recent ecological studies by Gravatt and Posey (Gypsy moth larvae as agents in dissemination of white pine blister rust); Roper (*Spartina* and coast erosion); Waller (Crop centers of the United States); and Watson (Relation of stimuli to cone production of western hemlock).

"Current Literature; Notes for Students." *Botanical Gazette*, 66, No. 4 (October 1918), 391–92.

Describes a study by Shantz and Piemeisel on fungous fairy rings in eastern Colorado and their effect on vegetation.

"Ecology." *Botanical Abstracts*, 1, No. 4 (December 1918), 140–45.

Cowles, as editor for ecology and plant geography, abstracts recent studies in ecology by Andrews (The relation between age and area in the distribution of plants); Dunnewald (Vegetation as an indicator of the fertility of sandy pine plains soils in northern Wisconsin); Fink (The distribution of fungi in Puerto Rico); and Pittier (Our present knowledge of the forest formations of the Isthmus of Panama).

"Current Literature; Notes for Students." *Botanical Gazette*, 66, No. 6 (December 1918), 540–42.

Describes studies by Rübel on the development of geobotany and Bews on the vegetation of Natal (South Africa).

1919

"The Present and Past Climates of Our Leading Crop Plants." *Annals of the Association of American Geographers*, 9 (1919), 73.

This paper was read before the Baltimore Meeting of the Association of American Geographers on December 27 or 28, 1918. According to the published abstract, Cowles stated that major crop plants originate in Indo-Malaysia, tropical America, and the Levant (countries along the eastern shore of the Mediterranean Sea). The great staple crop plants of northern Eurasia, the United States, Argentina, South Africa, and Australia are of Levantine origin. Five reasons may be given for this: (1) gradual, century-long acclimatization; (2) the origin, by mutation, of cold temperate races; (3) climatic changes during the period of human culture; (4) the fact that species are not necessarily best-suited to their place of origin; and (5) agricultural extension is possible without acclimatization. This paper is noticed in *The Geographical Review*, 7, No. 2 (February 1919), 108.

"Ecology and Plant Geography" *Botanical Abstracts*, 1, No. 5 (January 1919), 191–93.

Abstract of Cowles' study "Retrogressive and Progressive Successions in the Arkansas Sunk-lands." This is identical to the abstract in *Journal of Ecology*, 6 (1918), 95–96 (see above).

"Ecology and Plant Geography." *Botanical Abstracts*, 1, No. 6 (February 1919), 231–33.

Cowles abstracts a study by Helmsley on the palms of Seychelles and the Mascarene Islands in the western Indian Ocean.

"Ecology and Plant Geography." *Botanical Abstracts*, 2, No. 1 (March 1919), 2–3.

Cowles abstracts a study by Baker on aspen as a temporary forest type.

"Ecology and Plant Geography." *Botanical Abstracts*, 2, No. 2 (April 1919), 41–44.

Cowles abstracts a study by Coker on the principles and problems of fish culture in ponds.

"Ecology and Plant Geography." *Botanical Abstracts*, 2, No. 3 (May 1919), 67–69

Cowles abstracts studies by Guppy on plant distribution; and Skottsberg on Canada's phytogeographic provinces. The second abstract is co-authored with A.L. Bakke.

"Ecology in Reconstruction" and "The Illinois Forestry Survey." *Journal of Ecology*, 7 (May 1919), 120. "Ecology in Reconstruction" is the President's address before the American Meeting of the Ecological Society of America, Baltimore, Maryland, Dec. 26–28, 1918.

The one-line citation gives no details of the talk. The abstract of "The Illinois Forestry Survey" describes a forestry survey in progress that is "along ecological lines." The survey aims to determine the extent of Illinois' forests and to designate prospective preserves. Cowles will lead the work in Cook County (i.e., Chicago).

"Current Literature; Book Reviews." *Botanical Gazette*, 68, No. 6 (December 1919), 477–78. [Republished in this volume.]

Reviews *Plant Succession; An Analysis of the Development of Vegetation* by F.E. Clements. Cowles states that Clements has summarized everything important that has been written about succession and added to it. He finds Clements' elaborate Greek-derived terminology "unfortunate," preferring the vernacular, and disagrees sharply with his view of succession as inevitably progressive.

Succession "may be retrogressive as well as progressive," Cowles writes, "although of course progression is much more abundant and important."

1920

"Proceedings of the Ecological Society of America Annual Meeting, St. Louis, December 30, 1919–January 1, 1920." *Ecology*, 1 (1920), 63.

Describes a twenty-minute lantern presentation made by Cowles on "The Rising Rock Shores of Lake Michigan." Cowles says that the best examples of such shores are found in Door County, Wisconsin. An abstract of this paper also appears in *Journal of Ecology*, 8, No. 1 (March 1920), 87.

"Size of Preserves—Location" and "Grazing in Preserves," In "Preserves of Natural Conditions" by Victor E. Shelford *Transactions of the Illinois Academy of Science*, Vol. 13. (February 1920), 37–58.

Cowles contributes a single paragraph stating that the governor of Illinois wants nature preserves to average 1,000 acres (p. 43), and a statement that sheep grazing damages young trees in preserves (p. 44). The full article by Shelford contains quotations from several other people. This same text was published as a 32-page pamphlet by the Ecological Society of America in 1921 [see "Books, Pamphlets, and Contributions to Books" in this volume.]

"Current Literature; Book Reviews; Notes for Students." *Botanical Gazette*, 69, No. 4 (April 1920), 350–51, 356.

Reviews *Tidal Lands; A Study of Shore Problems* by A.E. Carey and F.W. Oliver, calling it "a masterpiece of applied ecology." The authors studied the shores of England and Brittany. (This review is abstracted in *Botanical Abstracts*, 11, No. 4 [September, October, November 1922] 523.) In "Notes for Students," Cowles reviews *Crop Centers of the United States* by A.E. Waller. He writes that the author has done a "great service in unifying ecology and agriculture" by showing close relationships between crop and vegetation centers, influenced by climate. (This review is noticed in *Botanical Abstracts*, 11, No. 4 [September, October, November 1922] 539.)

"Ecology and Plant Geography." *Botanical Abstracts*, 4, No. 1 (July 1920), 22–57.

Cowles abstracts the following studies: Hesselman (Influence of silvicultural practice on soil nitrification and its importance in the reproduction of coniferous forests); Denis (On certain thalii of *Aneura* devoid of chlorophyll); Garside (Pollen presentation in *Cryptostemma calendulaceum)*; Hayden (The ecologic foliar anatomy of some plants of a prairie province in central Iowa, The ecological subterranean anatomy of some plants of a prairie province in central Iowa); Lundegardh (Ecological and physiological studies on Hallands Vadero, Physiology and anatomy of the shore plants); MacDougal, Richards, and Spoehr (Basis of succulence in plants); Neger (Gas passageways in leaves); Rendle (Some cases of adaptation among plants); Rigg (Growth of trees in sphagnum); Small (Chapter IX in The origin and development of the *Compositae*.); Stakman and Levine (Effect of certain ecological factors on the morphology of the urediniospores of *Puccinia graminis*); Tischler (Studies on the anatomical structure of the stamens and pistils of *Lythrum salicaria* with relation to the problem of "illegitimacy"); Waterman (Development of root systems under dune conditions); Brenchley (Buried weed seeds); MacIntire (The growth of sheep sorrel in calcareous and dolomitic media); Turrill (Contributions to the flora of Macedonia: I); Heimlich (The trees of White County Indiana); MacCaughey (The pala or mule's-foot fern [*Marattia Douglasii* (Presl) Baker] in the Hawaiian Archipelago); and Sampson (Range preservation and its relation to erosion control on western grazing lands).

"State Park Conference." *Bulletin of the Garden Club of America*, #7 (December 1920), 17.
Says that forthcoming State Park Conference (January 10–12, Des Moines, Iowa), the first of its kind, will be a very important event that will "mark a new epoch in the preservation of natural areas."

1921

"Report of the Committee on Ecological Survey." *Transactions of the Illinois State Academy of Science*, 14 (1921), 14.
During the 14th annual meeting in Carbondale (April 29 and 30, 1921), Cowles reports that he and his students have surveyed Cook County, producing maps and descriptive texts. Others have surveyed Lake and Alexander counties.

"Ecology and Geographic Boundaries." *The Geographical Review*, 11, No. 1 (January 1921), 137.
Cowles delivered this paper to the Chicago meeting of the Association of American Geographers held on December 30–31, 1920 and January 1, 1921. According to the author of a one-paragraph notice, Cowles "sketched the ecological basis of the disputes in the sunk lands region of eastern Arkansas affected by the New Madrid earthquakes of 1811–1812." The paper "clearly demonstrated the great progress made in recent years in the study of physiographic conditions that affect rings of growth and the variation in ring habit, among different kinds of trees. Temperature, light, and rainfall all produce a composite effect, and the rain does not always have its chief effect in the years in which it falls." This paper is noticed by title in *Annals of the Association of American Geographers*, 11 (1921),122. Cowles delivered what is presumably another version of this paper ("Retrogressive and Progressive Successions in Arkansas Sunk Lands") to the Ecological Society of America in December 1917. It is abstracted in *Journal of Ecology*, 6, No. 1 (April 1918), 95–96.

"Imported Plants." *School Science and Mathematics*, 21, No. 6 (June 1921), 560–64.
Cowles presented this paper on November 26, 1920, at Englewood High School, Chicago, to the biology section of the Chicago Association of Science

and Math Teachers. After explaining that most U.S. crop plants were imported, he says that the time has come to experiment with the agricultural possibilities of native plants.

"Current Literature; Notes for Students." *Botanical Gazette*, 71, No. 6 (June 1921), 466–69.
Describes studies by Samson, Weyl, Jardine, Smith, and Coker on ecology applied to ranching, range preservation, erosion control, hill pastures, and fish culture

"Current Literature; Notes for Students." *Botanical Gazette*, 72, No. 1 (July 1921), 52–53.
Describes a study by Campbell on the origin of Hawaiian flora.

"Current Literature; Book Reviews; Notes for Students." *Botanical Gazette*, 72, No. 6 (December 1921), 407; 411–12.
Reviews *Lehrbuch der ökologischen Pflanzengeographie; dritte umgearbeitete Auflage* [Guide to Ecological Plant Geography; third revised edition] by Eugen Warming and P. Graebner, which is the third German edition of his ecological plant geography, much revised from earlier editions. In "Notes for Students," Cowles describes studies by McDougall on classification of symbiotic phenomena; and Whitford and Craig on forests of British Columbia.

"Ecology and Plant Geography." *Botanical Abstracts*, 10, No. 2 (December 1921), 73.
Cowles describes a study by Thiessen called "Notes on the Vertical Distribution of Temperature."

1922

"Ecology and Plant Geography." *Botanical Abstracts*, 10, No. 3 (January 1922), 147–48.
Cowles describes a study by Weaver entitled "Relative Transpiration of Coniferous and Broad-Leaved Trees in Autumn and Winter."

"Current Literature; Notes for Students." *Botanical Gazette*, 73, No. 1 (January 1922), 80.
Cowles describes a study by Harper on the forest geography of New Jersey.

"Current Literature; Notes for Students." *Botanical Gazette*, 73, No. 3 (March 1922), 246.
Cowles describes a study by Pool, Weaver, and Jean on the tension zone between prairie and woodland.

"Ecology and Plant Geography." *Botanical Abstracts*, 11, No. 1 (March–April 1922), 21–23.

Cowles describes work by Pool, Weaver, and Jean (Further studies in the eco-tone between prairie and woodland); Whitford (Forests of British Columbia); and Warming and Graebner (Eugen Warming's textbook of ecological plant geography; third revised edition).

"Current Literature; Notes for Students." *Botanical Gazette*, 73, No. 4 (April 1922), 334–35.
Describes studies by Gail on the vertical distribution of *Fucus* and Bowman on the botanical ecology of the Dry Tortugas.

"Mosses and Lichens." *Bulletin of the Garden Club of America*, #5 (May 1922), 265–66.
In this brief, popular account of mosses and lichens, Cowles writes that "every nature lover should make some effort to get acquainted with them."

"Ecology and Plant Geography." *Botanical Abstracts*, 11, No. 4 (September, October, November 1922), 520.
Cowles describes a study by Snow entitled "Diaphragms of Water Plants. II. Effect of Certain Factors upon Development of Air Chambers and Diaphragms."

1925

"Current Literature; Book Reviews; Minor Notices." *Botanical Gazette*, 80, No. 5 (November 1925), 341.
Reviews *A Guide to the Trees* by C. Curtis, which, says Cowles, is aimed at Boy Scouts and Campfire Girls.

"Current Literature; Notes for Students." *Botanical Gazette*, 80, No. 6 (December 1925), 452–53.
Describes a study by Fernald on the persistence of plants in unglaciated areas of boreal America.

1926

"Current Literature; Book Reviews; Notes for Students." *Botanical Gazette*, 81, No. 4 (April 1926), 233; 236.
Reviews *The Standard Cyclopedia of Horticulture* by L.H. Bailey, which he calls "very handsome and satisfactory." In "Notes for Students," Cowles describes a study by Babcock and Hall on *Hemizonia congesta*, a hayfield tarweed.

"Current Literature; Minor Notices." *Botanical Gazette*, 82, No. 5 (November 1926), 340.
Reviews *Ergebnisse der Biologie* [Research in Biology] by K. Frisch, R. von Goldschmidt, W. Ruhland, and H. Winterstein, which collects the latest research on biology with special emphasis on comparative physiology and

psychology of animals, plant physiology, the mechanics of development, and theories of inheritance.

"Current Literature; Minor Notices." *Botanical Gazette*, 82, No. 6 (December 1926), 447.

Reviews A Monograph on the British Lichens: A Descriptive Catalogue of The Species in the Department of Botany, British Museum by Annie Lorrain Smith. Cowles reviews the difference between this, the second edition, and the first edition.

1927

[Report of the Conservation Committee; Report of the Committee on Legislation and Finance.] *Transactions of the Illinois State Academy of Science*, 20 (1927), 17–18.

At the 20th Annual Meeting in Joliet (April 29 and 30, 1927), Cowles reports that R.B. Miller, an academy member, was appointed State Forester and is beginning to purchase lands for state forests. An upper Mississippi wildlife refuge continues to develop in Minnesota and there has been little progress in other state parks. He also reports on conservation-related legislation in Illinois.

"Current Literature; Minor Notices." *Botanical Gazette*, 83, No. 6 (June 1927), 428.

Cowles reviews *Cargoes and Harvests* by D.C. Peattie, a popular history of economic plants, calling it "one of the most attractively written books on botany that the reviewer has ever read."

"Current Literature; Minor Notices." *Botanical Gazette*, 84, No. 3 (September 1927), 109.

Reviews *An Outline of Plant Geography* by D.H. Campbell, which Cowles calls "a general book on plant geography" that "should be in the hands of all world travelers."

"Research Items: Forest and Prairie." *Nature*, 120, No. 3034 (December 24, 1927), 931.

Account of a paper given by Cowles at the National Academy of Sciences meeting, Washington, DC. Cowles discusses the probable fate of American grasslands that have yet to be plowed. He distinguishes edaphic prairies (which occur as interruptions in otherwise forested areas) from climatic (existence determined by climatic conditions). This is probably similar or identical to "The Persistence of Prairies," abstracted in *Ecology*, 9, No. 4 (October 1928), 380–82. See below.

1928

"The Persistence of Prairies." *Ecology*, 9, No. 4 (Oct. 1928), 380–82.

Paper presented Dec. 29, 1927, in Nashville, Tennessee, to the Ecological

Society of America. Presumably similar or identical to "Forest and Prairie," abstracted in *Nature*, 120, No. 3034 (December 24, 1927), 31. See above for description. [Republished in this volume.]

"The Department of Botany." *The University Record*, N.S. 14, No. 2 (April 1928), 117–19.
Cowles describes the history of the Botany Department at the University of Chicago, ignoring his personal contributions.

1929

"The Succession Point of View in Floristics," In *Proceedings of the International Congress of Plant Sciences, Ithaca, New York, August 16–23, 1926* (Menasha, Wisconsin: George Banta, 1929) 1, 687–91. [Republished in this volume.]
Paper presented August 20, 1926, in Ithaca, NY, to the ecology section of the International Congress of Plant Sciences. In this "successional study from a floristic angle," Cowles says that different plants dominated the Chicago region in turn as the glaciers receded, leaving relicts behind. He then describes different Chicago-area successions; northern species at the southwest edge of their ranges in Chicago; disjuncts of the north, south, east, and west range; and endemics. He closes by asking for more studies to clarify understanding of the subject.

"Report of the Committee on Conservation." *Transactions of the Illinois State Academy of Science*, 22 (1929), 6–7
At the 22nd Annual Meeting in Macomb (May 3 and 4, 1929), Cowles reports the acquisition by the State of Illinois of land for five state parks in Illinois: Blackhawk State Park; White Pine Forest Park; Giant City Park; Buffalo Rock Park; and Pierre Menard Homestead and Fort Gage. He announces acquisition by the State of Illinois of Horseshoe Lake State Forest, but regrets that more has not been done. On page 5 of this volume, Cowles co-signs the "Report of the Treasurer" with A.C. Noe and Joseph B. Hawkes.

"Some Aspects of Utah Crops and Vegetation." *Annals of the Association of American Geographers*, 19 (March 1929), 27–28.
Cowles read this paper to the Association of American Geographers in December 1928. He describes the different vegetation types of Utah and the abundant crop possibilities they suggest.

"John Merle Coulter; Current Literature; Minor Notices." *Botanical Gazette*, 87, No. 2 (March 1929), 211–17; 326–27. [Republished in this volume.]
Obituary describes the history of the *Botanical Gazette*, suggesting that it was one of Coulter's major achievements, then summarizes Coulter's career as botanist and teacher. In "Minor Notices," Cowles reviews *Studies in the Ecological Evolution of the Angiosperms* by J.W. Bews, He recommends the book to ecologists, but warns that it is "speculative and at times quite unorthodox."

"Current Literature; Book Reviews." *Botanical Gazette*, 88, No. 5 (November 1929), 343.

Reviews *Plant Succession and Indicators* by F.E. and Edith S. Clements, explaining that this is a combined and condensed edition of *Plant Succession* (1916) and *Plant Indicators* (1920). Cowles lists the changes and describes material that was omitted to make this edition.

"Current Literature; Minor Notices." *Botanical Gazette*, 88, No. 6 (December 1929), 457.

Reviews *Flora Photographica. II: Floral Province of the European "Mittelgebirge"* by H. Iltis and B. Schulz, a volume of plant photographs, which is part of a projected series that will cover all the world's plants, acting as a complement to herbaria and floras.

1930

"Report of the Committee on Conservation." *Transactions of the Illinois State Academy of Science*, 23, No. 1 (September 1930), 19–20.

Cowles describes the new White Pine Forest in Ogle County, protection measures for the "rapidly disappearing" prairie chicken, preservation of the Waukegan Flats in Lake County, and efforts toward protection of Stony Island in Chicago. Cowles also mentions that "conservation people" want to protect wild flowers along highways and railroad rights-of-way. On page 16 of this volume, Cowles co-signs the "Auditors' Report" with A.C. Noe and J.B. Hawkes.

1931

"President's Opening Speech to Section," In *Fifth International Botanical Congress, Cambridge, 16–23 August, 1930 Report of Proceedings*, edited by F.T. Brooks and T.F. Chipp (Cambridge: Cambridge University Press, 1931), 48.

Abstract of opening speech delivered on August 18, 1930, in Cambridge, England, to the Fifth International Botanical Congress, Section E (Phytogeography and Ecology). Cowles delivered it in his capacity as section president. He states that ecological study has developed rapidly "along many lines" in a single generation and praises its contributions to theoretical and applied science.

"Report of the Committee on Conservation." *Transactions of the Illinois State Academy of Science*, 23, No. 3 (March 1931), 617.

Cowles reports that the conservation movement is making "some progress" in the state of Illinois and urges establishment of a national forest. On p. 613, Cowles co-signs the "Report of the Auditor" with A.C. Noe and Lewis M. Turner.

"Conservation of Illinois Areas of Botanical Value." *Transactions of the Illinois State Academy of Science*, 24, No. 2 (Dec. 1931), 86–89. [An unknown number of offprints of this article were produced by Phillips Bros., Springfield, Illinois, in 1932. There is a single copy of this offprint at the LuEsther Mertz Library of the New York Botanical Gardens.]

Speech given on May 8 or 9, 1931, in Peoria, to the Illinois State Academy of Science. Cowles wants to preserve places of scenic value, which are often of ecological and botanical interest. After describing existing parks, he lists other sites that should be preserved: Apple River Canyon; the Rock River between Oregon and Dixon; Rock Canyon on the Kankakee River near Kankakee; and Waukegan Flats in Lake County.

1932

"Report of the Committee on Conservation." *Transactions of the Illinois State Academy of Science*, 24, No. 4 (June 1932), 626.

Cowles has "very little to report this year" except for efforts to help establish national forest units in Illinois.

"The Ever-Changing Landscape." *Scientific Monthly*, 34 (May 1932), 457–59.

Radio talk in the series "Science Service Radio Talks Presented over the Columbia Broadcasting System." In a popular manner, Cowles surveys plant succession, especially in forests.

1933

"Current Literature." *Botanical Gazette*, 95, No. 6 (December 1933), 349–50.

Reviews *Wild flowers of the Alleghenies* by J.E. Harned. Stating that this book is aimed at both technical botanists and flower lovers, Cowles calls it beautifully produced.

Chronology

NOTE: This chronology lists key events in Cowles' life. He spent his entire academic career teaching ecology and botany in the Department of Botany at the University of Chicago; leading University of Chicago students on summer field ecology trips; and occasionally teaching elsewhere. His lectures at professional meetings are listed here, but it would be impossible to compile a list of his talks to groups like garden clubs. This chronology is followed by a list of Cowles' professional memberships and the editorial positions that he held.

Early Life: Born February 27, 1869, Kensington, Connecticut, son of Henry Martyn and Eliza (Whittlesey) Cowles. A brother, Dwight, is born on September 9, 1874. (The Cowles family traces its lineage to John Cowles, who came to Massachusetts from England in about 1634.) Attends Kensington public schools during the 1870s and 1880s, graduates from New Britain (Connecticut) High School on March 27, 1888.

Spring 1893: Receives B.A. from Oberlin College, Ohio. Chief interests in college are taxonomic botany, local distribution of plants, geology, Latin, and Greek. Also studies German and French.

1893–94: Graduate study in geology, University of Chicago.

September 1894–June 1895: Professor of Natural Science, Gates College, Neligh, Nebraska. At Gates, leads students on geological and botanical collecting trips.

Summer 1895: Special Field Assistant, U.S. Geological Survey.
Receives fellowship to study geology at the University of Chicago for academic year 1895–96; studies Pleistocene paleobotany with Rollin D. Salisbury and Thomas C. Chamberlin.

January 1896: First publication: a book review in the *Journal of Geology.*
April 25: Observes Indiana dunes for the first time at Dunes Park, Indiana. Begins studying dune vegetation.

1897: Laboratory Assistant in Ecology, University of Chicago.
Summer: Travels up and down the east shore of Lake Michigan.

1898: Assistant in Ecology, University of Chicago.
March 18: Takes final exam for Ph.D.
April: Receives Ph.D. in Botany and Geology, University of Chicago.
September: Leads University of Chicago field class of twelve students for six weeks on North Manitou Island, Lake Michigan; probably also spends some

time on Beaver Island and possibly also on Mackinac.

Feb–May, 1899: Publishes a modified form of his dissertation in *Botanical Gazette*.

September: Spends several weeks at Marquette, Michigan, studying the flora with a party of advanced University of Chicago students.

June 1900: Conducts University of Chicago field study class through the Allegheny Mountains of eastern Tennessee.

June 25: Marries Elizabeth Lucretia Waller in Louisville, Kentucky.

Summer: Takes charge of botanical work at Cold Spring Harbor Biological Laboratory, Long Island, New York.

October: First visit to "Sunk Lands" in the Varney River area of Missouri.

July 1901: Conducts field party of about twenty University of Chicago students to study ecology in northwestern Montana, especially at Flathead Lake.

December: Promoted from Assistant to Associate in Ecology.

March 1902: Conducts University of Chicago student group to Gulf coast of Mississippi, with C.B. Davenport as co-leader.

July 2 to August 11: Teaches ecology in botany program at Woods Hole, Massachusetts.

August 12: Conducts student group of fourteen to Mount Katahdin and the coast of Maine for four weeks where they study the climatic and edaphic influences on the flora.

October: Promoted from Associate to Instructor in Botany.

September 1903: Leads a University of Chicago field party to Arizona, California, and southern California to study desert, rock, and dune vegetation.

March 1904: Sent to Florida by the Department of Botany to study the Everglades. Uses the U.S. Subtropical Laboratory in Miami as a base.

April: Visits the Apalachicola River region, Florida, between the Georgia border and about 30 miles south of the border, especially west of the Chattahoochee River.

Summer, Fall, and Winter 1905–06: In June attends International Botanical Congress, Vienna. Possibly holds summer Field Ecology class in Scotland for University of Chicago students. Studies dune vegetation in Belgium and Holland.

April 1, 1906: Returns from Europe.

Summer: Field research in northern Michigan.

Autumn and early Winter: Studies the Florida Everglades under a Carnegie Institution Grant in botany.

May 1907 or earlier: Promoted from Instructor to Assistant Professor of Botany.

June 15–July 24: Leads University of Chicago Field Ecology course in Oregon, Washington, and British Columbia.

July 25–August 30: Leads University of Chicago Field Ecology course in Alaska.

Jan 2–March 20, 1908: Leads University of Chicago Field Ecology course in south Florida.

June: Leads University of Chicago Field Ecology students to the north shore of Lake Superior.

Summer 1909: Field studies on the north shore of Lake Superior.

Winter term 1910: Field ecology trip to south Florida.

1911: Promoted from Assistant Professor to Associate Professor of Ecology.

August: Travels through Britain on the International Phytogeographical Excursion. Studies dunes and other vegetation of England, Scotland, and Ireland.

October: Attends the Tenth International Geographical Congress in Rome, Italy, as a delegate of the Association of American Geographers.

1912: Begins "a critical study of the sunken lands of northeastern Arkansas" at the instigation of the U.S. Department of Justice. This work continues off and on through 1918 and he testifies in several cases.

June: Leads University of Chicago Field Ecology students to Quebec. [Possibly led by George Fuller.]

June 29: Birth of daughter, Harriet Elizabeth Cowles.

April 7, 1913: Becomes Founding 1st Vice President of Friends of Our Native Landscape under founder Jens Jensen; serves in key capacities for fifteen years.

July 27–September 24: Conducts the International Phytogeographic Excursion in the United States.

November 14, 1914: Helps found the Conservation Council of Chicago.

1915: Promoted from Associate Professor to Professor of Ecology.

June 14–17, 1916: Leads four-day field trip to "Chicago Sand Dune Region" for members of the Ecological Society of America. There is a typewritten record of this trip with photographs among the Charles Olmsted Papers UC:BDR.

July 29–Sept 3: Leads University of Chicago Field Ecology students to the Lake Superior region.

October 30: Testifies at a public hearing in Chicago on the proposed Sand Dunes National Park in Indiana. His remarks are published in *Report on the Proposed Sand Dunes National Park* (1916) and reprinted in this volume.

May 22, 1918: Meets with Stephen Forbes and John M. Coulter to discuss how volunteers will assist with forestry survey of Illinois. During summer, does forestry surveys of northern Cook County with a party of students.

July 26–August 31: Leads University of Chicago Field Ecology students to the Lake Huron region.

June–July 1919: Leads University of Chicago Field Ecology students to Door County, Wisconsin.

December: First visit to Red River, the border between Texas and Oklahoma; testifies in the Red River Boundary Dispute.

Summer 1920: Leads University of Chicago Field Ecology students to California.

Summer, 1921: Leads University of Chicago Field Ecology students to California.

September 24: Testifies before the Supreme Court of the United States in the Red River Boundary Dispute lawsuit involving the states of Texas and Oklahoma and the United States government as intervener.

April 28, 1922: Helps to found Illinois Forestry Association in Chicago. The Association seeks to develop forests in Illinois for economic benefit and also to establish permanent forest preserves.

Summer: Leads University of Chicago Field Ecology students to Lake County, Illinois, and Mason County, Michigan.

June 1923: Receives honorary Doctor of Science degree from Oberlin College, Ohio.

June–July 1924: Leads University of Chicago Field Ecology students to Utah. Apparently works through Utah Agricultural College, Logan.

Mid-July through late August: Ecological work at Alpine School, Provo, Utah.

1925: Becomes Chairman of the Department of Botany, University of Chicago, succeeding John M. Coulter.

June 22–July 29: Leads University of Chicago Field Ecology students to Utah.

June 18–July 25, 1928: Leads University of Chicago Field Ecology students to Utah.

July–August: Leads University of Chicago Field Ecology students to British Columbia and Washington.

1929: Symptoms of Parkinson's disease begin to limit teaching and administrative work.

July 29–August 25: Leads University of Chicago Field Ecology students to New Mexico.

Winter Term 1930: Trip to France and Italy with wife and daughter.

1931: Classroom teaching ceases because of Parkinson's disease.

July 1934: Retires as Professor and Chairman of University of Chicago Department of Botany at age 65. Becomes Professor Emeritus. Retires as editor of the *Botanical Gazette.*

July 1935: Honored with a special issue of *Ecology.*

September 12, 1939: Dies at his home.

September 14: Honored at Memorial Service, Bond Chapel, University of Chicago at 2 p.m. Buried at Oak Woods Cemetery, Chicago. Moved to Cave Hill Cemetery, Louisville, in 1982.

Professional Societies

American Association for the Advancement of Science
Becomes member at Dec 1904 (Philadelphia) 54th meeting. Fellow after 1906; Secretary-Treasurer Section G, December 1907 (in absence of F. E. Lloyd). Elected Secretary for a five-year term: 1908–1912; Vice President of Section G (Botany): December 1913; Member Sectional Committee Section G: 1911–14; Member of the Council: 1911–17; Representative on the Council of the A.A.A.S. from the Botanical Society of America and Secretary of Botanists of the Central States (a section of A.A.A.S.): November 1905 to April 1907.

American Society of Naturalists ASN records (incomplete and fragmentary) list Cowles as a member in 1904, 1910, and 1911, and a sustaining member from 1919-1928. He lectures on "The Adaptation Viewpoint in Ecology" as part of a symposium on Adaptation at the 1913 annual meeting in Cleveland (January 2 morning session).

Association of American Geographers
One of fifty-eight founding members: December 29, 1904. Helps found the *Annals of the Association of American Geographers.* President 1910.

Botanical Society of America
Elected Associate in 1900; Member after 1904; Vice President: 1921; President: 1922; Councillor: 1923–25. Runs for many society offices.

British Ecological Society
Member: 1927–1934; Elected Honorary Life Member: January 3, 1934.

Chicago Academy of Sciences
Records are inaccessible. Vice President: 1912–1913; President: 1923–24.

Conservation Council of Chicago
Attends founding meeting on November 14, 1914, representing the Geographic Society of Chicago; During the mid and late 1920s presides over monthly meetings of this group, which he describes as a clearing house for information on Chicago-area conservation.

Dunes Pageant Association Trustee
Member of the Promotion Committee that helps to publicize the Historical Pageant of the [Indiana] Dunes, which took place on June 3, 1917.

Ecological Society of America
Charter Member: 1914; President: 1916 and 1918; Representative for Illinois to Committee on Preservation of Natural Conditions (1926).

Friends of Our Native Landscape
Attends founding meeting on April 7, 1913, joins committee for "Organization and a Constitution"; Helps write constitution; Becomes first Vice President, serves in this capacity and on the Board of Directors until the late 1920s.

Geographic Society of Chicago
Early records of the Geographic Society appear to be lost. Cowles may have joined as early as 1900, possibly invited by Prof. Rollin D. Salisbury, University of Chicago, who was a founder; Member of the Excursion Committee in 1907; President: 1912–14; Vice President: 1932–33; Very active with the Geographic Society, as a member of the Board of Directors or as an officer almost continuously from 1912 through 1934.

Illinois State Academy of Sciences
Charter Member: December 7, 1907; Member of Committee on "The Ecological Survey of the State of Illinois" beginning in 1912; Membership Committee: 1911–12; Chairman: 1914–1915; President: 1920; Program committee on ecological survey, 1922; Listed as a Life Member in 1929 Annual Report.

Illinois Forestry Association
Founding Member; At first meeting April 28, 1922. Later, President. According to the *Journal of the Illinois State Historical Society*, 15, Nos. 3–4 (October

1922–January 1923), 729–30, the Illinois Forestry Association, after months of research, has made public an extensive program for the protection and development of forests in Illinois." Produces a report for the Forestry Association that "describes the economic benefits that development of forestry would bring to Illinois."

International Association of Botanists
President of the section on phytogeography and ecology at the International Botanical Congress, Cambridge, England, August 1930.

National Conference on State Parks
Invited to organizing meeting for First National Conference on State Parks, Chicago, Illinois, October 1920; Attends First National Conference on State Parks, Des Moines, Iowa, Jan 10–12, 1921; Serves on the Conference Committee in 1923 and the Executive Committee in 1924 and 1925.

National Dunes Park Association
In July of 1916, attends a meeting at Waverly Beach, Indiana, subsequently joins the Board.

Playground Association of Chicago
Member: probably joins in 1905; serves with Jensen on committee that organizes Saturday Afternoon Walking Trips to raise public awareness of nearby natural sites. (Cowles' name appears in Playground Association literature dated April 14 and August 26, 1908). The walking trip activity eventually passes to the Prairie Club of Chicago, which Cowles never joins.

State of Illinois, Board of Natural Resources and Conservation
Appointed 1925 as representative in forestry.

Wild Flower Preservation Society
Member: Joins Chicago Chapter on May 5, 1913, sending dues to Mr. Millispaugh, a botanist at the Field Museum of Natural History; National Vice President; National President 1923.

Editorial Work

American Journal of Botany
Member of Editorial Board: 1925–1933.

American Journal of Geography
Associate Editor: 1902–9.

Botanical Abstracts
Member of Editorial Board: 1918–1923; Editor for Ecology and Plant Geography: 1918–23.

Botanical Gazette
Associate Editor: 1898–1926; Co-Editor with John M. Coulter: 1926–28; Editor: 1929–34; Associate Editor: 1934–1937.

Ecology
Member of Editorial Board: 1920.

Journal of Geography
Takes charge of special phytogeography department when the journal is created in February of 1902; Associate Editor: 1906.

Totius orbis flora photographica arte depicta Band 1 (1929) Band 2 (1930) (Brunn, Czechoslovakia: Rudolf M. Rohrer). Hugo Iltis, who is best known as the biographer of Mendel created and edited this serial publication. According to the first issue, the series was designed to "display in original photographic prints of uniform size (9 x 12 cm) the vegetation-cover of the earth in its typical associations, being thus a modern complement of the herbaria and Floras." The series was to be published in cooperation with an international group of botanists including Cowles. Only two issues appeared, the first on the flora of Trinidad and the second on central Europe. Cowles reviews the European volume in *Botanical Gazette*, 88, No. 6 (December 1929), 457.

INDEX

Adams, Charles C., 44–45, 45–47, 94, 321
"An Address to Be Given by Harriet Cowles Waller …," 11, 14n3, 17n7, 29n21, 41n13, 44n19, 77n27, 84n42
Agassiz Association, 21
American Environmental Photographs, 1891–1936 (website), ii, 8–9, 41n13
Arkansas Sunk Lands. *See* Sunk Lands Cases
"Aspects of the Species Question" (Arthur et al.), 48, 322
Association of American Geographers, 4, 30, 45n20, 47n24, 48, 72, 221, 304, 305, 326, 332, 334, 335, 339, 346

Badè, William F., 81
Biological Field and Farm proposal, 64–65, 66n11
The Book of Plants (Parker/HCC), 59, 77n27, 300–301
"Borderline Science: Expert Testimony and the Red River Boundary Dispute" (Cittadino), 9, 11
Botanical Gazette, 25, 28, 30, 33n5, 34, 37, 50n28, 53–54, 57, 91, 265, 269, 271, 273, 274, 276, 279, 280, 281, 282, 283, 298, 303, 304, 307–334, 336–341, 343, 346, 349
Botanical Society of America 47n25, 57, 241, 282, 322, 323, 346, 347
Botany 36 (Field Ecology), 7, 80–82, 306
Bowman, Isaiah, 61, 63n5
Burton, Ernest D., 90–91

"The Causes of Vegetational Cycles", 48–49, 221–240 (HCC Text), 326
Chamberlain, Charles J., 21n11, 28, 75, 90
Chamberlin, Thomas C., 22, 24–27, 36, 342
Chapman, Herman C., 89
Chicago Academy of Sciences, 5, 10, 30, 33n6, 49–50, 69, 302, 347
Chicago Textbook. See *Textbook of Botany for Colleges and Universities*
Christian Endeavor, 15–18, 19
Cittadino, Eugene, 9, 11, 44n18, 53n32, 58n2, 62n5, 72n20
Clements, Frederic E., 5, 53–56, 271, 305, 308
  statistical/quantitative methods of, 5, 55, 94–95
  views on succession, 53, 55
  The Development and Structure of Vegetation (HCC Review Text) 272–274
  The Phytogeography of Nebraska (HCC Review Text) 271–273
  Plant Succession: An Analysis of the Development of Vegetation (HCC Review Text) 276–277
  Research Methods in Ecology (HCC Review Text) 274–276
climax community, 4, 35, 276
Committee on Ecological Survey (IAS), 47n24, 70, 71, 300, 335, 347
congregationalism, 14–16
conservation, 68–74, 84–89, 94
Conservation Council of Chicago, 57, 69–70, 344